Collins

Perfect Maths ASSESSMENTS

Register online to get access to Analytics, Reports and Remedial

10

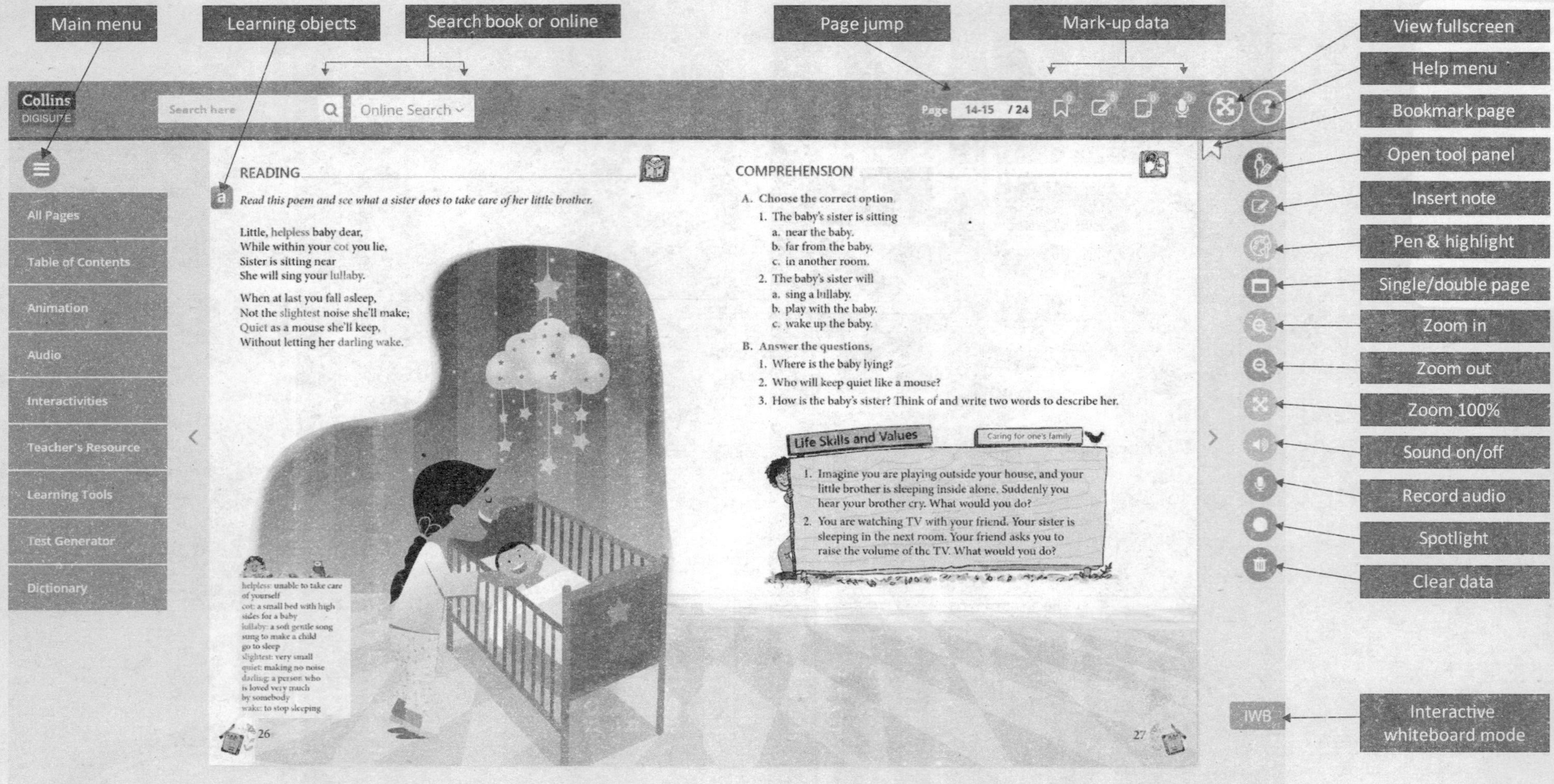

Student + Teacher			Teacher-only	
a animations	ia activities	g games	lp lesson plans	tn teacher's notes
ilt instructor-led tutorials	w worksheets	v videos	w worksheets	ak answer keys
	audio			

Preface

Collins Perfect Maths Assessments is a comprehensive maths self-assessment series for classes 6 to 10, for schools across all boards. This series adheres to the guidelines of the *National Education Policy* (NEP) 2020 in which self-assessment is stated as one of the tools for transforming the culture of assessment. This series follows a holistic approach and promotes active engagement with learning. It aims to make the students move away from rote learning; and hence, elevate the status of the student from a passive learner to an active learner and facilitate learner autonomy, higher cognitive abilities and metacognitive engagement. A smooth transition of questions from easy, average to difficult would enable better understanding of concepts, self-analysis and hence excellence in any competitive exam.

The workbooks can also be used by teachers for review and assessments in an academic year, if they want to, as each assessment paper has a variety of questions.

Key Features

Each book contains the following features.

Part 1 (Multiple Choice Questions)

Prior Knowledge Test	Questions to assess pre-existing knowledge and identify misconceptions
Keywords	Definitions of important terms giving an overview of concepts in a chapter
Concept Map	Summary of a chapter in the form of a graphic organizer for quick revision
Self-Assessments	One or two carefully graded, differentiated and topic-specific, self-assessment papers per chapter with 25 questions per assessment paper

- Questions tagged with three difficulty levels: Easy 🙂, Average 😐 or Difficult 🙁

Part 2 (Subjective Type Questions)

Self-Assessment	One chapter-wise assessment paper containing only short answer and long answer (+ picture-based) type questions

- In Grades 9 and 10, sample questions based on the Organisation for Economic Co-operation and Development's (OECD's) Programme for International Student Assessment (PISA) maths framework included within the assessment paper

End of the book

General Tips	Suggested tools and techniques that can be used to ease the process of learning
Quick Tips	Suggested strategies for effective learning and acing exams
Solutions	Answers to all the questions for easy self-evaluation
Hints for Difficult Questions	Supporting texts to help in answering difficult questions
Sample OMR Answer Sheets	Answer sheets in the form of an OMR sheet for students to mark the answers

Online Version

Subscription-based online version of the assessment papers in Part 1 is available where students can try the assessment online via digital OMR sheets, and have access to analytics, reports and remedial.

We would like to take this opportunity to thank all the teachers who reviewed the workbooks and provided their feedback, which helped in improving the quality of the content.

Feedback, invaluable comments and suggestions from users are welcome.

Authors

Key Features

Collins Perfect Maths Assessments series is aligned with the *National Education Policy* (NEP) 2020. The key features have been designed to provide students with a comprehensive understanding of the fundamental concepts and their applications, to reinforce critical thinking and problem-solving skills; and thus, move away from rote learning. Each book consists of two main parts.

PART 1

Multiple choice questions

PRIOR KNOWLEDGE TEST

Choose the correct option.

1. Which of the following has a

Assess your pre-existing knowledge and identify misconceptions

KEYWORDS

Euclid's division lemma: For positi
atisfying $a = bq + r, 0 \leq r < b$

Overview the concepts of a chapter with the definitions of important terms

CONCEPT MAP

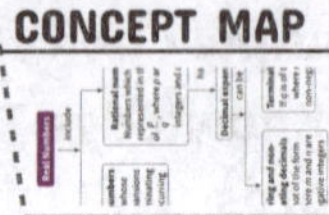

Summarize and revise quickly with the help of the graphic organizer

PART 1
CHAPTER 1: Real Numbers
SELF-ASSESSMENT 1

PART 1
CHAPTER 1: Real Numbers
SELF-ASSESSMENT 2

34. A paper tree is made by mounting a cone on top of a cylinder. The height and the radius of the cone is double than that of the cylinder. Find the curved surface ...tree if the radius of the cone is 5 cm and height is 12 cm.
A. 65π cm²
B. 85π cm²
C. 90π cm²
D. 95π cm²

35. The surface areas of two spheres are in the ratio 16 : 81. Find the ratio of their volumes.
A. 729 : 64
B. 64 : 729
C. 12 : 27
D. 27 : 12

38. A hemispherical metal container has inner and outer radii as 6 cm and 9 cm, respectively. Find the weight of the container, if the density of th... 8.05 g per cm³.
A. 9.4 kg
B. 8.6 kg
C. 8.4 kg
D. 7.5 kg

39. The water filled in a conical vessel is transferred into a cylindrical flask with the same radius. Find the minimum height of the flask so that it can be filled without overflow if the height of conical vessel is 18 cm.
A. 6 cm
B. 6.25 cm
C. 8 cm
D. 9 cm

Average questions are tagged with this smiley!

Pick the right (or best) option from the distracters!

Difficult questions are tagged with this smiley!

Easy questions are tagged with this smiley!

PART 2

Subjective type questions

PART 2
CHAPTER 1: Real Numbers
SELF-ASSESSMENT 3

- Assess your reasoning, detailing, explaining, describing or schematic representation skills
- Think and plan how you can organize and structure your answer

19. Vinay has a piece of land of area 28,000 sq. m which is in the shape of a quadrilateral. He wants to grow potatoes and tomatoes as shown in the figure. Find the area of the field used to grow tomatoes.
    A. 28,000 sq. m
    B. 12,000 sq. m
    C. 16,000 sq. m
    D. 14,000 sq. m

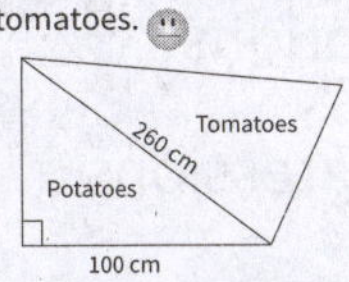

20. The nameboard of a school which is in the form of a triangle has to be painted. If the sides of the board are

23. A gardener wants to grow grass at the corners of a field which are in the form of triangles, leaving a rectangular area as shown in the figure. If the length and breadth of the rectangular area are 25 m and 20 m, respectively, find the area of the field in which he has grown the grass.
    A. 28,000 sq. m
    B. 12,000 sq. m
    C. 16,000 sq. m
    D. 14,000 sq. m

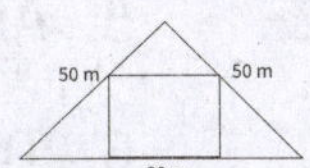

24. Use the given figure to find the area of

- In classes 9 and 10, PISA based questions as per PISA Maths framework included for extended learning

AT THE END OF THE BOOK

GENERAL TIPS

Use these tools and techniques to ease the process of your learning

QUICK TIPS

Apply these strategies for effective learning and ace your exams

SOLUTIONS

Compare your marked answers with the solutions and find the areas where you need an extra effort

Hints for Difficult Questions

Take help from the supporting texts and find answers to difficult questions

Mark your answer for Part 1 questions, in this, and measure your progress

Collins Perfect Maths Assessments 10

CHAPTER 1

SAMPLE OMR ANSWER SHEET

IMPORTANT: PLEASE FILL IN NAME, SCHOOL CODE, CLASS, SECTION & ROLL NO. CORRECTLY

PERSONAL DETAILS

1. STUDENT NAME (IN ENGLISH CAPITAL LETTERS ONLY)

2. SCHOOL CODE   3. CLASS

MARK YOUR ANSWERS

1.	A	B	C	D	26.	A	B	C	D
2.	A	B	C	D	27.	A	B	C	D
3.	A	B	C	D	28.	A	B	C	D
4.	A	B	C	D	29.	A	B	C	D

Contents

PART 1

Multiple choice questions

CHAPTER 1

Real Numbers

PRIOR KNOWLEDGE TEST

Choose the correct option.

1. Which of the following has a non-terminating and recurring decimal representation?
   A. A rational number
   B. A whole number
   C. An integer
   D. An irrational number

2. Which of the following is equal to 924?
   A. $2 \times 3 \times 7 \times 9$
   B. $2^2 \times 3 \times 7 \times 11$
   C. $2 \times 3 \times 7 \times 4$
   D. $2 \times 3 \times 17$

3. Which of the following represents the third root of *x* divided by the fourth root of *x*?
   A. x B. $\sqrt{x}$ C. $\sqrt[12]{x}$ D. $\frac{1}{\sqrt[12]{x}}$

4. Which of the following is an irrational number?
   A. $\sqrt[4]{16}$ B. $\sqrt[4]{625}$
   C. $\sqrt[2]{225}$ D. $\sqrt[2]{216}$

5. Simplify: $4\sqrt{3}+6\sqrt{7}-5\sqrt{3}-4\sqrt{7}$
   A. $2\sqrt{7}-\sqrt{3}$ B. $\sqrt{3}+2\sqrt{7}$
   C. $8\sqrt{3}+\sqrt{7}$ D. $6\sqrt{7}$

KEYWORDS

Euclid's division lemma: For positive integers *a* and *b*, there exist whole numbers *q* and *r* satisfying $a = bq + r, 0 \le r < b$

Fundamental Theorem of Arithmetic: The prime factorisation of any natural number is unique, except for the order of its factors

Real numbers: Rational numbers together with irrational numbers

Rational number: A number which can be written in the form of $\frac{p}{q}$, where *p* and *q* are integers and $q \neq 0$; it is denoted by the letter Q

Irrational number: A number which cannot be written in the form of $\frac{p}{q}$, where *p* and *q* are integers and $q \neq 0$

Terminating decimal expansion: For any rational number $n = \frac{p}{q}$, if the prime factorisation of *q* is of the form 2^n5^m, where *n*, *m* are non-negative integers, then *n* has a terminating decimal expansion

Non-terminating decimal expansion: For any rational number $n = \frac{p}{q}$, if the prime factorisation of *q* is not of the form 2^n5^m, where *n*, *m* are non-negative integers, then *n* has a non-terminating or recurring decimal expansion

CONCEPT MAP

Real Numbers include:

- **Irrational numbers**
  Numbers whose decimal expansions are non-terminating and non-recurring
- **Rational numbers**
  Numbers which can be represented in the form of $\frac{p}{q}$, where p and q are integers and $q \neq 0$

Rational numbers have **Decimal expansions**, which can be:

- **Recurring and non-terminating decimals**
  If q is not of the form 2^n5^m, where m and n are non-negative integers
- **Terminating decimals**
  If q is of the form 2^n5^m, where m and n are non-negative integers

Rational numbers follow:

Euclid's division lemma:
If a and b are integers, there exist whole numbers q and r satisfying $a = bq + r, 0 \leq r < b$.

Euclid's division lemma is used in:

Euclid's division algorithm:
According to this, the HCF of any two positive integers a and b, with $a > b$, is obtained as follows:
Step 1: Apply the division lemma to find q and r, where $a = bq + r, 0 \leq r < b$.
Step 2: If $r = 0$, the HCF is b.
If $r \neq 0$, apply Euclid's lemma to b and r.
Step 3: Continue the process till the remainder is zero.
The divisor at this stage will be HCF(a, b).
Also, HCF(a, b) = HCF(b, r).

The Fundamental Theorem of Arithmetic:
The prime factorisation of any natural number is unique, except for the order of its factors.

The Fundamental Theorem of Arithmetic is used to prove:

- If p is a prime number and p divides a^2, then p divides a, where a is a positive integer.
- For any two positive integers a and b, HCF(a, b) and LCM(a, b) satisfy:
  HCF(a, b) × LCM(a, b) = $a \times b$

PART 1

CHAPTER 1: Real Numbers

SELF-ASSESSMENT 1

Choose the correct option.

1. The highest common factor (HCF) of 495 and 54 is equal to __________.
   A. 495×54
   B. 54
   C. 9
   D. 3

2. Given positive integers a and b, there exists unique integers q and r satisfying the equation $a = bq + r$, such that __________.
   A. $0 < r < b$
   B. $0 < r \leq b$
   C. $0 \leq r \leq b$
   D. $0 \leq r < b$

3. The prime factorisation of 6468 is equal to __________.
   A. $2 \times 3 \times 7 \times 11$
   B. $2^2 \times 3 \times 7^2 \times 11$
   C. $12 \times 7 \times 11 \times 13$
   D. $2^2 \times 3 \times 7 \times 13$

4. There are 315 sofa chairs and 180 stools to be arranged in a conference hall in the same number of columns. Find the maximum number of columns in which the sofa chairs and stools can be arranged.
   A. 5
   B. 45
   C. 60
   D. 90

5. The prime factorisation of any natural number is unique, except for the order of its factors. This statement is known as __________.
   A. Fundamental theorem of algebra
   B. Euclid's division of algorithm
   C. Euclid's prime factorisation theorem
   D. Fundamental Theorem of Arithmetic

6. For any two positive integers a and b such that $a \neq b$, HCF(a, b) and LCM(a, b) satisfy the condition __________.
   A. HCF(a, b) = LCM (a, b)
   B. HCF(a, b) > LCM(a, b)
   C. HCF(a, b) × LCM(a, b) = $a \times b$
   D. HCF(a, b) + LCM(a, b) = $a \times b$

7. If the HCF(238, 511) = 7, then the LCM(238, 511) = __________.
   A. 34×511
   B. $(238 \times 511) \times 7$
   C. $(238 + 511) \div 7$
   D. $(511 - 238) \div 7$

8. $\sqrt{2}$ is an irrational number because its __________.
   A. decimal representation is non-terminating
   B. decimal representation is non-recurring
   C. decimal representation is neither terminating nor recurring
   D. decimal value is approximately 1.41

9. If p is a prime number such that p^2 divides 123456, then ______________.

   A. p also divides 123456
   B. p^2 divides 456
   C. p divides 456
   D. p does not divide 123456

10. Find the value of x.

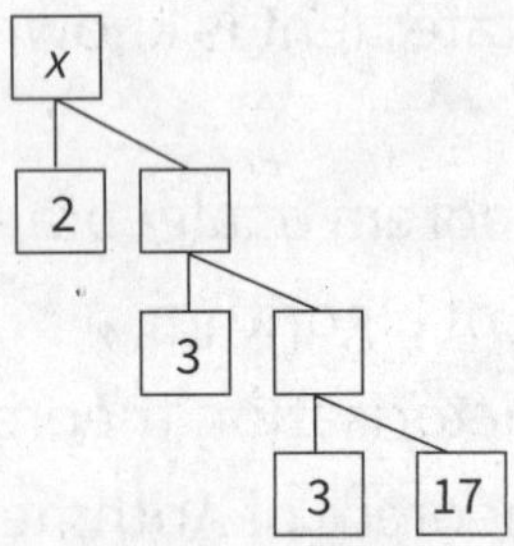

   A. 306
   B. 304
   C. 286
   D. 102

11. Denny and Shatsang take a circular path from the same point. Denny takes 39 minutes to complete a round, while Shatsang takes 91 minutes. Suppose they both start from the same point at the same time and go in the same direction, then after how minutes will they meet at the starting point?

   A. 39 minutes
   B. 91 minutes
   C. 273 minutes
   D. 3549 minutes

12. The LCM of two numbers is 441 and their HCF is 21. If one of the numbers is 63, find the other number.

   A. 21
   B. 129
   C. 147
   D. 294

13. Find the largest number that divides 197 and 349, leaving a remainder of 7.

   A. 19 B. 21
   C. 38 D. 39

14. The HCF(14, 91, 147) is equal to ________.

   A. $14 \times 91 \times 147$
   B. 14
   C. 7
   D. 2

15. Find the LCM of two positive integers $n = x^3y^2$ and $m = x^5y$, where x and y are prime numbers.

   A. xy
   B. x^5y^2
   C. x^3y^2
   D. x^5y

16. Lekha has three ribbons of length 42 m, 54 m and 78 m. Find the least possible number of equal pieces of ribbon she can cut from the given ribbons.

   A. 6 B. 7
   C. 12 D. 29

17. If n is a natural number, $5^{2n} - 3^{2n}$ is always divisible by ______.

   A. 2
   B. 5
   C. 8
   D. Both A and C

18. $5 \times 7 \times 11 \times 13 + 26$ is a composite number because it is divisible by _____.

   A. 2 B. 7
   C. 11 D. 13

19. Which of the following statements is correct for the number $6-\sqrt{5}$?

A. It is a rational number.

B. It is an irrational number.

C. It is a prime number.

D. Both A and C

20. Which of the following is true for the number 0.12012001200012000......?

A. It cannot be expressed in the form $\frac{p}{q}$.

B. It can be expressed in the form $\frac{p}{q}$.

C. It is a rational number.

D. It is a repeating decimal expansion.

21. An irrational number is a number which has ____________.

A. a terminating decimal expansion

B. a non-terminating decimal expansion

C. a recurring decimal expansion

D. neither a recurring nor a terminating decimal expansion

22. The number $\frac{18524}{1375}$ can be expressed as __________.

A. $\frac{2^5 \times 421}{2^3 \times 5^3}$

B. $\frac{13472}{10^3}$

C. 13.472

D. All of these

23. The decimal expansion of $\frac{88769}{2^2 \times 5^3}$ will terminate after ____________.

A. one decimal place

B. two decimal places

C. three decimal places

D. four decimal places

24. The decimal expansion of $\frac{78939}{2^2 \times 3^2 \times 5^3}$ is a ____________.

A. terminating decimal

B. non-terminating but recurring decimal

C. non-terminating and non-recurring decimal

D. whole number

25. Which of the following is the simplest form of the decimal number 0.104?

A. $\frac{21}{200}$

B. $\frac{13}{125}$

C. $\frac{13}{25}$

D. $\frac{23}{125}$

SELF-ASSESSMENT 2

Choose the correct option.

26. Find the value of a, if the HCF of 76 and 133 is expressed as $76a - 133$.
    A. 1
    B. 2
    C. 3
    D. 4

27. Given positive integers a and 5, there exist unique integers q and r satisfying the equation $a = 5q + r$, such that ___________.
    A. $0 < r < 5$
    B. $1 \leq r \leq 5$
    C. $0 \leq r < 5$
    D. $1 \leq r < 5$

28. Find the HCF of 459 and 135.
    A. 7
    B. 9
    C. 21
    D. 27

29. Find the HCF of 1001 and 266.
    A. 1
    B. 7
    C. 11
    D. 13

30. If the HCF(238, 406) = 14, then the LCM(238, 406) is equal to ______.
    A. 6902 B. 5992
    C. 5684 D. 4012

31. The LCM(16, 48, 64) is equal to _________.
    A. $16 \times 48 \times 64$
    B. 192
    C. 64
    D. 4

32. Find the HCF of two positive integers $n = x^6y^4$ and $m = x^2y^3$, where x and y are prime numbers.
    A. xy B. x^2y^3
    C. x^4y D. x^8y^7

33. Find the smallest 5-digit number which when divided by 5, 7, 14, 21 and 56 leaves no remainder.
    A. 10,000
    B. 10,080
    C. 11,060
    D. 11,680

34. A gardener has to arrange flower pots for a flower show. He has 135 pots with red roses, 195 pots with yellow roses and 105 pots with white roses. The gardener wants to arrange the pots in such a way that each row has an equal and the maximum number of pots. Find the total number of rows in the arrangement if each row can have only one type of flower.
    A. 29
    B. 21
    C. 15
    D. 13

35. Find the HCF of $2^4 \times 3^4$ and $4^2 \times 3^5$.

A. $4^2 \times 3^4$

B. $2^4 \times 3^5$

C. $4^4 \times 3^5$

D. $2^2 \times 3^4$

36. Find the maximum length of the equal-sized rod pieces that can be cut from 2 m 52 cm, 3 m 36 cm and 4 m 20 cm rods.

A. 86 cm

B. 84 cm

C. 54 cm

D. 48 cm

37. The LCM of two numbers is 322 and the product of the numbers is 7406. Find the HCF of the numbers.

A. 23 B. 27

C. 46 D. 49

38. Find the least number which is divisible by the first six natural numbers.

A. 12

B. 24

C. 60

D. 120

39. What is the HCF of two consecutive natural numbers *n* and *m*?

A. 1

B. *n*

C. *m*

D. *nm*

40. Find the number of prime factors in the prime factorisation of 1045.

A. 3 B. 4

C. 5 D. 6

41. $3 \times 5 \times 11 \times 19 + 22$ is a composite number because it is divisible by ___.

A. 2 B. 6

C. 11 D. 13

42. Find the value of *x*.

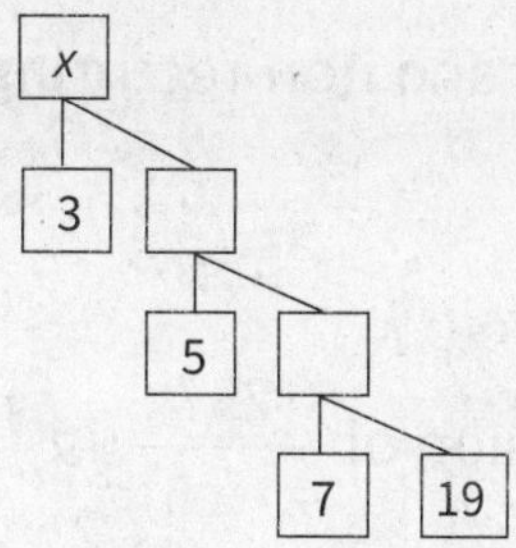

A. 665

B. 1995

C. 1985

D. 2793

43. Which of the following statements is correct for the product of $2\sqrt{5}$ and $3+\sqrt{5}$?

A. It is a rational number.

B. It is an irrational number.

C. It is a prime number.

D. It is a multiple of 5.

44. Which of the following is not an irrational number?

A. $2-\sqrt{2}$ B. $2\times\sqrt{3}$

C. $5\div\sqrt{5}$ D. $\sqrt{5}\times\sqrt{5}$

45. The decimal expansion of $\frac{24175}{2^2 \times 5^3}$ will terminate after __________.

A. one decimal place

B. two decimal places

C. three decimal places

D. four decimal places

46. The decimal expansion of $\frac{4521}{2^2 \times 7 \times 5^3}$ is a ___________________.

A. terminating decimal

B. non-terminating but recurring decimal

C. non-terminating and non-recurring decimal

D. whole number

47. The decimal expansion of $\frac{237}{2^2 \times 5^2}$ is __________.

A. 47.5

B. 23.7

C. 4.75

D. 2.37

48. If $37.\overline{37}$ is represented as a rational number of the form $\frac{p}{q}$, what can be concluded about the prime factors of q?

A. It is of the form $2^n 5^m$.

B. It is not of the form $2^n 5^m$.

C. $q > p$

D. q is a prime number.

49. Pick the odd one out with respect to their decimal places.

A. $\frac{3425}{2^4 \times 5^3}$

B. $\frac{6325}{2^3 \times 5^4}$

C. $\frac{5622}{2^4 \times 5^3}$

D. $\frac{3696}{2^3 \times 3 \times 5^3}$

50. Which of the following has a non-terminating decimal expansion?

A. $\frac{285}{45}$

B. $\frac{456}{15}$

C. $\frac{723}{8}$

D. $\frac{832}{25}$

CHAPTER 2

Polynomials

PRIOR KNOWLEDGE TEST

Choose the correct option.

1. Which of the following is not a polynomial?

   A. $\frac{x}{\sqrt{5}}$ B. $4-3\sqrt{x}$

   C. $\frac{x^3}{5}-\frac{x}{25^{-2}}$ D. $\frac{x}{2^{-3}}$

2. Which of the following is a linear polynomial?

   A. $a+\frac{1}{a}$ B. $a+7$

   C. $5\sqrt{5}a^3-3$ D. a^2+6a+9

3. What is the zero of the polynomial $2x+3$?

   A. 3 B. $\frac{2}{3}$ C. $\frac{-3}{2}$ D. −2

4. What is the remainder when $(x^{72}+72)$ is divided by $(x+1)$?

   A. 0 B. 71

   C. 72 D. 73

5. Which of the following is a factor of the polynomial $x^3+12x^2+47x+60$?

   A. $(x+3)$ B. $(x-4)$

   C. $(x-5)$ D. All of these

KEYWORDS

Linear polynomial: A polynomial of degree 1

Quadratic polynomial: A polynomial of degree 2

Cubic polynomial: A polynomial of degree 3

- If $p(x)$ is a polynomial in x, and if k is any real number, then the value obtained by replacing x by k in $p(x)$ is called the value of $p(x)$ at $x = k$, and is denoted by $p(k)$

Zero of a polynomial: If k is a zero of the polynomial $p(x) = ax + b$, then

$$p(k) = ak + b = 0, \text{ that is, } k = \frac{-b}{a}$$

- Graph of a linear polynomial $ax + b$, $a \neq 0$, is a straight line.
- Graph of a quadratic polynomial $ax^2 + bx + c$, $a \neq 0$, is a parabola.
- If α and β are the zeros of a quadratic polynomial $p(x) = ax^2 + bx + c$, $a \neq 0$, then the sum of the zeros $= \alpha + \beta = \frac{-b}{a}$ and the product of the zeros $= \alpha\beta = \frac{c}{a}$

Division algorithm: If $p(x)$ and $g(x)$ are any two polynomials with $g(x) \neq 0$, then we can find polynomials $q(x)$ and $r(x)$ such that $p(x) = g(x) \times q(x) + r(x)$, where $r(x) = 0$ or degree of $r(x)$ < degree of $g(x)$

CONCEPT MAP

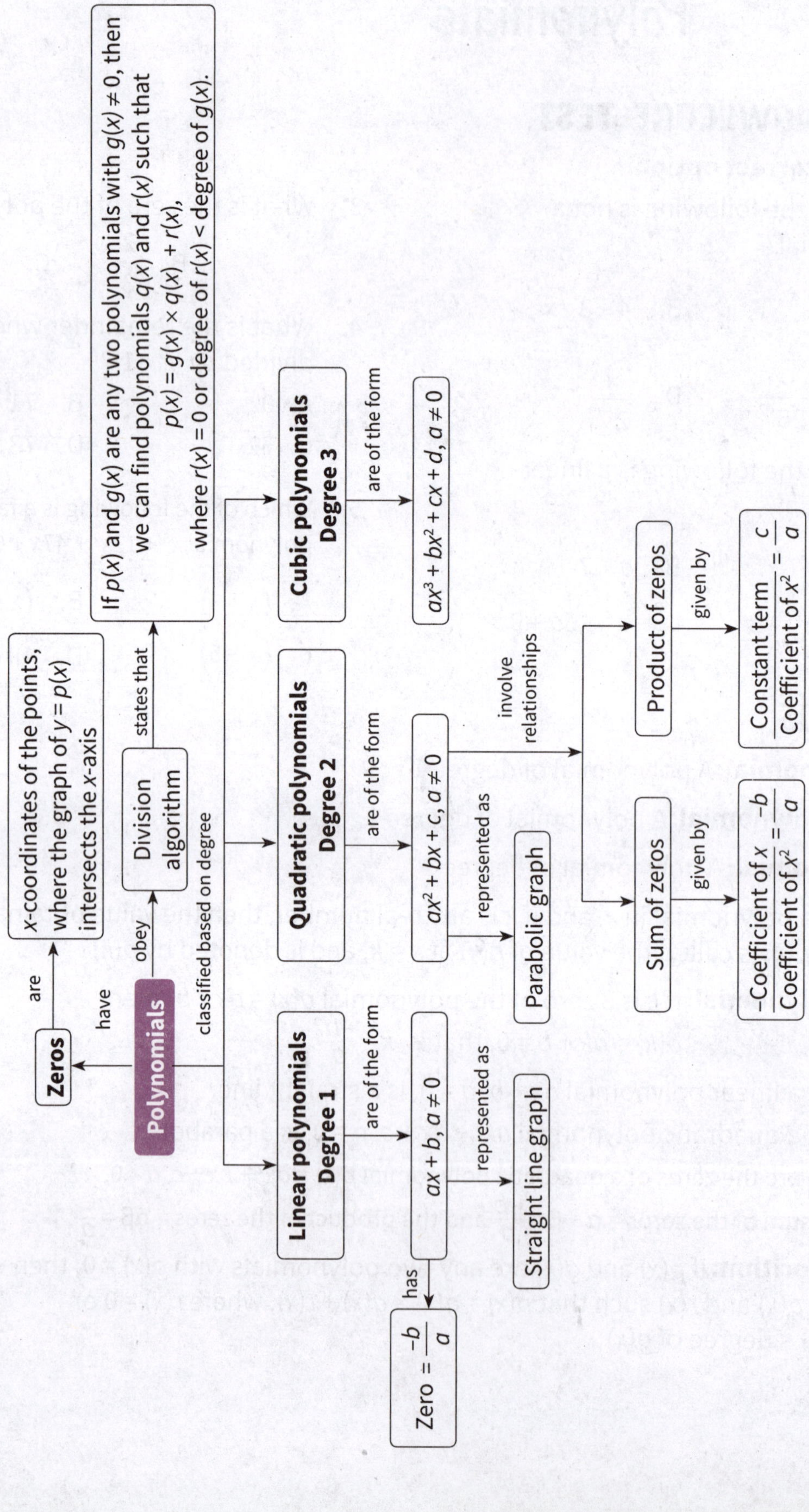
Zeros
are
x-coordinates of the points, where the graph of $y = p(x)$ intersects the x-axis
have
Polynomials
obey
Division algorithm
states that
If $p(x)$ and $g(x)$ are any two polynomials with $g(x) \neq 0$, then we can find polynomials $q(x)$ and $r(x)$ such that $p(x) = g(x) \times q(x) + r(x)$, where $r(x) = 0$ or degree of $r(x)$ < degree of $g(x)$.
classified based on degree
Linear polynomials Degree 1
Quadratic polynomials Degree 2
Cubic polynomials Degree 3
are of the form
are of the form
are of the form
$ax + b, a \neq 0$
$ax^2 + bx + c, a \neq 0$
$ax^3 + bx^2 + cx + d, a \neq 0$
has
Zero = $\frac{-b}{a}$
represented as
Straight line graph
represented as
Parabolic graph
involve relationships
Sum of zeros
Product of zeros
given by
given by
$\frac{-\text{Coefficient of } x}{\text{Coefficient of } x^2} = \frac{-b}{a}$
$\frac{\text{Constant term}}{\text{Coefficient of } x^2} = \frac{c}{a}$

PART 1

CHAPTER 2: Polynomials

SELF-ASSESSMENT 1

Choose the correct option.

1. Which of the following is a quadratic polynomial?
   A. $5x+7$
   B. $x^2+15x-34$
   C. $3x^3+5x^2-8x-53$
   D. x^4-16

2. Which of the following is a zero of the polynomial $3x+12$?
   A. 3 B. 4
   C. –4 D. –6

3. What is the value of the polynomial x^3-3x^2-3x-6 if $x=3$?
   A. 3 B. –3
   C. –60 D. –15

4. Which of the following is not a factor of the polynomial x^3-7x-6?
   A. $(x+1)$ B. $(x+2)$
   C. $(x+3)$ D. $(x-3)$

5. Find the number of zeros of the polynomial $p(x)$ from the given graph.

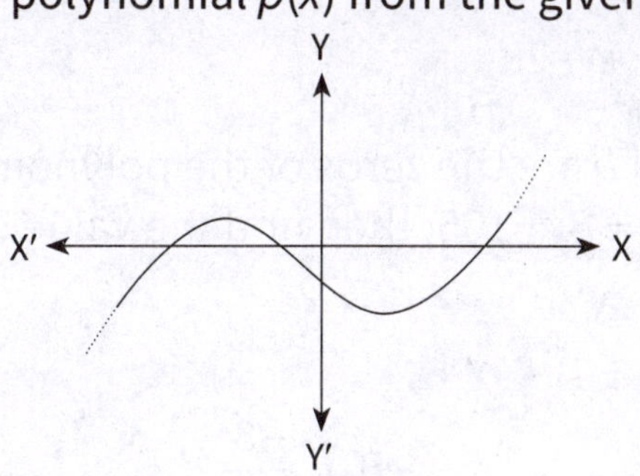

   A. 1 B. 2
   C. 3 D. 4

6. Which of the following is the graph of a quadratic polynomial?
   A. Straight line
   B. Parabola
   C. Circle
   D. Ellipse

7. If the graph of a polynomial touches x-axis at one point and y-axis at two points, find the number of zeros of the polynomial.
   A. 0
   B. 1
   C. 2
   D. 3

8. Find the polynomial for the following graph.

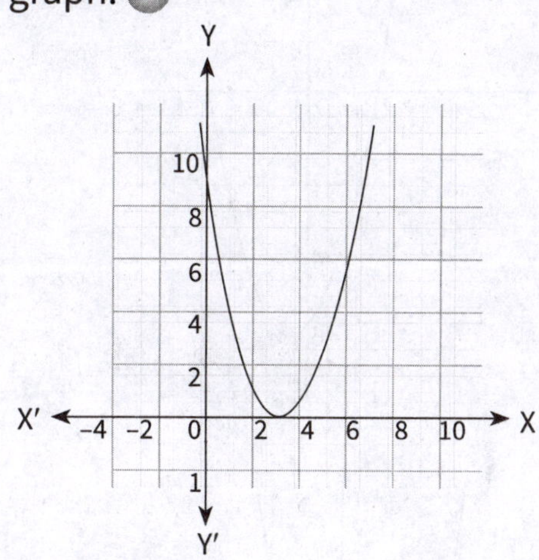

   A. x^2+6x+9
   B. x^2-6x+9
   C. x^2-9
   D. $x-3$

9. Which of the following graphs represents the polynomial $x^2 - 5x + 6$?

A.

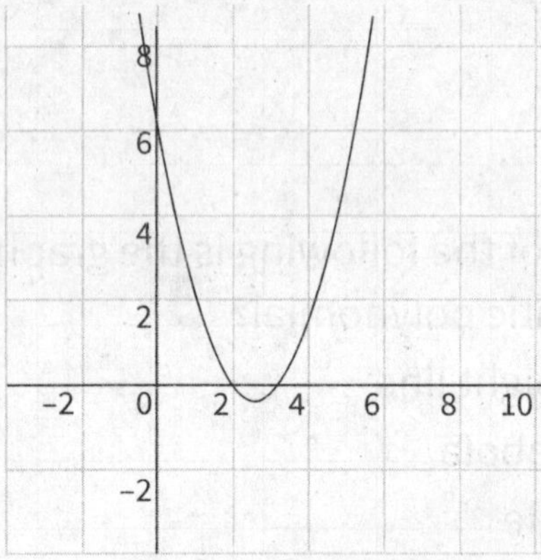

B.

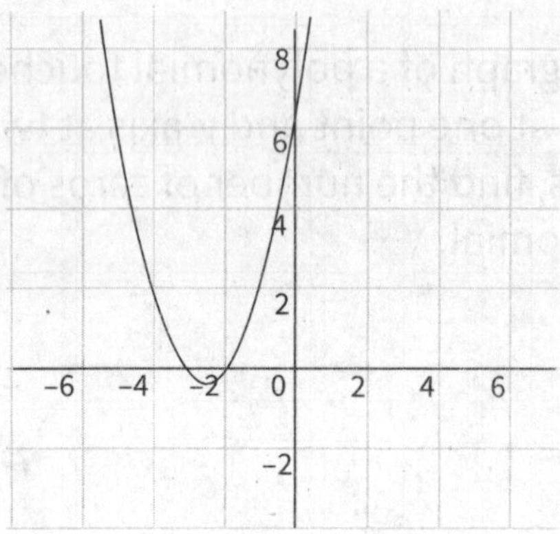

C.

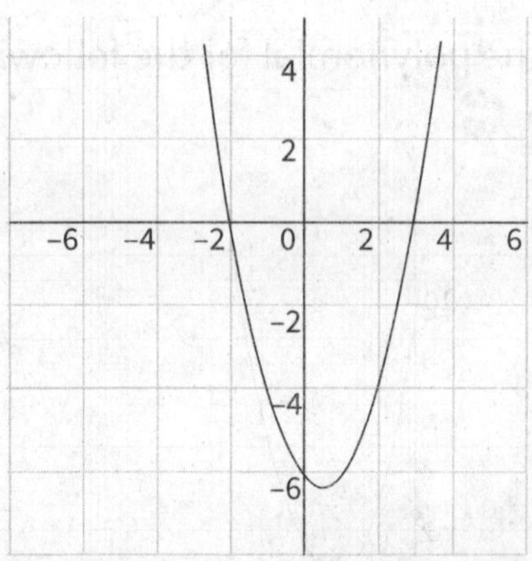

D.

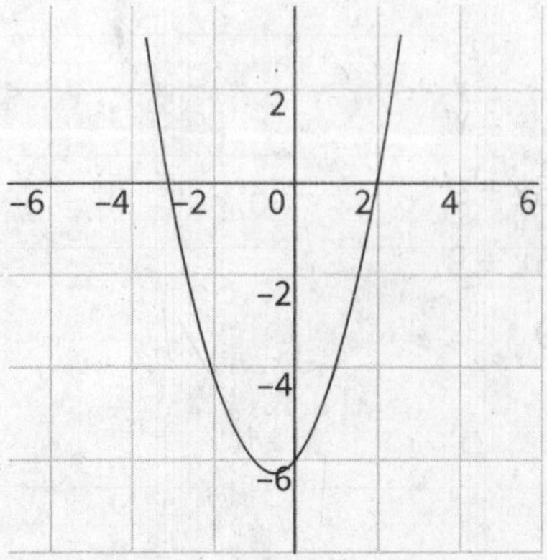

10. If the zeros of the polynomial $ax^2 + bx + c, c \neq 0$, are equal, then which of the following is always true?

A. *c* and *a* have opposite signs.

B. *c* and *b* have opposite signs.

C. *c* and *a* have the same sign.

D. *c* and *b* have the same sign.

11. What are the zeros of the polynomial $x^2 - 2x - 24$?

A. 6 and 4

B. –6 and 4

C. –6 and –4

D. 6 and –4

12. The zeros of a polynomial are $\frac{3}{2}$ and $\frac{5}{2}$. Find the polynomial.

A. $x^2 - 8x + 15$

B. $x^2 + 8x + 15$

C. $4x^2 - 16x - 60$

D. $4x^2 - 16x + 15$

13. Find the quadratic polynomial if the sum of their zeros is 1 and the product of their zeros is –20.

A. $x^2 + x + 20$

B. $x^2 - x + 20$

C. $x^2 - x - 20$

D. $x^2 + x + 20$

14. If *a* and *b* are the zeros of the polynomial $f(x) = x^2 - 8x - 105$, then find the value of $\frac{1}{a} + \frac{1}{b}$.

A. $\frac{8}{105}$

B. $\frac{-8}{105}$

C. $\frac{-105}{8}$

D. $\frac{105}{8}$

15. If one zero of the polynomial $p(x)=x^2+ax+18$ is twice the other, find the value of a.

A. 3 B. -6

C. 9 D. -3

16. If the sum of the zeros of the polynomial $kx^2+(2k+3)x+4$ is –5, find the value of k.

A. 1 B. 2

C. 4 D. -4

17. Find the quadratic polynomial if the sum and the product of its zeros are $\sqrt{2}$ and -4, respectively.

A. $x^2+\sqrt{2}x-4$

B. $x^2-\sqrt{2}x+4$

C. $x^2+\sqrt{2}x+4$

D. $x^2-\sqrt{2}x-4$

18. What can you say about the zeros of the polynomial $x^2-77x+360$?

A. Both are positive.

B. Both are negative.

C. One is positive and one is negative.

D. Both are equal.

19. If the product of the zeros of the polynomial $x^2-kx+(k+4)$ is 12, find the zeros of the polynomial.

A. 6 and 2 B. -6 and -2

C. 3 and 4 D. -3 and -4

20. If $(x-2)$ is a factor of the polynomial x^2+ax+b and $(a+b)=-7$, what is the other factor?

A. $(x-5)$ B. $(x+5)$

C. $(x+2)$ D. $(x+8)$

21. Find the quotient and the remainder when the polynomial $p(x)=x^3+x^2-22x-35$ is divided by the polynomial $g(x)=(x-5)$.

A. Quotient = x^2+6x+8, remainder = 5

B. Quotient = x^2+6x+8, remainder = –5

C. Quotient = x^2+6x-8, remainder = –5

D. Quotient = x^2-6x+8, remainder = 5

22. Which of the following is a factor of the polynomial x^3-6x^2-6x-7?

A. x^2+x-1 B. x^2-x-1

C. x^2+x+1 D. x^2-x+1

23. On dividing the polynomial $x^3+8x^2-9x-69$ by a polynomial $g(x)$, the quotient and the remainder obtained are x^2-9 and 3, respectively. Find $g(x)$.

A. $(x+3)$ B. $(x+8)$

C. $(x-8)$ D. $(x-3)$

24. If two zeros of the polynomial $x^4-x^3-9x^2+3x+18$ are $\sqrt{3}$ and $-\sqrt{3}$, what are the other two zeros?

A. 2, 3 B. -2, -3

C. 2, -3 D. -2, 3

25. Which of the polynomials leaves the remainder zero when divided by x^2+3?

A. $x^4-3x^3-25x^2-9x-84$

B. x^4+9

C. x^4+3x^2+9

D. x^4-6x^2+9

PART 1

CHAPTER 2: Polynomials

SELF-ASSESSMENT 2

Choose the correct option.

26. How many zeros does a polynomial of degree *n* always have?
    A. Only 1 zero
    B. At most *n* zeros
    C. Exactly *n* zeros
    D. At least *n* zeros

27. Find the odd one out.
    A. $25x^3+7$
    B. $x^2+15x-34$
    C. $x^2-8x-53$
    D. x^2-81

28. Find the zero of the polynomial $2x+8$.
    A. 8
    B. -8
    C. 4
    D. -4

29. Find the value of the polynomial $2x^3+4x^2+11x+12$, if $x=-2$.
    A. -10
    B. 10
    C. 34
    D. 66

30. Which of the following is a factor of the polynomial x^8-256?
    A. x^4-16
    B. x^2+4
    C. $(x-2)$
    D. All of these

31. Find the graph in which the number of zeros of the polynomial is 2.

A.

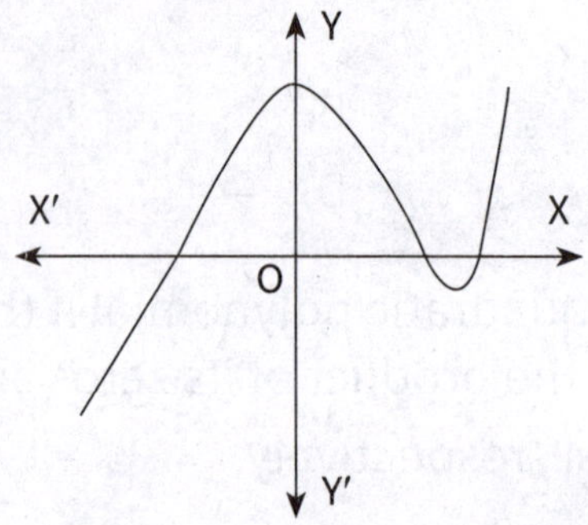

B.

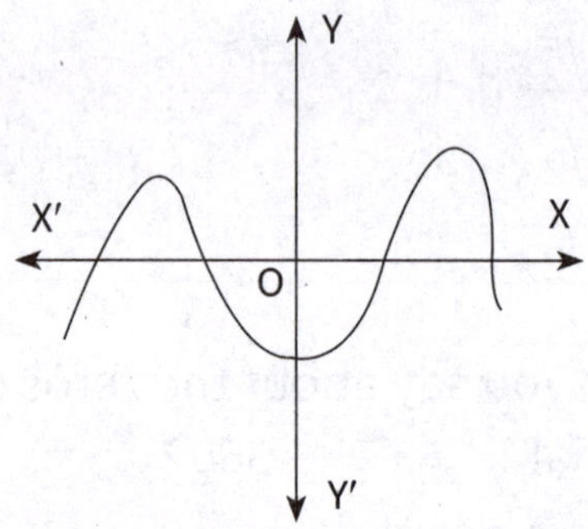

C.

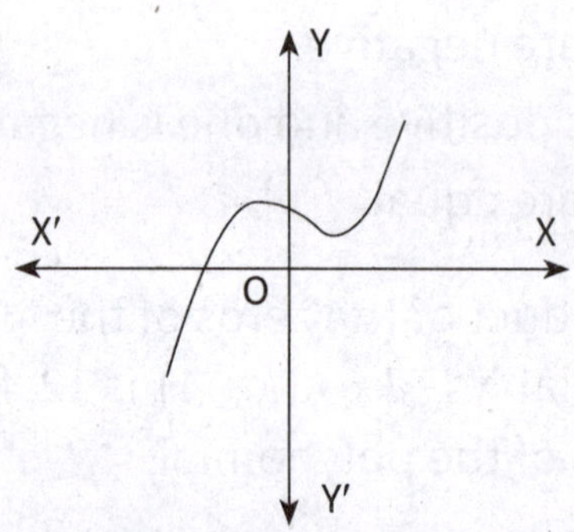

D.

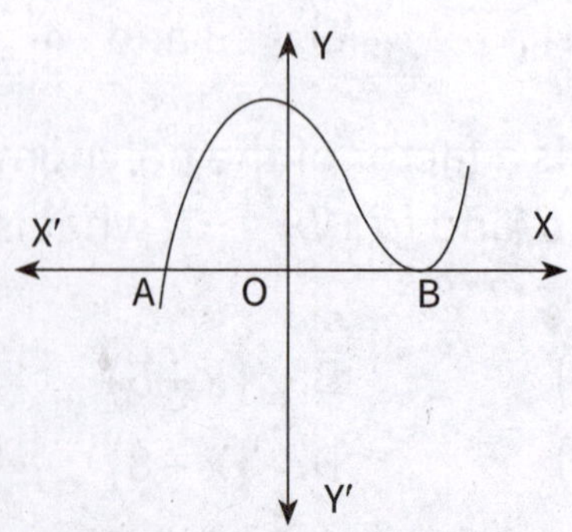

32. Find the number of zeros of the polynomial represented by the graph given below.

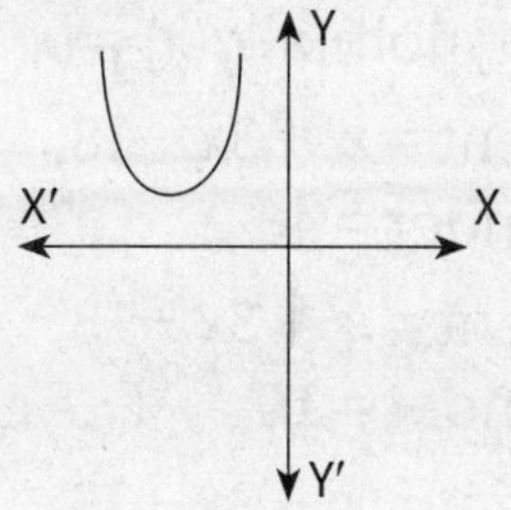

A. 0
B. 1
C. 2
D. 3

33. Find the quadratic polynomial from the given graph.

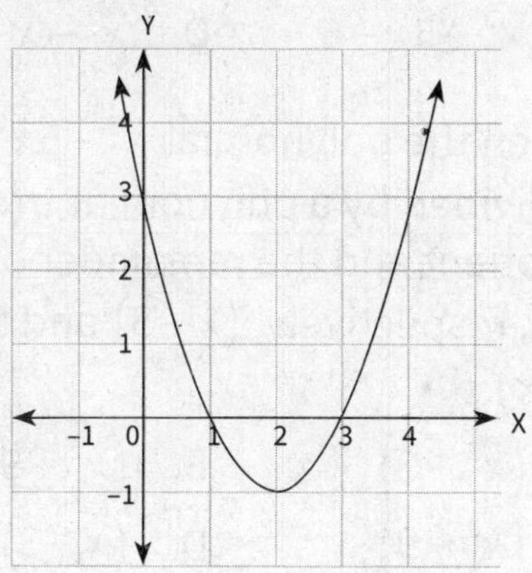

A. x^2+4x+3
B. x^2-4x+3
C. x^2+4x-3
D. x^2-4x-3

34. If the graph of a polynomial does not intersect the y-axis at any point, but intersects the x-axis at three points, find the number of zeros of the polynomial.

A. 0
B. 1
C. 2
D. 3

35. For a given quadratic polynomial of the form ax^2+bx+c, which of the following represents the sum and the product of the zeros, respectively?

A. $\frac{b}{a}, \frac{c}{a}$

B. $\frac{-b}{a}, \frac{c}{a}$

C. $\frac{b}{a}, \frac{-c}{b}$

D. $\frac{-b}{c}, \frac{c}{a}$

36. If one zero of the polynomial x^2-2x+k is 5, find the other zero.

A. 3 B. −3
C. −5 D. −2

37. What are the zeros of the polynomial $2x^2-5x-18$?

A. 9 and −4
B. −9 and 4
C. −2 and $\frac{9}{2}$
D. 2 and $\frac{-9}{2}$

38. The zeros of a polynomial are $\frac{7}{2}$ and 4. Find the polynomial.

A. $x^2-14x+28$
B. $2x^2+15x+14$
C. $2x^2-15x+28$
D. $x^2-15x+14$

39. If one zero of the polynomial $x^2-kx+(k+1)$ is 2, find its other zero.

A. −3 B. 3
C. −2 D. 5

40. If l and m are the zeros of the polynomial $f(x) = 2x^2 - 7x - 30$, then find the value of $l^2 + m^2$.

A. $\frac{49}{4}$ B. -30

C. $\frac{169}{4}$ D. $\frac{-169}{4}$

41. If one zero of the polynomial $p(x) = x^2 + ax + 27$ is thrice the other, find the value of a.

A. -12 B. 9

C. 3 D. -9

42. If the product of the zeros of the polynomial $px^2 - 2x + (p-4)$ is -3, find the zeros of the polynomial.

A. $3, \frac{1}{2}$ B. $-2, \frac{1}{2}$

C. $3, -1$ D. $-3, 1$

43. Which of the following polynomials has the sum of its zeros equal to zero?

A. $x^2 - 12x + 36$ B. $x^2 + 12x - 36$

C. $x^2 - 36$ D. $x^2 - x - 2$

44. Which of the polynomials has the sum of its zeros equal to the product of its zeros?

A. $x^2 + 4x + 4$ B. $x^2 - 4x + 4$

C. $x^2 - 2x + 1$ D. $x^2 - 2x + 2$

45. If $(x - 1)$ and $(x - 8)$ are the two factors of the polynomial $x^3 - ax^2 + bx - 24$, find the values of a and b.

A. 12 and 35

B. -12 and -35

C. -12 and 35

D. 12 and -35

46. Find the quotient and the remainder when the polynomial $p(x) = x^4 + 3x^3 - 19x^2 - 3x + 28$ is divided by the polynomial $g(x) = (x^2 - 1)$.

A. Quotient $= x^2 + 3x - 18$, remainder $= 46$

B. Quotient $= x^2 + 3x - 18$, remainder $= 10$

C. Quotient $= x^2 - 3x - 18$, remainder $= 10$

D. Quotient $= x^2 - 3x + 18$, remainder $= -10$

47. Which of the following is not a factor of the polynomial $x^4 + 4x^3 - 5x^2 - 36x - 36$?

A. $x^2 - 9$ B. $x^2 + 4x + 4$

C. $x^2 + 5x + 6$ D. $x^2 - x + 6$

48. When the polynomial $x^3 + 5x^2 - 9x - 40$ is divided by a polynomial $g(x)$, the quotient and the remainder obtained are, respectively, $(x+5)$ and 5. Find $g(x)$.

A. $(x^2 + 3)$ B. $(x^2 + 9)$

C. $(x^2 - 9)$ D. $(x - 3)$

49. If two zeros of the polynomial $4x^4 - 16x^3 + 11x^2 + 16x - 15$ are $\frac{3}{2}$ and $\frac{5}{2}$, find the other two zeros.

A. 1 and -1 B. -1 and -2

C. 1 and -2 D. -1 and 2

50. What should be subtracted from the polynomial $2x^3 + 3x^2 - 5x - 60$ so that it is exactly divisible by $(x - 3)$?

A. 6

B. -6

C. 12

D. -12

CHAPTER 3

Pair of Linear Equations in Two Variables

PRIOR KNOWLEDGE TEST

Choose the correct option.

1. The equation $4x - 5y = 6$ has __________.
   A. a unique solution
   B. two solutions
   C. no solution
   D. many solutions

2. The sum of two numbers is 4 more than thrice their difference. Express this as a linear equation in two variables.
   A. $x - y = 3(x + y + 4)$
   B. $x + y = 3(x - y) + 4$
   C. $x + y = 3(x - y + 4)$
   D. $x + y + 4 = 3(x - y)$

3. Which of the following is not the solution for $3x + 5y = 21$?
   A. (2, 3) B. (–3, 6)
   C. (9, –1) D. (7, 0)

4. If (3, –1) is a solution to the linear equation $9x - 2y = t$, find the value of t.
   A. 25 B. 27
   C. 29 D. 31

5. Find the linear equation which has (–1, 2), (0, 2) and (2, 2) as solution.
   A. $y - x = 2$ B. $x + 2y = 0$
   C. $-2x + 2 = 2$ D. $0 \times x + y = 2$

KEYWORDS

Linear equation in two variables: An equation with two variables, where the highest power of the variables is 1

Solution of an equation: The value of the variable(s) which satisfies the equation

Consistent: A pair of linear equations is consistent if they have a unique solution or the lines represented by them intersect at a single point

Dependent/equivalent: A pair of linear equations is said to be dependent if they have infinitely many solutions or the lines represented by them coincide

Inconsistent: A pair of linear equations is said to be inconsistent if they have no solution or the lines represented by them are parallel

Substitution method: The value of one variable is substituted by expressing it in terms of the other variable to solve a given pair of linear equations

Elimination method: The method of eliminating one variable first, to get a linear equation in the other variable

Cross-multiplication: In the pair of linear equations $a_1x + b_1y + c_1 = 0$ and $a_2x + b_2y + c_2 = 0$,

$$\frac{x}{b_1c_2 - b_2c_1} = \frac{y}{c_1a_2 - c_2a_1} = \frac{1}{a_1b_2 - a_2b_1}$$

CONCEPT MAP

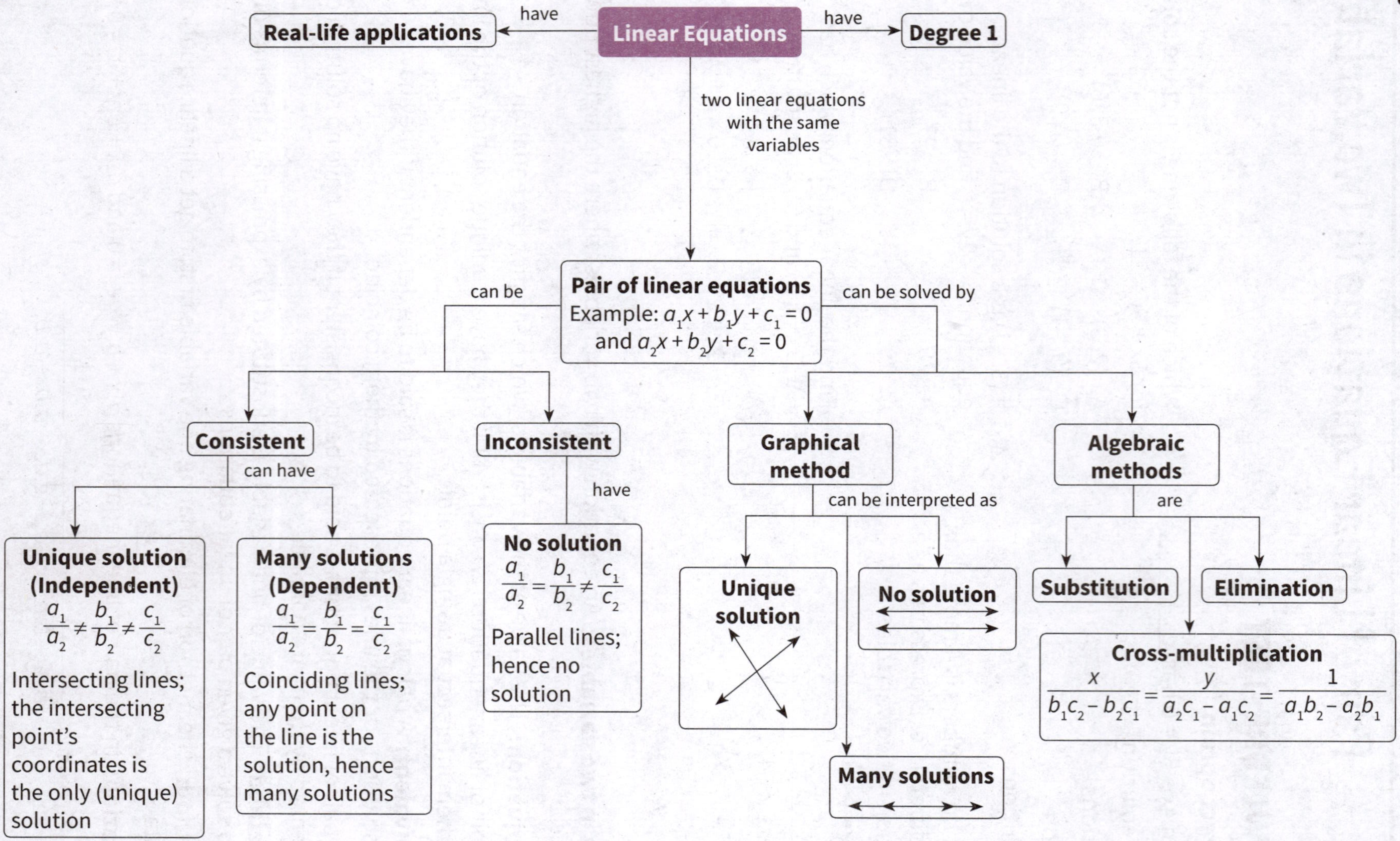

Linear Equations
have
Real-life applications
have
Degree 1
two linear equations with the same variables
Pair of linear equations
Example: $a_1x + b_1y + c_1 = 0$ and $a_2x + b_2y + c_2 = 0$
can be
can be solved by
Consistent
can have
Unique solution (Independent)
$\frac{a_1}{a_2} \neq \frac{b_1}{b_2} \neq \frac{c_1}{c_2}$
Intersecting lines; the intersecting point's coordinates is the only (unique) solution
Many solutions (Dependent)
$\frac{a_1}{a_2} = \frac{b_1}{b_2} = \frac{c_1}{c_2}$
Coinciding lines; any point on the line is the solution, hence many solutions
Inconsistent
have
No solution
$\frac{a_1}{a_2} = \frac{b_1}{b_2} \neq \frac{c_1}{c_2}$
Parallel lines; hence no solution
Graphical method
can be interpreted as
Unique solution
No solution
Many solutions
Algebraic methods
are
Substitution
Elimination
Cross-multiplication
$\frac{x}{b_1c_2 - b_2c_1} = \frac{y}{a_2c_1 - a_1c_2} = \frac{1}{a_1b_2 - a_2b_1}$

PART 1

CHAPTER 3: Pair of Linear Equations in Two Variables

SELF-ASSESSMENT 1

Choose the correct option.

1. The linear equations $x + y = 2$ and $3x + 3y = 6$ have __________.
   A. no common point
   B. a single common point
   C. many common points
   D. only two common points

2. Select the pair of equations which is consistent and independent.
   A. $3x - 7y - 9 = 0$ and $6x - 14y - 2 = 0$
   B. $4x + 3y = 5$ and $3x + 4y = 5$
   C. $5x + 3y - 12 = 0$ and $65x + 39y - 156 = 0$
   D. $2x - y = 9$ and $14x - 7y - 63 = 0$

3. If we consider the two linear equations $x - 2y = 0$ and $3x + 4y = 20$ and compare them with the general equations $a_1x + b_1y + c_1 = 0$ and $a_2x + b_2y + c_2 = 0$, then the value of $\frac{a_1}{a_2}$ is equal to _____.
   A. $\frac{-2}{4}$
   B. $\frac{0}{20}$
   C. $\frac{1}{-2}$
   D. $\frac{1}{3}$

4. Which of the following is the geometrical representation for the equations $3x - 15y = 0$ and $13x - 65y = 1$?
   A. 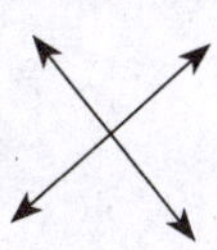
   B. 
   C. 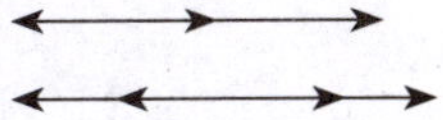
   D. 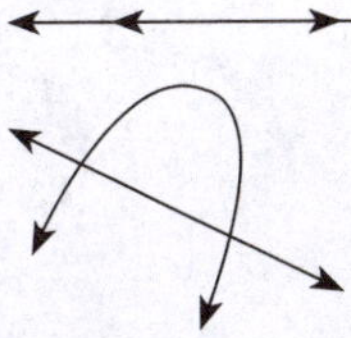

5. Select the correct statement for the following pair of linear equations in two variables: $x + y = 2$ and $2x + 2y = 4$.
   A. $\frac{a_1}{a_2} = \frac{b_1}{b_2} = \frac{c_1}{c_2} = 4$
   B. $\frac{a_1}{a_2} = \frac{b_1}{b_2} = \frac{c_1}{c_2} = \frac{1}{2}$
   C. $\frac{a_1}{a_2} \neq \frac{b_1}{b_2} \neq \frac{c_1}{c_2}$
   D. $\frac{a_1}{a_2} = \frac{b_1}{b_2} \neq \frac{c_1}{c_2}$

6. Select the correct statement.
   A. The lines represented by the equations $x + y = 1$ and $2x + 2y = 4$ are intersecting.
   B. The lines represented by the equations $2x + 2y = 4$ and $4x + 4y = 8$ are parallel.
   C. The lines represented by the equations $2x + 3y = 4$ and $2x + 3y = 7$ are parallel.
   D. The lines represented by the equations $2x + 3y = 4$ and $2x + 3y = 9$ are intersecting.

7. Which of the following is correct for the straight lines given by the equations $x + 3y = 6$ and $2x - 3y = 12$?
   A. They meet at the point (0, 0).
   B. They meet at the point (6, 0).
   C. They do not meet at all.
   D. They overlap.

8. Which of the following is the graphical representation of the pair of equations $x = -7$ and $y = 2$?
   A. Straight lines intersecting at (7, 2)
   B. Parallel lines
   C. Straight lines intersecting at (–2, 7)
   D. Straight lines intersecting at (–7, 2)

9. Which of the following gives a unique solution for the equation $4x + 6y = 18$?
   A. $-14x - 21y = 63$
   B. $3x + 9y = 27$
   C. $4x + 6y = 56$
   D. $2x + 3y = 9$

10. The sum of a two-digit number and the number obtained by reversing the order of its digits is 88. This statement can be written as ___________.
   A. $(x + y) + (y + x) = 88$
   B. $(10x + y) + (10y + x) = 88$
   C. $(x - y) + (y - x) = 88$
   D. $(10x - y) + (10y - x) = 88$

11. For what values of p, the following pair of equations $4x + py + 8 = 0$ and $2x + 2y + 4 = 0$ have many solutions?
   A. All values of p
   B. All values of p except $p = 4$
   C. $p = 4$
   D. $p = 0$

12. For what values of t, the pair of equations $x + (2t - 1)y - 2 = 0$ and $(2t - 1)x + 25y = t + 7$ have infinitely many solutions?
   A. $t = 5$ B. $t = 3$
   C. $t = 2$ D. $t = 0$

13. One year ago, Harish's age was twice the age of his sister. Four years from now, Harish's age will be 10 more than half the age of his sister. Find the present age of Harish and his sister.
   A. 11, 6
   B. 13, 7
   C. 5, 12
   D. 6, 10

14. Find the value of y by solving the pair of equations $\sqrt{2}x + \sqrt{3}y = 0$ and $\sqrt{3}x - 2\sqrt{2}y = \sqrt{2}$.
   A. $y = \sqrt{2}$
   B. $y = 0$
   C. $y = \frac{-2}{7}$
   D. $y = \frac{-\sqrt{2}}{\sqrt{3}}$

15. Which of the following substitutions is the most suitable for solving the pair of equations $\frac{2}{\sqrt{x}} + \frac{3}{\sqrt{y}} = 2$ and $\frac{4}{\sqrt{x}} - \frac{4}{\sqrt{y}} = -1$?
   A. $x = a$ and $y = b$
   B. $\frac{1}{x} = 4$ and $\frac{1}{y} = -4$
   C. $\frac{1}{\sqrt{x}} = 4$ and $\frac{1}{\sqrt{y}} = 4$
   D. $\frac{1}{\sqrt{x}} = a$ and $\frac{1}{\sqrt{y}} = b$

16. Find the solution to the pair of linear equations $\frac{2}{x}+\frac{3}{y}=13$ and $\frac{5}{x}-\frac{4}{y}=-2$.

A. $x=2, y=3$

B. $x=\frac{1}{3}, y=\frac{1}{2}$

C. $x=\frac{1}{2}, y=\frac{1}{2}$

D. $x=\frac{1}{2}, y=\frac{1}{3}$

17. Find the solution to the pair of linear equations $\frac{10}{x-1}+\frac{2}{y+1}=4$ and $\frac{15}{x-1}-\frac{5}{y+1}=-2$.

A. $x=5, y=2$

B. $x=\frac{1}{2}, y=\frac{1}{5}$

C. $x=6, y=0$

D. $x=\frac{1}{6}, y=1$

18. The cost price of two types of bags is in the ratio of 4 : 5; and the selling price of the bags is in the ratio of 5 : 6. If both the bags earn a profit of ₹30, find the cost price of both the bags.

A. ₹300, ₹330

B. ₹150, ₹180

C. ₹120, ₹150

D. ₹30, ₹30

19. The cost of 10 masks and 15 sanitizer bottles is ₹945; and the cost of 15 masks and 10 sanitizer bottles is ₹755. Find the cost of one mask and a sanitizer bottle.

A. ₹15, ₹53

B. ₹50, ₹55

C. ₹20, ₹50

D. ₹17, ₹51

20. Three girls and four boys can do a piece of work in 3 days, whereas five girls and three boys can do the same work in 2 days. Find the number of days required by one girl to finish the same work.

A. 11 days

B. 12 days

C. 15 days

D. 60 days

21. The sum of a two-digit number and the number obtained by reversing its digits is 99. The difference of the two-digit number and the number obtained by reversing its digits is 45. Find the number.

A. 72

B. 71

C. 63

D. 54

22. A houseboat package includes a fixed amount as cleaning charges in the price quoted per day. For 4 days, Mahendra paid ₹16,750, whereas Sohail paid ₹28,000 for his 7-day stay there. What are the fixed cleaning charges?

A. ₹1570

B. ₹1750

C. ₹2370

D. ₹3750

23. A fraction becomes $\frac{1}{3}$ when 2 is added to the numerator, and it becomes $\frac{1}{4}$ when 1 is subtracted from the denominator. Find the fraction.

A. $\frac{4}{18}$ B. $\frac{5}{21}$

C. $\frac{4}{13}$ D. $\frac{5}{16}$

24. A fisherman can row downstream 33 km in 3 hours and upstream 14 km in 2 hours. Find the speed of the stream.
    A. 9 km/h
    B. 7 km/h
    C. 4 km/h
    D. 2 km/h

25. A motorboat can cover 30 km upstream and 72 km downstream in 11 hours, and 36 km upstream and 24 km downstream in 8 hours. Find the speed of the boat in still water.
    A. 11 km/h
    B. 9 km/h
    C. 8 km/h
    D. 7.5 km/h

SELF-ASSESSMENT 2

Choose the correct option.

26. When two straight lines are coincident, then their solutions are ________.
 A. independent B. dependent
 C. inconsistent D. no solution

27. The lines represented by the equations $y = 2x - 2$ and $y = 4x - 4$ have ________.
 A. one common point (2, 2)
 B. one common point (1, 0)
 C. many common points
 D. no common point

28. In the equations $mx + ny = p$ and $rx + sy = t$, if $ms \neq nr$, then the equation has ________.
 A. a unique solution
 B. no solution
 C. infinitely many solutions
 D. two solutions

29. Identify the point where the line represented by the equation $x + 2y - 4 = 0$ crosses the x-axis.
 A. (–4, 2) B. (4, 0)
 C. (0, 2) D. (–4, 0)

30. Given a pair of equations $mx + ny = p$ and $ax + by = p$, which of the following conditions results in infinitely many solutions?
 A. $am = bn$ B. $ap = bn$
 C. $an = bp$ D. $mb = an$

31. The linear equations $5x - 4y = -8$ and $7x + 6y = 9$ have ________.
 A. no common point
 B. a single common point
 C. infinite common points
 D. only two common points

32. Select the pair of equations which is consistent.
 A. $4x - 4y - 5 = 0$ and $2x - 2y - 2 = 0$
 B. $x + y = 5$ and $2x + 2y = 20$
 C. $2x + y - 6 = 0$ and $4x - 2y - 4 = 0$
 D. $x - y = 8$ and $3x - 3y - 2 = 16$

33. Pick the odd one out based on the comparison of ratios of the coefficients of the given equations.
 A. $x - 3y = 0$ and $2x - 2y = 2$
 B. $5x = 5$ and $2y = -14$
 C. $y - 6 = 3x$ and $2y = 5x$
 D. $x + y = 3$ and $3x + 3y = 9$

34. Which of the following is the graphical representation of the pair of linear equations $x = -5$ and $y = -2$?
 A. Straight lines intersecting at (5, 2)
 B. Parallel lines
 C. Perpendicular lines intersecting at (–5, –2)
 D. Coincident lines passing through the origin

35. The sum of the digits of a two-digit number is 13. If 45 is added to the number, the digits of the number get reversed. Find the original number.

A. 94

B. 85

C. 58

D. 49

36. Find the equivalent equations to the given pair of linear equations: $\frac{xy}{x+y}=\frac{1}{11}$ and $\frac{xy}{x-y}=\frac{1}{7}$.

A. $\frac{1}{x}+\frac{1}{y}=11;\ \frac{1}{x}-\frac{1}{y}=7$

B. $\frac{1}{x}+\frac{1}{y}=11;\ \frac{1}{y}-\frac{1}{x}=7$

C. $\frac{1}{x}+\frac{1}{y}=7;\ \frac{1}{x}-\frac{1}{y}=11$

D. $\frac{1}{x}+\frac{1}{y}=7;\ -\frac{1}{x}-\frac{1}{y}=11$

37. Given a pair of linear equations $2x+\frac{3}{y}=12$ and $4x-\frac{5}{y}=2$, find the value of $t=6y$.

A. $\frac{1}{2}$

B. $-\frac{1}{3}$

C. 3

D. 2

38. Shekhar has some ₹20 and ₹50 notes. If he had a total of 47 notes and a total amount of ₹2170 with him, find the number of ₹20 and ₹50 notes.

A. 7, 40

B. 5, 42

C. 6, 41

D. 9, 38

39. Five years ago, Ram's age was 7 times the age of his son. After five years from now, Ram's age will be 3 times the age of his son. Find the present ages of Ram and his son.

A. 40, 15

B. 40, 10

C. 50, 20

D. 55, 25

40. Find the solution to the pair of linear equations $\frac{6}{3x-1}+\frac{3}{y-x}=6$ and $\frac{2}{3x-1}+\frac{4}{y-x}=5$.

A. $x=1, y=2$

B. $x=\frac{1}{2}, y=\frac{1}{3}$

C. $x=2, y=1$

D. $x=\frac{1}{3}, y=\frac{1}{2}$

41. Find the solution to the pair of linear equations $\frac{2}{\sqrt{x}}+\frac{3}{\sqrt{y}}=2$ and $\frac{4}{\sqrt{x}}-\frac{9}{\sqrt{y}}=-1$.

A. $x=2$ and $y=3$

B. $x=-2$ and $y=-3$

C. $x=4$ and $y=9$

D. $x=-4$ and $y=9$

42. For what values of p, the pair of equations $-3x+py+2=0$ and $(p-6)x+3y+(p-1)=0$ have infinitely many solutions?

A. $p=-3$

B. $p=3$

C. $p=-9$

D. $p=9$

43. Two trains are at two different stations, which are 120 km apart. The trains started at the same time at different speeds. They will cross each other in 12 hours when travelling in the same direction, and in 1 hour when travelling in the opposite direction. Find the speed of both the trains.

A. 60 km/h and 70 km/h
B. 55 km/h and 75 km/h
C. 60 km/h and 80 km/h
D. 65 km/h and 55 km/h

44. Ridhima bought 20 kg of rice at ₹53 per kg and pulses at ₹108 per kg. Find the amount of rice and pulses purchased by her if she spent a total of ₹1445.

A. Rice = 6 kg, Pulses = 14 kg
B. Rice = 11 kg, Pulses = 9 kg
C. Rice = 13 kg, Pulses = 7 kg
D. Rice = 15 kg, Pulses = 5 kg

45. The sum of a two-digit number and the number obtained by reversing its digits is 66. The difference of the two-digit number and the number obtained by reversing its digits is 36. Find the number.

A. 61 B. 51
C. 43 D. 42

46. A fraction becomes $\frac{1}{9}$ when 4 is subtracted from the numerator, and it becomes $\frac{1}{4}$ when 1 is added to the denominator. Find the fraction.

A. $\frac{8}{36}$ B. $\frac{7}{24}$
C. $\frac{7}{27}$ D. $\frac{5}{9}$

47. A fisherman can row upstream 18 km in 6 hours and downstream 42 km in 2 hours. Find the speed of the stream.

A. 12 km/h
B. 9 km/h
C. 8 km/h
D. 6 km/h

48. The area of a rectangle reduces by 13 square units if its length is reduced by 4 units and its breadth is increased by 1 unit. Its area increases by 7 square units if the length increases by 1 unit. Find the length and the breadth of the given rectangle.

A. 19 units, 7 units
B. 17 units, 9 units
C. 18 units, 7 units
D. 15 units, 8 units

49. Two women and five men can complete a piece of work in 4 days, whereas four women and two men can complete the same work in 3 days. Find the number of days required by one man to complete the same work.

A. 7 days
B. 42 days
C. 48 days
D. 60 days

50. In ΔXYZ, $\angle X = 4\angle Y = 3(\angle Z + \angle Y)$. Find all the three angles of the triangle.

A. $\angle X = 90°, \angle Y = 30°, \angle Z = 60°$
B. $\angle X = 100°, \angle Y = 25°, \angle Z = 55°$
C. $\angle X = 130°, \angle Y = 40°, \angle Z = 10°$
D. $\angle X = 135°, \angle Y = 33.75°, \angle Z = 11.25°$

CHAPTER 4

Quadratic Equations

PRIOR KNOWLEDGE TEST

Choose the correct option.

1. What is the product of $(x-2)(2x+3)$?

   A. x^2-x-6 B. $2x^2-x-6$

   C. $2x^2+x+6$ D. $2x^2+x-6$

2. Which of the following is a factor of $x^2-7x+12$?

   A. $(x-3)$ B. $(x+3)$

   C. $(x+4)$ D. $(x-6)$

3. What is the value of $1.11^2-0.89^2$?

   A. 0.0044 B. 0.044

   C. 0.44 D. 4.4

4. Find the factors of $49a^2-25b^2+40bc-16c^2$.

   A. $(7a-5b+4c)(7a+5b+4c)$

   B. $(7a+5b+4c)(7a-5b-4c)$

   C. $(7a+5b-4c)(7a+5b+4c)$

   D. $(7a-5b+4c)(7a+5b-4c)$

5. Which of the following is not a factor of $2x^4-32$?

   A. 2 B. x^2-4

   C. $x+2$ D. x^2+8

KEYWORDS

Quadratic equation: An algebraic equation having the highest power of the variable as 2

Standard form of a quadratic equation: $ax^2+bx+c=0, a\neq 0$, is the standard form of a quadratic equation

Root of a quadratic equation: A real number α is called a root of the quadratic equation $ax^2+bx+c=0, a\neq 0$, if $a\alpha^2+b\alpha+c=0$

Discriminant of a quadratic equation: If $ax^2+bx+c=0, a\neq 0$, is a quadratic equation, then b^2-4ac is called the discriminant

A quadratic equation $ax^2+bx+c=0$ has

- two distinct real roots, if $b^2-4ac>0$
- two equal real roots, if $b^2-4ac=0$
- no real roots, if $b^2-4ac<0$

Quadratic formula: If $b^2-4ac\geq 0$, then the roots of the quadratic equation $ax^2+bx+c=0$ are given by the formula $\dfrac{-b\pm\sqrt{b^2-4ac}}{2a}$

CONCEPT MAP

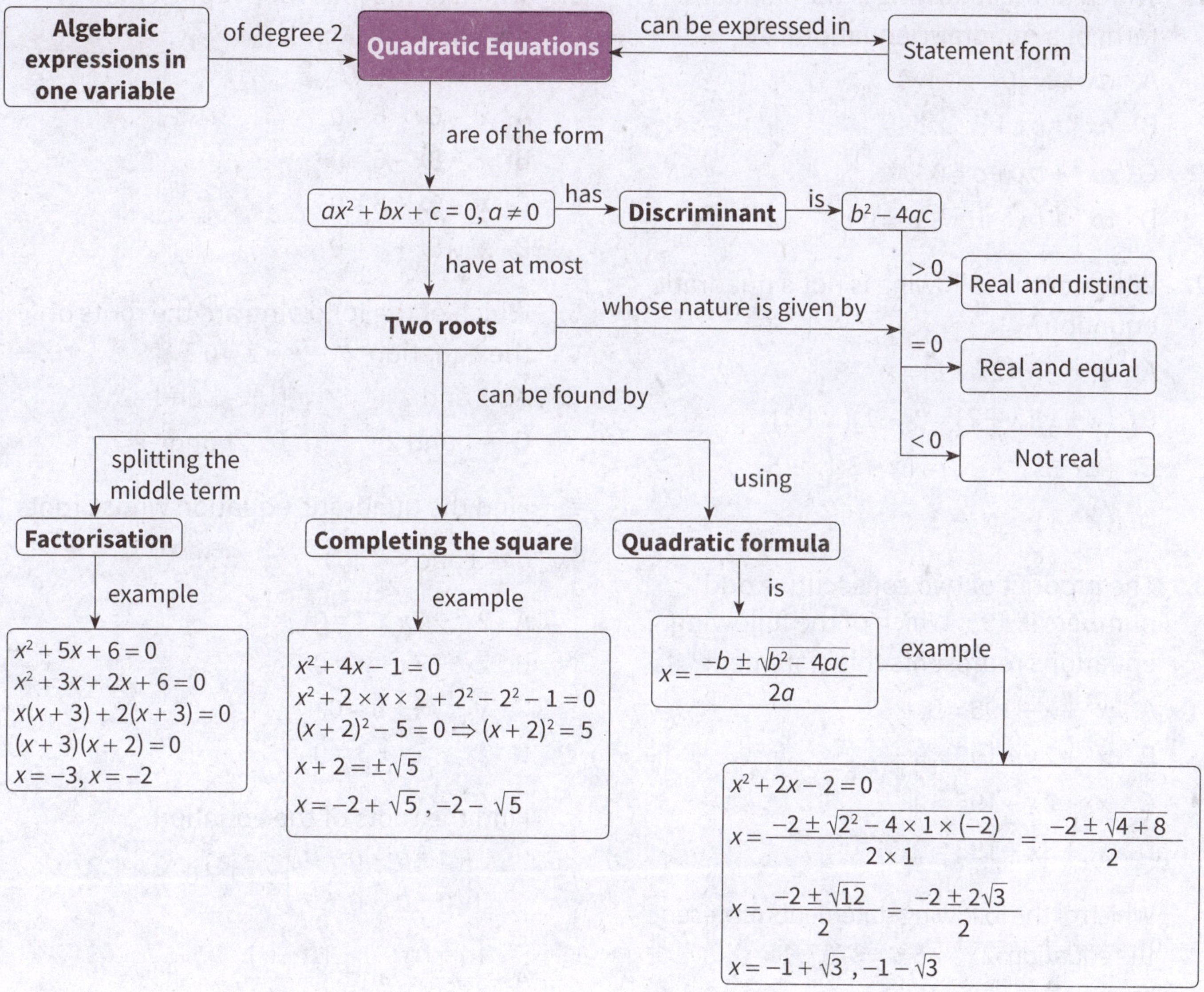

Algebraic expressions in one variable
of degree 2
Quadratic Equations
can be expressed in
Statement form
are of the form
$ax^2 + bx + c = 0, a \neq 0$
has
Discriminant
is
$b^2 - 4ac$
have at most
Two roots
whose nature is given by
> 0
Real and distinct
$= 0$
Real and equal
< 0
Not real
can be found by
splitting the middle term
using
Factorisation
Completing the square
Quadratic formula
example
$x^2 + 5x + 6 = 0$
$x^2 + 3x + 2x + 6 = 0$
$x(x + 3) + 2(x + 3) = 0$
$(x + 3)(x + 2) = 0$
$x = -3, x = -2$
example
$x^2 + 4x - 1 = 0$
$x^2 + 2 \times x \times 2 + 2^2 - 2^2 - 1 = 0$
$(x + 2)^2 - 5 = 0 \Rightarrow (x + 2)^2 = 5$
$x + 2 = \pm\sqrt{5}$
$x = -2 + \sqrt{5}, -2 - \sqrt{5}$
is
$x = \frac{-b \pm \sqrt{b^2 - 4ac}}{2a}$
example
$x^2 + 2x - 2 = 0$
$x = \frac{-2 \pm \sqrt{2^2 - 4 \times 1 \times (-2)}}{2 \times 1} = \frac{-2 \pm \sqrt{4 + 8}}{2}$
$x = \frac{-2 \pm \sqrt{12}}{2} = \frac{-2 \pm 2\sqrt{3}}{2}$
$x = -1 + \sqrt{3}, -1 - \sqrt{3}$

PART 1

CHAPTER 4: Quadratic Equations

SELF-ASSESSMENT 1

Choose the correct option.

1. Which of the following is the standard form of a quadratic equation?
   A. $ax+c=0$
   B. ax^2+bx+c
   C. $ax^2+bx+c=0$
   D. $ax^3+bx^2+cx+d=0$

2. Which of the following is not a quadratic equation?
   A. $3(x-5)(2x+1)=x^2$
   B. $(x+1)(x+2)=(x-1)(x+3)$
   C. $(2x-1)(x-3)=(x+3)(x+5)$
   D. $(x+1)^3=x^3-1$

3. The product of two consecutive odd numbers is 195. Which of the following equations represents this statement?
   A. $x^2+x-195=0$
   B. $x^2+2x+195=0$
   C. $x^2+2x-195=0$
   D. $x^2+3x-195=0$

4. Which of the following statements represents the equation $2x^2-5x=375$?
   A. The square of the hypotenuse of a right triangle is 375 sq. cm. The other two sides are in the ratio 2 : 5.
   B. The area of a rectangle is 375 sq. m, whose length is 5 m less than twice its breadth.
   C. The product of two consecutive odd numbers is 375.
   D. The square of the ages of Anant and Awungshi is 375.

5. Which of the following represents the equation $(x-2)^2+1=2x-3$ in its standard form?
   A. $x^2-6x-6=0$
   B. $x^2-8x-6=0$
   C. $x^2-6x+8=0$
   D. $x^2-8x+6=0$

6. Which of the following are the roots of the equation $x^2-x-2=0$?
   A. 1 and 2 B. –1 and –2
   C. –1 and 2 D. 1 and –2

7. Find the quadratic equation whose roots are 3 and $\frac{1}{2}$.
   A. $2x^2+7x+3=0$
   B. $2x^2-7x-3=0$
   C. $x^2-7x+6=0$
   D. $2x^2-7x+3=0$

8. Find the roots of the equation $x^2-\left(\frac{a+b}{a-b}+\frac{a-b}{a+b}\right)x+1=0.$
   A. $\frac{(a+b)}{(a-b)}$ and $\frac{(b-a)}{(a+b)}$
   B. $\frac{(a+b)}{(a-b)}$ and $\frac{(a+b)}{(a-b)}$
   C. $\frac{(a-b)}{(a+b)}$ and $\frac{(a-b)}{(a+b)}$
   D. $\frac{(a+b)}{(a-b)}$ and $\frac{(a-b)}{(a+b)}$

9. Find two numbers whose sum is 33 and their product is 270.

A. 10 and 27

B. 12 and 21

C. 20 and 13

D. 15 and 18

10. The sum of the squares of two consecutive numbers is 365. Find the numbers.

A. 11 and 12

B. 12 and 13

C. 13 and 14

D. 14 and 15

11. If 2 and 3 are the roots of the equation $3x^2 - px - q = 0$, find the values of *p* and *q*.

A. –15 and –42

B. 15 and 42

C. 15 and –18

D. –15 and –18

12. A two-digit number is 27 less than the number formed by reversing its digits. If the product of the digits is 18, find the number.

A. 29

B. 63

C. 92

D. 36

13. Which is the first step to solve the equation $5x^2 - 6x + 16 = 0$ by the method of completing the square?

A. Divide the equation by 5

B. Multiply the equation by 5

C. Either A or B

D. Neither A nor B

14. Identify the formula to find the roots of a quadratic equation.

A. $x = -b\dfrac{\pm\sqrt{b^2 - 4ac}}{2a}$

B. $x = \dfrac{-b \pm \sqrt{b^2 + 4ac}}{2a}$

C. $x = \dfrac{b \pm \sqrt{b^2 - 4ac}}{2a}$

D. $x = \dfrac{-b \pm \sqrt{b^2 - 4ac}}{2a}$

15. Find the roots of the quadratic equation $x^2 - 2x - 5 = 0$.

A. $2 \pm \sqrt{24}$

B. $4 \pm \sqrt{24}$

C. $2 \pm \sqrt{6}$

D. $1 \pm \sqrt{6}$

16. Find the roots of the equation $\dfrac{2}{x-1} + \dfrac{4}{x-2} = \dfrac{8}{x-4}$, where $x \neq 1, 2, 4$.

A. $2 \pm 2\sqrt{5}$

B. $4 \pm 4\sqrt{3}$

C. $2 \pm \sqrt{3}$

D. $-2 \pm 2\sqrt{3}$

17. A truck travels a distance of 540 km at a uniform speed. If the speed had been 9 km/h more, it would have taken 2 hours less for the same journey. Find the speed of the truck.

A. 40 km/h

B. 45 km/h

C. 50 km/h

D. 55 km/h

18. If the sum of a rational number and its reciprocal is $\frac{13}{6}$, find the number.

A. $\frac{7}{2}$ B. $\frac{5}{3}$

C. $\frac{2}{3}$ D. $\frac{2}{5}$

19. Two water taps together can fill a cistern in $3\frac{3}{7}$ hours. The tap with the smaller diameter takes 2 hours more than the larger one to fill the tank completely. Find the time taken by the larger tap alone to fill the cistern completely.

A. 4 hours

B. 5 hours

C. 6 hours

D. 8 hours

20. A dealer sells an article at ₹39 and gains the same percentage as the cost price of the article. What is the cost price of the article?

A. ₹20 B. ₹25

C. ₹30 D. ₹35

21. The numerator of a fraction is 3 less than the denominator. If 1 is added to both the numerator and the denominator, then the sum of the new fraction and the original fraction is $\frac{9}{10}$. Find the original fraction.

A. $\frac{4}{7}$

B. $\frac{2}{5}$

C. $\frac{5}{8}$

D. $\frac{1}{4}$

22. The quadratic equation $ax^2 + bx + c = 0$ has no real roots if __________.

A. $b^2 - 4ac = 0$

B. $b^2 - 4ac > 0$

C. $b^2 - 4ac < 0$

D. $b^2 + 4ac < 0$

23. Find the value of the discriminant of the quadratic equation $x^2 + 7x - 61 = 0$.

A. 49

B. 244

C. 289

D. 293

24. Find the value of k if the equation $x^2 - 4kx + 256 = 0$ has equal roots.

A. 8

B. 16

C. 24

D. –16

25. Find the nature of the roots of the equation $2x^2 + 9x - 12 = 0$.

A. Real and distinct roots

B. Real and equal roots

C. No real roots

D. Equal and imaginary roots

SELF-ASSESSMENT 2

Choose the correct option.

26. Which of the following is an example of a quadratic equation?
A. $1 - 3x^2 + 300 + x^2 = 4 - 2x^2$
B. $2x^2 + 7x - 2x - x^2 - x^2 = 0$
C. $7x + 4y + 13 = 0$
D. $x(x - 3) + x(x + 3) = 0$

27. Rakhi is 5 years younger than her brother. The product of their ages after 11 years will be equal to 266. Which of the following quadratic equations will represent this situation?
A. $(x + 11)(x + 6) = 266$
B. $(x + 11)(x + 16) - 266 = 0$
C. $x^2 + 27x - 90 = 0$
D. All of these

28. The length of a rectangle is 5 units less than three times the breadth. The area of the rectangle is 112 square units. Which of the following quadratic equations will represent this situation?
A. $(3x + 5)(x) = 112$
B. $(x - 5)(3x) + 112 = 0$
C. $3x^2 - 5x - 112 = 0$
D. $3x^2 - 5x + 5 = 112$

29. Which of the following is the standard form of the equation $x^2 + x(x + 1) + 7 = x^2 - 7x + 15$?
A. $x^2 - 8x - 22 = 0$
B. $x^2 + 8x - 8 = 0$
C. $x^2 + 8x + 8 = 0$
D. $x^2 - 6x - 22 = 0$

30. Which of the following are the roots of the equation $x^2 - \sqrt{2}x - 4 = 0$?
A. $\sqrt{2}$ and $2\sqrt{2}$
B. $\sqrt{2}$ and $-2\sqrt{2}$
C. $-\sqrt{2}$ and $2\sqrt{2}$
D. $-\sqrt{2}$ and $-2\sqrt{2}$

31. Find the quadratic equation whose roots are $\sqrt{2}$ and $5\sqrt{2}$.
A. $x^2 + 6\sqrt{2}x + 10 = 0$
B. $x^2 - 6\sqrt{2}x + 10 = 0$
C. $x^2 + 6\sqrt{2}x - 10 = 0$
D. $x^2 - 6\sqrt{2}x - 10 = 0$

32. Find the roots of the equation $5(x + 1)(x + 2) = 4(2x - 1)(x + 3)$.
A. $\frac{11}{3}$ and 2
B. $\frac{-11}{3}$ and 2
C. $\frac{11}{3}$ and -2
D. $\frac{-11}{3}$ and -2

33. An express train takes 1.5 hours less than a passenger train to travel 288 km between Bengaluru and Chennai. If the average speed of the passenger train is 16 km/h less than that of the express train, find the average speed of the express train.
A. 48 km/h
B. 54 km/h
C. 64 km/h
D. 72 km/h

34. Each side of a square is 5 cm less than that of another square. If the sum of their areas is 1025 sq. cm, find the side of the smaller square.
   A. 15 cm
   B. 20 cm
   C. 25 cm
   D. 30 cm

35. Find the other root of the equation $x^2 - kx + 12 = 0$, if one root of the equation is 3.
   A. 4   B. -4
   C. -3   D. 7

36. Divide 14 into two parts such that twice the square of the larger number exceeds thrice the square of the smaller number by 20. Find the numbers.
   A. 4 and 10
   B. 5 and 9
   C. 6 and 8
   D. 3 and 11

37. The sum of two numbers is 18. If the sum of their reciprocals is $\frac{9}{40}$, find the smallest number.
   A. 6
   B. 8
   C. 10
   D. 12

38. If –3 and –4 are the roots of the equation $x^2 - ax - b = 0$, find the values of *a* and *b*.
   A. 7 and 12
   B. 7 and –12
   C. –7 and –12
   D. –7 and 12

39. A two-digit number is four times the sum of its digits and two times the product of its digits. Find the number.
   A. 63
   B. 45
   C. 36
   D. 27

40. Vinay was asked to find the roots of the equation $3x^2 - 4x - 6 = 0$ by the method of completing the square. The method followed by him is as follows:
   Step 1: $3x^2 - 4x - 6 = 0$
   Multiply the equation by 3.
   Step 2: $9x^2 - 12x - 18 = 0$
   Step 3: $(3x)^2 - 2 \times 3x \times 2 + 2^2 - 2^2 - 18 = 0$
   Identify the next step.
   A. $(3x - 2)^2 = 22$
   B. $(3x + 2)^2 = 22$
   C. $(3x - 2)^2 = 18$
   D. $(3x + 2)^2 = 18$

41. Which of the following is the most suitable method for finding the roots of the equation $x^2 - 3x + 1 = 0$?
   A. By splitting the middle term
   B. By using algebraic identities
   C. By using quadratic formula
   D. Any of these

42. Find the roots of the quadratic equation $x^2 - 2\sqrt{2}x - 8 = 0$.
   A. $2\sqrt{2} \pm \sqrt{40}$
   B. $2 \pm \sqrt{10}$
   C. $\sqrt{2} \pm 2\sqrt{10}$
   D. $\sqrt{2} \pm \sqrt{10}$

43. Find the roots of the equation $\frac{x}{x+5}+\frac{x+1}{x+3}=\frac{2}{3}$, where $x \neq -5, -3$.

A. $1, \frac{15}{4}$

B. $-1, \frac{15}{4}$

C. $1, \frac{-15}{4}$

D. $-1, \frac{-15}{4}$

44. A shopkeeper buys a number of paper bags for ₹480. If the cost of each paper bag is increased by ₹3, the number of paper bags bought will reduce by 8. Find the cost price of each paper bag.

A. ₹12

B. ₹15

C. ₹40

D. ₹48

45. A motorboat whose speed is 20 km/h in still water takes 1 hour more to go 48 km upstream than to return downstream to the same spot. Find the speed of the stream.

A. 2 km/h

B. 3 km/h

C. 4 km/h

D. 5 km/h

46. The perimeter of a right-angled triangle is 120 cm. If the hypotenuse is 50 cm, find the area of the triangle.

A. 1500 sq. cm

B. 1200 sq. cm

C. 1025 sq. cm

D. 600 sq. cm

47. The quadratic equation $ax^2 + bx + c = 0$ has two distinct real roots, if ________.

A. $b^2 - 4ac = 0$

B. $b^2 - 4ac > 0$

C. $b^2 - 4ac < 0$

D. $-b + b^2 - 4ac < 0$

48. Which of the following is true if the equation $4a^2b^2x^2 - 12abx + k = 0$ has equal roots?

A. $2abx = 3$

B. $abx = 3$

C. $abx = \frac{2}{3}$

D. $abx = 2$

49. Find the value of k if the equation $kx^2 - 12x + (2k+1) = 0$ has equal roots.

A. –4

B. 4

C. $\frac{9}{2}$

D. 8

50. Find the nature of the roots of the equation $4x^2 + 8x + 12 = 0$.

A. Real and distinct roots

B. Real and equal roots

C. No real roots

D. None of these

CHAPTER 5

Arithmetic Progressions

PRIOR KNOWLEDGE TEST

Choose the correct option.

1. What is the next term in the given sequence?

   2, 3, 5, 8, 12, 17, ____

   A. 20 B. 22

   C. 23 D. 25

2. Safina is arranging different number of counters in the pattern given below. How many counters are needed to make the next pattern?

   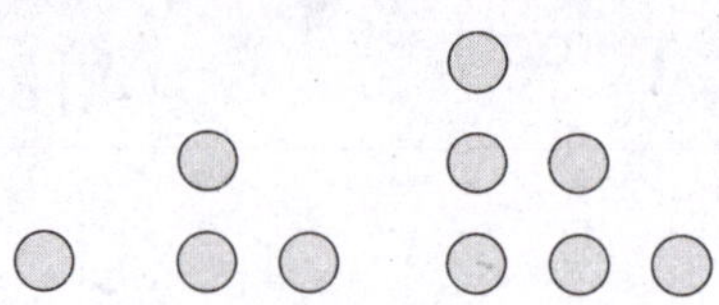

   A. 12

   B. 10

   C. 9

   D. 4

3. Which is the next number in the given pattern?

   1 4 9 16 ____

   A. 20 B. 25 C. 30 D. 36

4. What is the rule being followed in the following pattern?

   12, 24, 48, 96, 192 ...

   A. Double the number

   B. Multiples of 12

   C. Multiples of 6

   D. Sum of two consecutive numbers

5. Which is the next number in the following pattern?

   $\frac{1}{3}, \frac{3}{9}, \frac{9}{27}, \frac{27}{81} \ldots$

   A. $\frac{3}{243}$ B. $\frac{9}{243}$

   C. $\frac{27}{243}$ D. $\frac{81}{243}$

KEYWORDS

Arithmetic progression (AP): A sequence of numbers with a constant difference between the consecutive terms in the list

Term: Each number in the sequence

First term (a): The first number in the sequence

Common difference (d): The difference between any two consecutive terms of an AP; it is always a constant and can be positive, negative or zero

nth term: The nth number of an arithmetic progression is found by using the formula, $a_n = a + (n-1)d$

Sum of n terms: The sum of the n terms of an arithmetic progression is calculated by using the formula $S = \frac{n}{2}\left[2a + (n-1)d\right]$

CONCEPT MAP

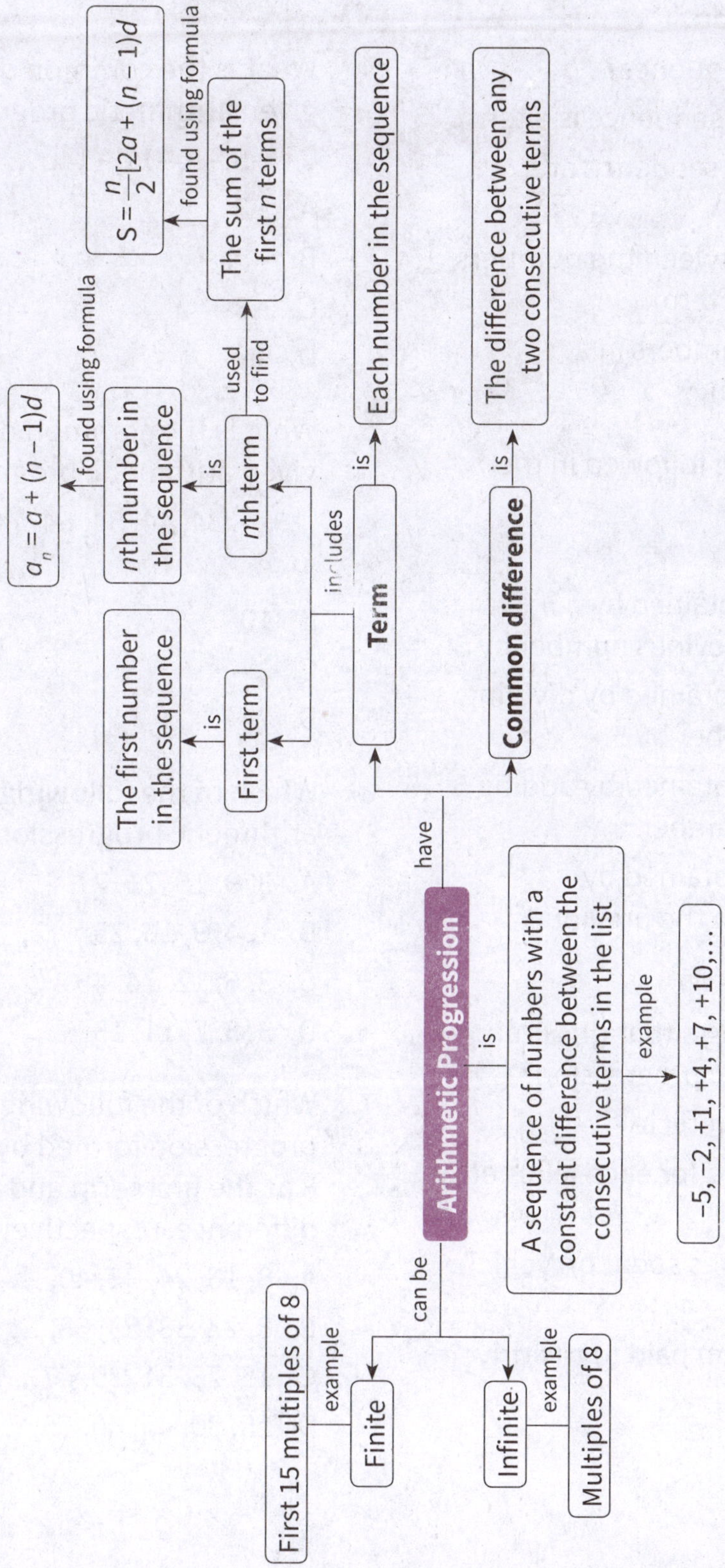

Arithmetic Progression
is
A sequence of numbers with a constant difference between the consecutive terms in the list
example
−5, −2, +1, +4, +7, +10,...
can be
Finite
example
First 15 multiples of 8
Infinite
example
Multiples of 8
have
Term
Common difference
is
The difference between any two consecutive terms
is
Each number in the sequence
includes
First term
is
The first number in the sequence
nth term
is
nth number in the sequence
found using formula
$a_n = a + (n - 1)d$
used to find
The sum of the first n terms
found using formula
$S = \frac{n}{2}[2a + (n - 1)d]$

SELF-ASSESSMENT 1

Choose the correct option.

1. What is a term in a sequence?
   A. Each number in a sequence is a term.
   B. Few numbers in a sequence are terms.
   C. The difference between the numbers in a sequence is a term.
   D. The sum of the numbers in a sequence is a term.

2. What is the rule being followed in the following pattern?
   3, 8, 13, 18, 23, …
   A. Each number is obtained by multiplying the previous number by 5.
   B. Each number is obtained by dividing the previous number by 5.
   C. Each number is obtained by adding 5 to the previous number.
   D. Each number is obtained by subtracting 5 from the previous number.

3. Which of the following situations is an example of arithmetic progression?
   A. Rent paid for the vehicle
   B. Travelling fare paid for each kilometre of travel
   C. Additional expenses spent on vehicle for repair
   D. Fixed remuneration paid to the driver

4. What is the common difference (*d*) in the given arithmetic progression?
   −5, −8, −11, −14, ….
   A. −3
   B. −9
   C. +3
   D. +9

5. What is the common difference in the given arithmetic progression?
   24, 34, 44, 54, 64, 74, …
   A. 6
   B. 10
   C. 24
   D. 74

6. Which of the following forms an arithmetic progression?
   A. 3, 9, 15, 21, 27
   B. 1, 4, 9, 16, 25
   C. 3, 6, 12, 24, 48
   D. 3, 5, 7, 11, 13

7. Which of the following is an arithmetic progression formed by taking 15 and 8 as the first term and the common difference, respectively?
   A. 8, 16, 24, 32, 40, …
   B. 8, 23, 38, 53, 68, …
   C. 15, 23, 31, 39, 47, …
   D. 15, 30, 45, 60, 75, …

8. Which of the following is an arithmetic progression formed by taking −12 and −20 as the first term and the common difference, respectively?

A. −12, −32, −52, −72, −92, …
B. 12, −8, −26, −48, −68, …
C. 20, 8, −4, −16, −28, −40, …
D. −20, −32, −44, −56, −68, …

9. What is the next number in the given pattern?

−0.5, 2.5, 5.5, 8.5, …

A. 9.5
B. 10.5
C. 11.5
D. 12.5

10. Which of the following formulas is used to find the *n*th term of an arithmetic progression?

A. $a_n = a + (n+1)d$
B. $a_n = a + (n-1)d$
C. $a_n = a + (n \times 1)d$
D. $a_n = a + (n \div 1)d$

11. What is the 20th term of an arithmetic progression, if $a = 5$ and $d = -2$?

A. −45
B. −40
C. −35
D. −33

12. What is the 10th term of an arithmetic progression, if $a = 5.5$ and $d = 4.2$?

A. 30.3
B. 33.3
C. 40.3
D. 43.3

13. Which term of the given arithmetic progression $-5, -4\frac{3}{4}, -4\frac{1}{2}, -4\frac{1}{4}, \ldots$ is $1\frac{1}{4}$?

A. 23rd
B. 24th
C. 25th
D. 26th

14. What is the common difference and the first term if the 4th term and the 8th term of an arithmetic progression are 11 and 23, respectively?

A. $a = 2$ and $d = 2$
B. $a = 2$ and $d = 3$
C. $a = 3$ and $d = 3$
D. $a = 3$ and $d = 2$

15. Which term of the arithmetic progression 3.65, 1.40, −0.85, −3.1, … is −34.6?

A. 16th
B. 17th
C. 18th
D. 19th

16. How many two-digit numbers are divisible by 6?

A. 13
B. 14
C. 15
D. 16

17. What is the 8th term from the last term of the arithmetic progression 11, 15, 19, 23, …, 107?

A. 79
B. 83
C. 87
D. 91

18. The fixed taxi fare is ₹50 for the first 4 km of travelling. After 4 km, the cost of each kilometre is ₹6. Find the number of kilometres travelled by a person if he pays a taxi fare of ₹140.

A. 12

B. 14

C. 16

D. 19

19. What is the sum of the first 15 terms of the given arithmetic progression?

$5\frac{1}{2}, 3, \frac{1}{2}, -2, -4\frac{1}{2}, \ldots$

A. $-177\frac{1}{2}$

B. −180

C. $-182\frac{1}{2}$

D. −185

20. What is the 20th term of an arithmetic progression if the sum of the first 20 terms is −1180 and the first term is −2?

A. −112

B. −114

C. −116

D. −118

21. How many terms of the given arithmetic progression −9, −12, −15, −18, … must be added to get the sum as −450?

A. 12

B. 13

C. 14

D. 15

22. An apartment committee has conducted various competitions for its residents on account of Independence Day celebrations. A sum of ₹7500 is distributed as cash prize among five winners. If the amount of each prize is ₹500 more than the preceding prize, find the value of the maximum amount of the prize given.

A. ₹3000

B. ₹2500

C. ₹2000

D. ₹1500

23. What is the sum of the first 15 terms of an arithmetic progression whose terms are found by using $a_n = 2 + 3n$?

A. 390

B. 960

C. 790

D. 930

24. Ziad's fitness coach has asked him to do plank exercise. He told him to start with 9 seconds and increase it by 9 seconds every day. If he can meet his target in 60 days, how much total time would he spend in doing the exercise?

A. 10,467 seconds

B. 14,670 seconds

C. 16,470 seconds

D. 17,460 seconds

25. A coin box was gifted to Thoibi with some money in it. She started adding three 2-rupee coins in it every day. On the 16th day, she had ₹140 in her coin box. How much money was there in the coin box on the 1st day?

A. 50   B. 70

C. 80   D. 90

PART 1

CHAPTER 5: Arithmetic Progressions

SELF-ASSESSMENT 2

Choose the correct option.

26. What is the rule being followed in the given pattern?

    4, 10, 16, 22, 28, ...

    A. Each number is obtained by multiplying the previous number by 6.
    B. Each number is obtained by dividing the previous number by 6.
    C. Each number is obtained by adding 6 to the previous number.
    D. Each number is obtained by subtracting 6 from the previous number.

27. Which of the following situations is not an example of arithmetic progression?
    A. Cost of machinery
    B. Cost of raw material spent on each product
    C. Time taken to produce each product
    D. Profit made by selling each product

28. Which of the following does not form an arithmetic progression?
    A. 4, 7, 10, 13, 16, ...
    B. 4, 8, 12, 16, 20, ...
    C. 4, 8, 16, 32, 64, ...
    D. 4, 6, 8, 10, 12, ...

29. What is the common difference (*d*) of the given arithmetic progression?

    18, 27, 36, 45, 54, 63, ...

    A. 6 B. 9
    C. 18 D. 63

30. Which of the following is an arithmetic progression formed by taking 35 as the first term and 12 as the common difference?
    A. 12, 24, 36, 48, 60, ...
    B. 12, 47, 82, 117, 152, ...
    C. 35, 47, 59, 71, 83, ...
    D. 35, 70, 105, 140, 175, ...

31. Which of the following is an arithmetic progression formed by taking 25 as the first term and –8 as the common difference?
    A. –8, –16, –24, –32, –40, ...
    B. 8, 0, –8, –16, –24, ...
    C. –25, –33, –41, –49, –57, ...
    D. 25, 17, 9, 1, –7, ...

32. What is the next number in the given pattern?

    $6-\sqrt{5},\ 6+\sqrt{5},\ 6+3\sqrt{5},\ \ldots$

    A. $6+4\sqrt{5}$ B. $6+5\sqrt{5}$
    C. $6+6\sqrt{5}$ D. $6+7\sqrt{5}$

33. What is the common difference of the following arithmetic progression?

    $\frac{1}{\sqrt{x}},\ \frac{1+\sqrt{x}}{x},\ \frac{2+\sqrt{x}}{x},\ldots.$

    A. $\frac{1}{\sqrt{x}}$ B. $\frac{1}{x}$
    C. $\sqrt{x}$ D. x

34. What is the 35th term of an arithmetic progression if $a = 4$ and $d = -3$?

A. −35

B. −89

C. −95

D. −98

35. What is the 12th term of an arithmetic progression if $a = 4.5$ and $d = 3.8$?

A. 33.3

B. 36.3

C. 43.3

D. 46.3

36. If three times the 6th term of an arithmetic progression is equal to two times the 8th term, what is the 2nd term of the same arithmetic progression?

A. 0

B. 3

C. 16

D. 18

37. Which term of the given arithmetic progression 8, 4, 0, ... is −68?

A. 18th

B. 17th

C. 20th

D. 21st

38. What is the common difference and the first term, if the 2nd term and the 8th term of an arithmetic progression are 6 and 36, respectively?

A. $a = 5$ and $d = 1$

B. $a = 1$ and $d = 1$

C. $a = 5$ and $d = 5$

D. $a = 1$ and $d = 5$

39. Which term of the arithmetic progression $4\frac{1}{4}, \frac{1}{2}, -3\frac{1}{4}, -7, \ldots$ is $-18\frac{1}{4}$?

A. 7th

B. 10th

C. 12th

D. 18th

40. How many two-digit numbers are divisible by 7?

A. 13

B. 14

C. 15

D. 16

41. Find the 7th term from the last term of the arithmetic progression 16, 21, 26, 31, ..., 151.

A. 121

B. 123

C. 125

D. 127

42. A customer deposits ₹15,000 in a bank, which pays him an interest of ₹500 per year. What will be his bank balance at the end of 9 years?

A. ₹18,000

B. ₹18,500

C. ₹19,000

D. ₹19,500

43. What is the sum of the first 25 terms of the given arithmetic progression?

$$4.2, 2.6, 1, -0.6, -2.2, \ldots$$

A. −325

B. −355

C. −375

D. −395

44. What is the 14th term of an arithmetic progression if the sum of the first 14 terms is –406 and the first term is –3?

A. –65

B. –55

C. –45

D. –35

45. How many terms of the given arithmetic progression –6, –10, –14, –18, ... must be taken so that their sum is –336?

A. 12

B. 13

C. 14

D. 15

46. A textile industry sent a consignment of 5000 uniforms in five lots, each increased by 250. Find the number of uniforms sent as the first consignment.

A. 500

B. 750

C. 1000

D. 1500

47. What is the sum of the first 28 terms of an arithmetic progression whose terms are found using the expression $a_n = 3n - 2$?

A. 1026

B. 1062

C. 1162

D. 1126

48. A theatre has seats arranged in rows in increasing order. Each row has the number of seats in multiples of 7. How many seats can be arranged in 20 rows?

A. 1400

B. 1435

C. 1470

D. 1495

49. A gardener started to plant saplings around a circular fountain in different circles. If the number of saplings planted in the first circle is 12 and is increased by 12 in each circle, how many saplings would be planted in the 5th circle?

A. 40

B. 50

C. 60

D. 80

50. The fixed cost of printing is ₹15 for 20-page printouts. The additional printing cost is charged, after 20 pages, at ₹0.75 per page. What is the cost of printing 50 pages?

A. ₹15

B. ₹22.5

C. ₹37.5

D. ₹60

CHAPTER 6

Triangles

PRIOR KNOWLEDGE TEST

Choose the correct option.

1. If $\Delta ABC \cong \Delta PQR$, $\angle A = 65°$ and $\angle B = 50°$, what is the measurement of $\angle R$?

   A. 65° B. 75°

   C. 100° D. 130°

2. If $AB = YZ$ and $\angle B = \angle Z$, then which of the following data is required to prove that $\Delta ABC \cong \Delta YZX$ by the SAS congruence rule?

   A. $AC = XY$ B. $\angle C = \angle X$

   C. $BC = ZX$ D. $\angle A = \angle Y$

3. If $\Delta KLM \cong \Delta PQR$, $KL = 8$ cm, $PR = 10.8$ cm and the perimeter of the $\Delta KLM = 22.8$ cm, what is the length of QR?

   A. 6 cm B. 4 cm

   C. 8 cm D. 10.8 cm

4. In ΔXYZ, XD is the perpendicular bisector of YZ. $\Delta XYD \cong \Delta XZD$ by the ________ congruence rule.

   A. RHS B. SSS

   C. SAS D. ASA

5. If $AB = PQ$, $\angle B = \angle Q$ and $AC = PR$, then how are the triangles ABC and PQR related?

   A. They are congruent by SAS.

   B. They are congruent by ASA.

   C. They are congruent by RHS.

   D. They may not be congruent.

KEYWORDS

Congruent figures: Two figures having the same shape and size

Similar figures: Two figures having the same shape (and not necessarily the same size)

All congruent figures are similar, but all similar figures may not be congruent.

The ratio of the areas of two similar triangles is equal to the square of the ratio of their corresponding sides.

Basic Proportionality theorem: If a line drawn parallel to one side of a triangle intersects the other two sides in two distinct points, the other two sides are divided in the same ratio; converse is also true

Pythagoras theorem: In a right-angled triangle, the square of the hypotenuse is equal to the sum of the squares of the other two sides; converse is also true

CONCEPT MAP

Triangles — having:
- Same shape and size → **Congruent Triangles**
- Same shape → **Similar Triangles**

Congruent Triangles — are → Similar Triangles

Similar Triangles — may not be → Congruent Triangles

Similar Triangles — conditions → Two triangles are similar if
i. their corresponding angles are equal and
ii. their corresponding sides are in the same ratio (or proportion)

Similar Triangles — criteria:

AAA Criterion

If in two triangles, the corresponding angles are equal, then their corresponding sides are in the same ratio and hence the two triangles are similar.

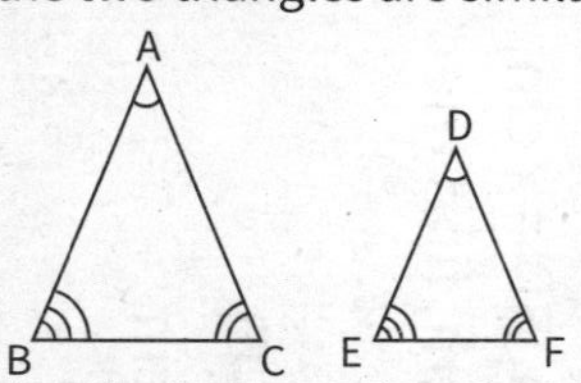

SSS Criterion

If in two triangles, the corresponding sides are in the same ratio, then their corresponding angles are equal and hence the triangles are similar.

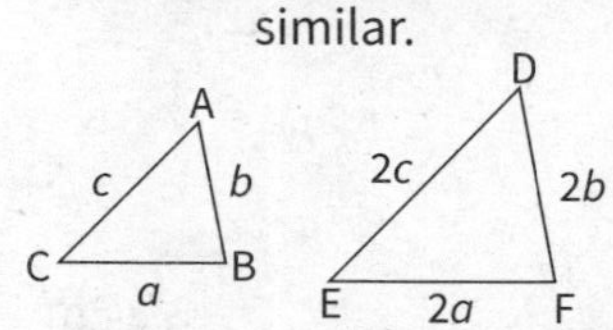

AA Criterion

If two angles of one triangle are respectively equal to the two angles of another triangle, then the two triangles are similar.

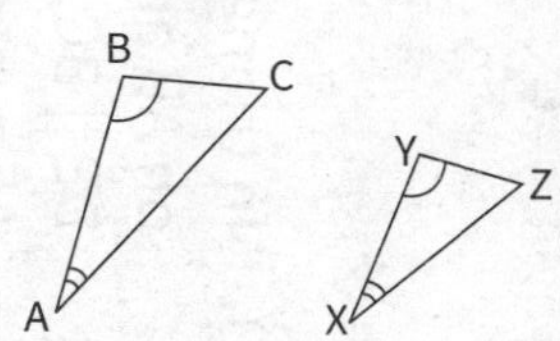

SAS Criterion

If one angle of a triangle is equal to one angle of another triangle and the sides including these angles are in the same ratio (proportional), then the triangles are similar.

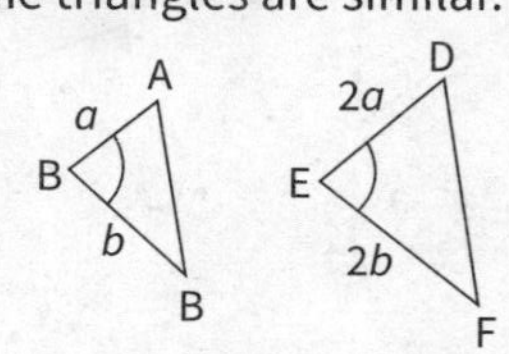

Similar Triangles — of → **Areas** — follow → The ratio of the areas of two similar triangles is equal to the square of the ratio of their corresponding sides.

Similar Triangles — applications:

Basic proportionality theorem: If a line drawn parallel to one side of a triangle intersects the other two sides in distinct points, the other two sides are divided in the same ratio.

converse → If a line divides any two sides of a triangle in the same ratio, then the line is parallel to the third side.

Pythagoras Theorem: In a right-angled triangle, the square of the hypotenuse is equal to the sum of the squares of the other two sides.

converse → If in a triangle, the square of one side is equal to the sum of the squares of the other two sides, then the angle opposite to the first side is a right angle.

PART 1

CHAPTER 6: Triangles

SELF-ASSESSMENT 1

Choose the correct option.

1. Given that $\Delta ABC \sim \Delta XYZ$, if $\angle A = 52°$ and $\angle Z = 68°$, find the measurement of $\angle B$.

   A. 30°   B. 52°

   C. 68°   D. 60°

2. Find the odd one out.

   A.

   B.

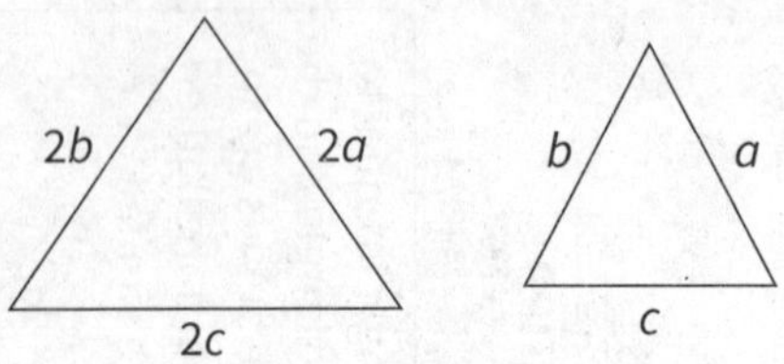

   C.

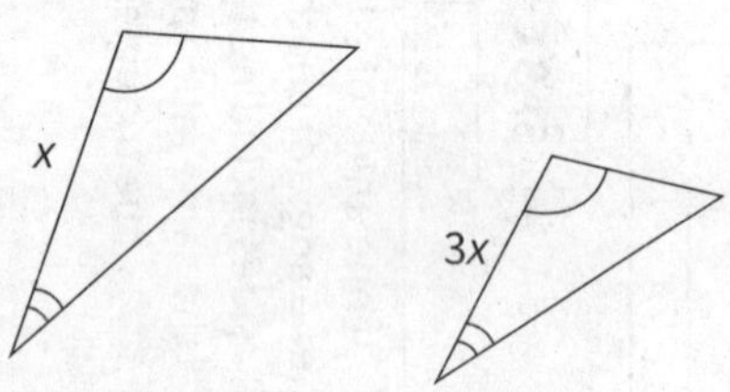

   D.

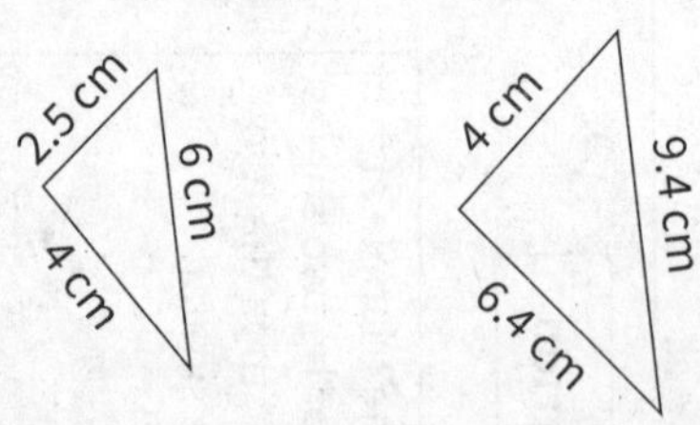

3. In triangle ABC, D and E are points on AB and AC, respectively, such that DE || BC. If AD = $(2x - 2)$ cm, BD = x cm, AE = $4x$ cm and EC = 12.5 cm, find the length of AB.

   A. 5 cm   B. 10 cm

   C. 13 cm   D. 16 cm

4. In triangle ABC, AD is the bisector of $\angle A$ and $\angle B = \angle C$. By which of the following similarity criterion is $\Delta ABD \sim \Delta ACD$?

   A. AA similarity

   B. SAS similarity

   C. SSS similarity

   D. They may not be similar.

5. In triangles PQR and XYZ, $\angle P = \angle X = 55°$, $\angle Q = 45°$ and $\frac{PQ}{XY} = \frac{PR}{XZ}$. Find the measurement of $\angle Z$.

   A. 45°   B. 55°

   C. 80°   D. 100°

6. Find the length of QR for the given figure.

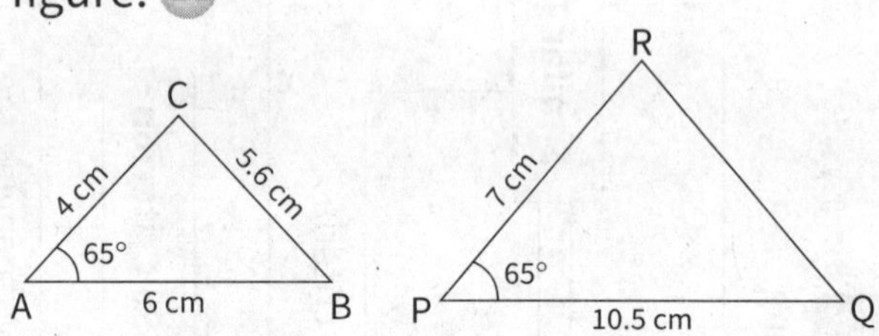

   A. 7.8 cm   B. 8.4 cm

   C. 9.6 cm   D. 9.8 cm

7. If $\Delta ABC \sim \Delta XYZ$, AB = 8 cm, BC = 7.6 cm, XY = 6 cm and XZ = 9.6 cm, find the perimeter of ΔXYZ.

   A. 21.3 cm

   B. 23.2 cm

   C. 25.2 cm

   D. 28.4 cm

8. Which of the following angles is equal to $\angle RPS$?

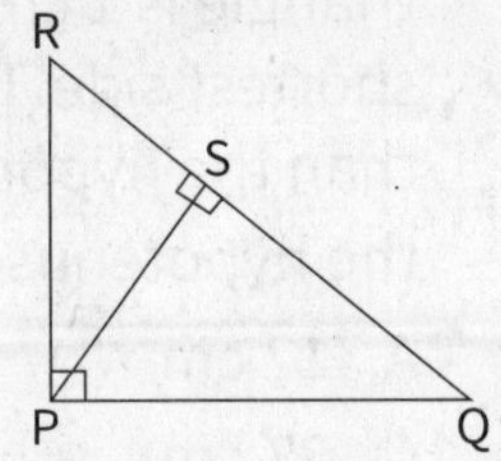

A. $\angle Q$
B. $\angle R$
C. $\angle SPQ$
D. $\angle PSR$

9. A 40-m long vertical pole casts a shadow with a length of 25 m on the ground. What is the height of the tower, if it casts a shadow with the length of 100 m on the ground at the same time and place?

A. 160 m B. 200 m
C. 240 m D. 320 m

10. In the given figure, XY || PQ || AC. If BX = AP = x cm, BY = $(x + 1)$ cm, QY = 7.5 cm, PX = $(2x - 2)$ cm, find the length of BC.

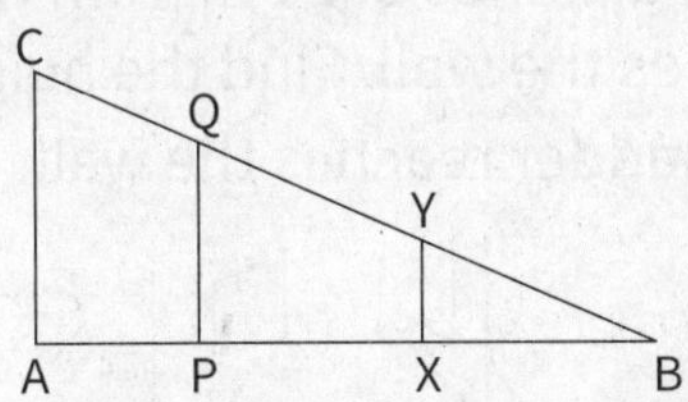

A. 14 cm B. 15 cm
C. 16 cm D. 17.5 cm

11. The areas of two similar triangles are 225 sq. cm and 625 sq. cm. If the shortest side of the larger triangle is 19 cm, find the shortest side of the smaller triangle.

A. 7.5 cm B. 9.5 cm
C. 11. 4 cm D. 12.5 cm

12. If the sides of two similar triangles are in the ratio 9 : 16, find the ratio of their areas.

A. 3 : 4 B. 9 : 16
C. 81 : 256 D. 256 : 81

13. ABC is an equilateral triangle in which D and E are the points of trisection on BC, such that D is nearer to B. Find the ratio of areas of triangles ABD and AEC.

A. 1 : 2 B. 1 : 4
C. 1 : 1 D. 1 : 9

14. In triangle PQR, X and Y are points on PR and QR, respectively, such that XY || PQ. If XY : PQ = 4 : 5, find ar(XYR) : ar(PQYX).

A. 4 : 5 B. 16 : 25
C. 4 : 3 D. 16 : 9

15. ABCD is a parallelogram, in which F is a point on AB and E is a point on diagonal AC, such that FE || BC. If AF : BF = 3 : 2, find ar(AFE) : ar(ABCD).

A. 9 : 34 B. 9 : 64
C. 9 : 25 D. 9 : 50

16. The areas of two equilateral triangles are in the ratio 16 : 9. If the height of the bigger triangle is $8\sqrt{3}$ cm, find the height of the smaller triangle.

A. $6\sqrt{3}$ cm B. $5\sqrt{3}$ cm
C. $4.5\sqrt{3}$ cm D. $4\sqrt{3}$ cm

17. In an equilateral triangle PQR, if $PX \perp QR$, then which of the following is equal to $4PX^2$?

A. PR^2 B. $2PR^2$
C. $3PR^2$ D. $4PR^2$

18. In an isosceles triangle ABC, if $AD \perp BC$ and AB = AC, then which of the following is true?

A. $AD^2 = 3CD^2$
B. $AC^2 + BD^2 = AB^2 + CD^2$
C. $AC^2 - BD^2 = AB^2 + CD^2$
D. $AC^2 + AD^2 = BD.DC$

19. A science museum is in the form of a triangular prism whose base is an equilateral triangle. If each side of the triangle is 160 m and the height of the prism is 30 m, find the height of the triangular base.

A. 160 m B. $80\sqrt{3}$ m
C. $160\sqrt{3}$ m D. 130 m

20. Two poles of heights 28 m and 38 m stand vertically on a plane ground. If the distance between their feet is 24 m, then find the distance between their tops.

A. 10 m B. 12 m
C. 18 m D. 26 m

21. The lengths of the diagonals of a rhombus are 40 cm and 42 cm. Find the perimeter of the rhombus.

A. 82 cm
B. 116 cm
C. 164 cm
D. 232 cm

22. The area of a square ABCD is 1600 sq. cm. X is a point on AB such that AX : XB = 3 : 5, and Y is a point on AD such that AY : YD = 1 : 4. Find the length of XY.

A. 8 cm
B. 15 cm
C. 17 cm
D. 18 cm

23. The hypotenuse of a right-angled triangle is 1 cm more than 3 times its shortest side. If the third side is 2 cm less than the hypotenuse, find the length of the hypotenuse.

A. 12 cm B. 35 cm
C. 37 cm D. 45 cm

24. A tree breaks due to heavy winds and the broken part touches the ground at a distance of 24 m from the foot of the tree. If the height of the tree is 36 m, find the height at which it is broken.

A. 10 m B. 12 m
C. 26 m D. 60 m

25. A wall needs to be painted by a group of workers. They need to find out the height to which a ladder of length 29 m, placed at a distance of 21 m from the wall, reaches the wall. Find the height at which the ladder reaches the wall.

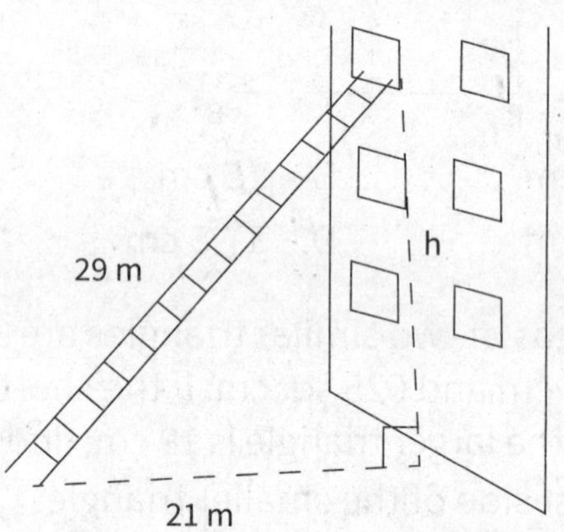

A. 20 m B. 18 m
C. 17 m D. 15 m

SELF-ASSESSMENT 2

Choose the correct option.

26. In triangles ABC and XYZ, $\angle A = 70°$, $\angle C = 50°$, $\angle Y = 60°$ and $\angle Z = 50°$. What can we say about these two triangles?
   A. Congruent by ASA criterion
   B. Similar by AA criterion
   C. Isosceles triangles
   D. Similar by SAS criterion

27. In triangle ABC, D and E are points on AC and BC, respectively, such that DE || AB. F and G are the midpoints of DE and CE, respectively. If CD = $(2x + 3)$ cm, AD = x cm, CE = $(3x + 2)$ cm and BE = $(x + 2)$ cm, find the length of GF.

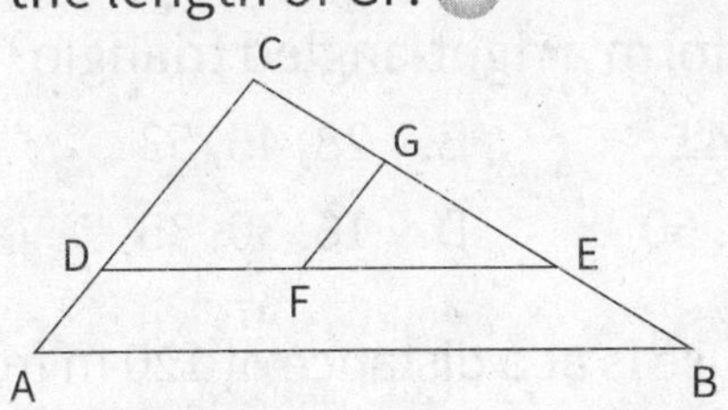

   A. 15 cm B. 10 cm
   C. 7.5 cm D. 6 cm

28. KL and MN are the line segments which intersect each other at O. Points K and N are joined with points M and L, respectively. If KO = 8 cm, LO = 4 cm, MO = 6 cm and ON = 3 cm, by which of the following similarity criterion is $\Delta KMO \sim \Delta LON$?
   A. AA similarity
   B. SAS similarity
   C. SSS similarity
   D. They may not be similar.

29. In triangles ABC and XYZ, $\frac{AB}{XY} = \frac{AC}{XZ} = \frac{BC}{YZ} = \frac{2}{3}$. Find the length of AC, if XZ = 15.6 cm.
   A. 31.2 cm B. 23.4 cm
   C. 9.6 cm D. 10.4 cm

30. In ΔABC, D and E are points on AB and AC, respectively, such that DE || BC. If AD = 3 cm, BD = 7.5 cm, AC = 17.5 cm and DE = 4 cm, find the perimeter of the trapezium BCED.
   A. 42 cm B. 38 cm
   C. 34 cm D. 24 cm

31. Which of the following is true with respect to the figure given below?

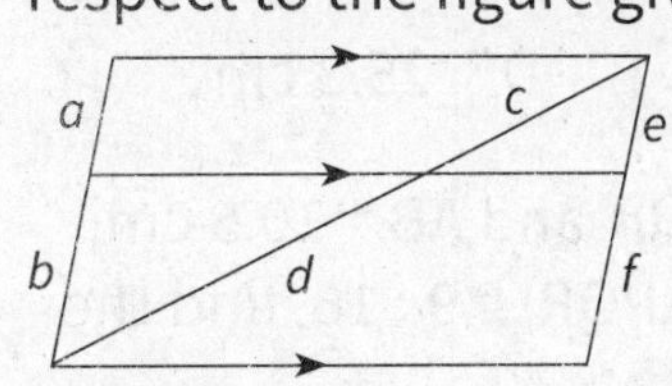

   A. $\frac{a}{b} = \frac{c}{d}$ B. $\frac{e}{f} = \frac{c}{d}$
   C. $\frac{a+b}{b} = \frac{c+d}{d}$ D. All of these

32. Two isosceles triangles have equal vertical angles equal to a right angle. Which of the following is true about these two triangles?
   A. Congruent triangles
   B. Similar triangles
   C. Both similar and congruent
   D. Neither similar nor congruent

33. The perimeters of two similar triangles are 42 cm and 36 cm. If one side of the first triangle is 14 cm, what is the corresponding side of the other triangle?

A. 14 cm B. 18 cm
C. 15 cm D. 12 cm

34. For what value of x, is PQ || XY?

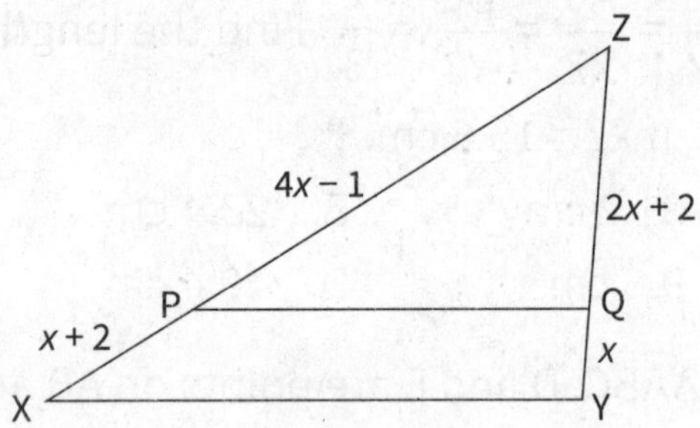

A. 8 B. 6
C. 5 D. 4

35. The areas of two similar triangles are 256 sq. cm and 324 sq. cm. If the median of the larger triangle is 22.5 cm, find the median of the smaller triangle.

A. 10 cm B. 11.4 cm
C. 20 cm D. 25.3 cm

36. If $\Delta ABC \sim \Delta PQR$ and AB = 10.5 cm, ar(ΔABC) : ar(ΔPQR) = 9 : 16, find the length of PQ.

A. 12.5 cm B. 14 cm
C. 17.5 cm D. 22.5 cm

37. In a triangle ABC, D and E are any points on AB and BC, respectively, such that BE : EC = 3 : 2 and DE || AC. Find the ratio of the area of ΔBDE and the area of trapezium ADEC.

A. 8 : 15 B. 16 : 25
C. 16 : 9 D. 9 : 16

38. PQRS is a parallelogram in which X and Y are the midpoints of PQ and QR, respectively. If the area of parallelogram PQRS is 128 sq. cm, find the area of triangle XQY.

A. 64 sq. cm B. 32 sq. cm
C. 16 sq. cm D. 8 sq. cm

39. The areas of two right-angled similar triangles are in the ratio 36 : 49. If the height of the smaller triangle is 9 cm, find the height of the bigger triangle.

A. 7 cm B. 10.5 cm
C. 14 cm D. 15 cm

40. Two sides of a right-angled triangle are 33 cm and 56 cm. Which of the following is the hypotenuse of the triangle?

A. 61 cm B. 63 cm
C. 65 cm D. 69 cm

41. Which of the following measurements does not form a right-angled triangle?

A. 9, 40, 41 B. 28, 45, 53
C. 36, 48, 60 D. 16, 30, 35

42. A lighthouse is at a distance of 120 m from a ship. If the distance between the ship and the tip of the lighthouse is 169 m, find the height of the lighthouse.

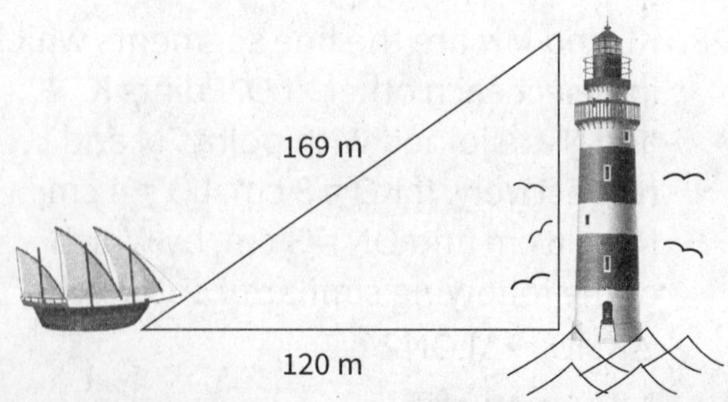

A. 118 m B. 119 m
C. 116 m D. 112 m

43. A man goes 20 km due North, 12 km due East and then 15 km due South. How far is he from the starting point?

A. 12 km B. 13 km

C. 15 km D. 18 km

44. A chord of a circle is at a distance of 21 cm from its centre. If the radius of the circle is 29 cm, find the length of the chord.

A. 10 cm B. 20 cm

C. 30 cm D. 40 cm

45. The diagonal of a square is 24 cm. Find its area.

A. 216 sq. cm B. 576 sq. cm

C. 144 sq. cm D. 288 sq. cm

46. The diagonals of a rhombus divide it into four triangles. One diagonal is 2 cm less than thrice the other. If the area of each triangle is 210 sq. cm, find the length of each side of the rhombus.

A. 24 cm B. 35 cm

C. 37 cm D. 74 cm

47. The hypotenuse of a right-angled triangle is 29 cm and the sum of other two sides is 41 cm. Find the length of the shortest side.

A. 16 cm B. 18 cm

C. 20 cm D. 21 cm

48. If the length of the hypotenuse of an isosceles right-angled triangle is $24\sqrt{2}$ cm, what is the perimeter of the triangle?

A. 72 cm

B. $48 + 24\sqrt{2}$ cm

C. $48(1 + \sqrt{2})$ cm

D. $72\sqrt{2}$ cm

49. The length and breadth of a rectangle are 15 cm and 8 cm, respectively. Find the length of its diagonal.

A. 24 m B. 20 m

C. 18 m D. 17 m

50. In an isosceles triangle, the base is 2 cm less than twice its side. If the altitude of the triangle is 7 cm, find its perimeter.

A. 56 cm B. 74 cm

C. 98 cm D. 121 cm

CHAPTER 7

Coordinate Geometry

PRIOR KNOWLEDGE TEST

Choose the correct option.

1. In which quadrant does the point A(3, –7) lie?
   A. Quadrant IV
   B. Quadrant III
   C. Quadrant II
   D. Quadrant I

2. Identify the coordinates and quadrant of a point with ordinate –4 and abscissa 6.
   A. (–4, 6); IV quadrant
   B. (–4, 6); II quadrant
   C. (6, –4); IV quadrant
   D. (6, –4); II quadrant

3. Which of the following lies on *y*-axis at a distance of 3 units in the negative direction?
   A. (–3, 0) B. (0, –3)
   C. (3, 0) D. (0, 3)

4. What is the perpendicular distance of point C(–8, –7) from *y*-axis?
   A. –8 B. –7
   C. 8 D. 7

5. What can be concluded about the line formed by plotting the following points? (– 3, 3); (3, 3); (– 6, 3); (0, 3); (1, 3)?
   A. The line is parallel to *x*-axis.
   B. The line is parallel to *y*-axis.
   C. The line is perpendicular to *x*-axis.
   D. Both B and C

KEYWORDS

Coordinate axes: Two intersecting straight lines (horizontal *x*-axis and vertical *y*-axis) used as reference lines in coordinate geometry

Origin: The point where *x*-axis and *y*-axis intersect each other; its coordinates are (0, 0)

Quadrants: The four equal regions formed by the intersection of the coordinate axes

Coordinate points: Locate the position of a point on the plane with a pair of numbers

***x*-coordinate:** The distance of the point from *y*-axis; also called abscissa (meaning: to cut)

***y*-coordinate:** The distance of the point from *x*-axis; also called ordinate (meaning: to keep in order)

CONCEPT MAP

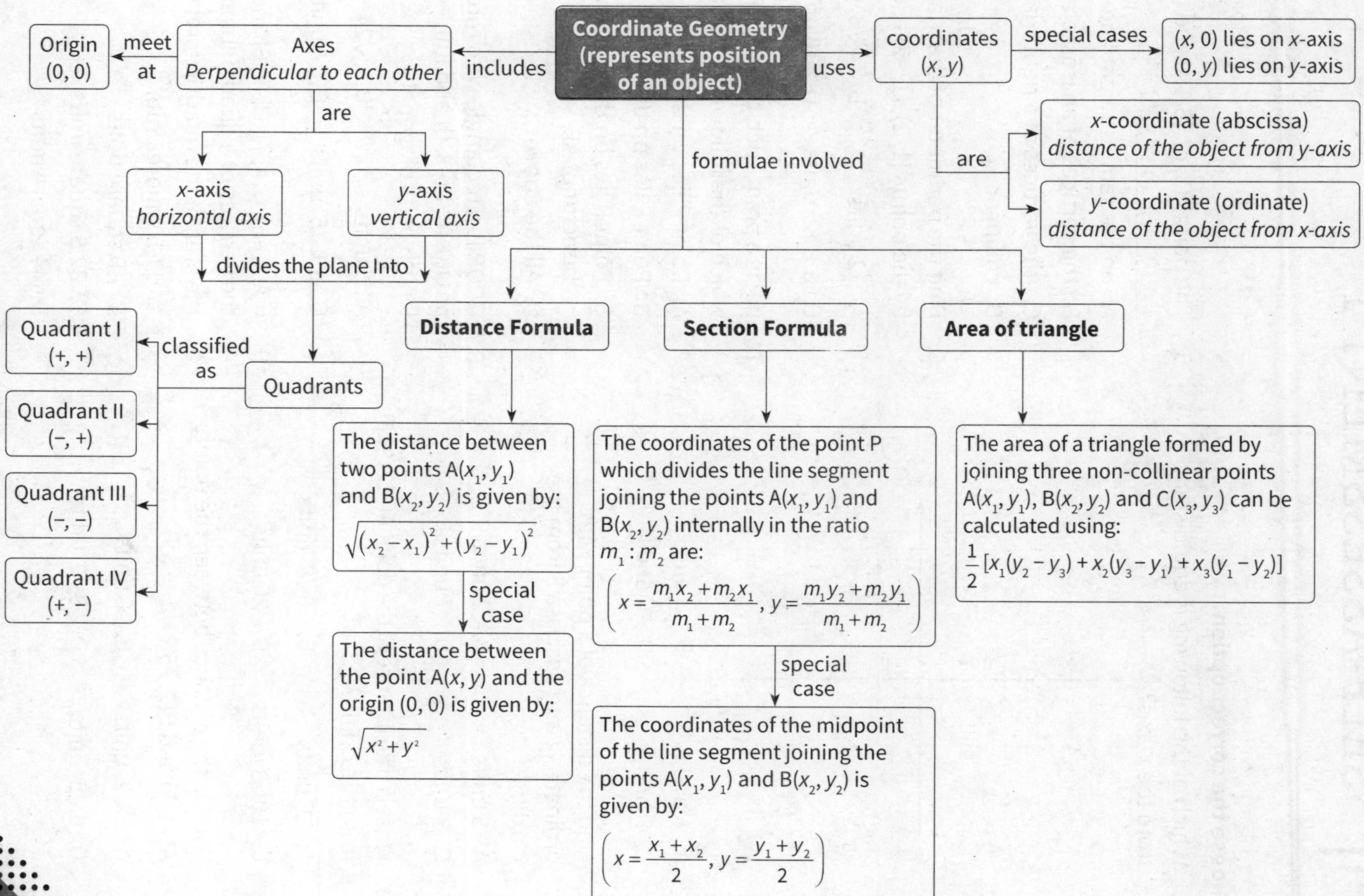

Coordinate Geometry (represents position of an object)
includes
Axes
Perpendicular to each other
meet at
Origin (0, 0)
are
x-axis
horizontal axis
y-axis
vertical axis
divides the plane Into
Quadrants
classified as
Quadrant I (+, +)
Quadrant II (−, +)
Quadrant III (−, −)
Quadrant IV (+, −)
uses
coordinates (x, y)
special cases
(x, 0) lies on x-axis
(0, y) lies on y-axis
are
x-coordinate (abscissa)
distance of the object from y-axis
y-coordinate (ordinate)
distance of the object from x-axis
formulae involved
Distance Formula
The distance between two points $A(x_1, y_1)$ and $B(x_2, y_2)$ is given by:
$\sqrt{(x_2 - x_1)^2 + (y_2 - y_1)^2}$
special case
The distance between the point A(x, y) and the origin (0, 0) is given by:
$\sqrt{x^2 + y^2}$
Section Formula
The coordinates of the point P which divides the line segment joining the points $A(x_1, y_1)$ and $B(x_2, y_2)$ internally in the ratio $m_1 : m_2$ are:
$\left(x = \frac{m_1x_2 + m_2x_1}{m_1 + m_2}, y = \frac{m_1y_2 + m_2y_1}{m_1 + m_2}\right)$
special case
The coordinates of the midpoint of the line segment joining the points $A(x_1, y_1)$ and $B(x_2, y_2)$ is given by:
$\left(x = \frac{x_1 + x_2}{2}, y = \frac{y_1 + y_2}{2}\right)$
Area of triangle
The area of a triangle formed by joining three non-collinear points $A(x_1, y_1)$, $B(x_2, y_2)$ and $C(x_3, y_3)$ can be calculated using:
$\frac{1}{2}[x_1(y_2 - y_3) + x_2(y_3 - y_1) + x_3(y_1 - y_2)]$

PART 1

CHAPTER 7: *Coordinate Geometry*

SELF-ASSESSMENT 1

Choose the correct option.

1. Which of the following is equidistant from the *x*-axis?

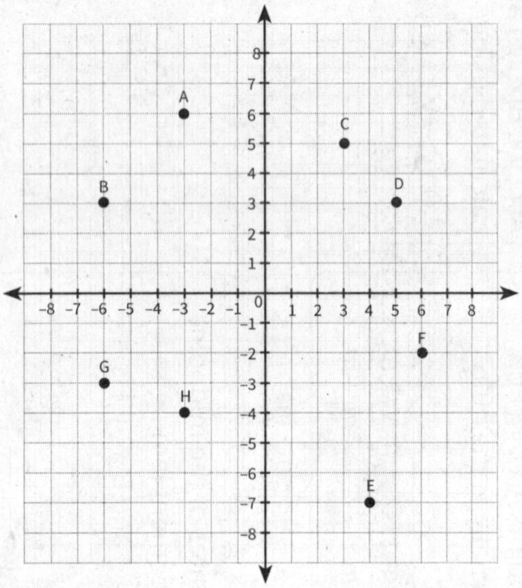

A. A and E B. B and F
C. D and G D. C and H

2. Find the distance of a point with ordinate –2 and abscissa 5 from the *y*-axis.

A. 5 units B. 2 units
C. 3 units D. 7 units

3. What is the distance of the point A(–12, –16) from the origin?

A. 16 units B. $8\sqrt{2}$ units
C. $10\sqrt{3}$ units D. 20 units

4. What is the distance between the points A(–4, 7) and B(2, –5)?

A. $5\sqrt{2}$ units B. 6 units
C. $6\sqrt{5}$ units D. $3\sqrt{2}$ units

5. The points (3, 4), (5, –4) and (7, 4) are ______________.

A. on the same straight line
B. the vertices of an isosceles triangle
C. the vertices of a right triangle
D. collinear

6. Find the perimeter of the triangle formed by the points (1, 2), (1, –2) and (4, –2).

A. 12 units B. $4\sqrt{3}$ units
C. $6+\sqrt{2}$ units D. 10 units

7. If P is a point such that AP = PB, then which of the following is always true?

A. Point P lies on the *x*-axis
B. Point P lies on the *y*-axis
C. Point P lies on the perpendicular bisector of AB
D. All the above

8. OPQR is a rectangle with three vertices as O(0, 0), P(–3, 0) and R(0, –4). Find the length of its diagonal.

A. 5 units B. $\sqrt{24}$ units
C. $3+\sqrt{5}$ units D. 4 units

9. If A(3, –5), B(4, 7), C(–2, 6) and D(1, –4) are the vertices of a quadrilateral, then find the area of the quadrilateral ABCD.

A. 11.5 square units
B. 19 square units
C. 32.5 square units
D. 44 square units

10. Find the value of x for which A(−3, −2), B(x, 1) and C(−8, 3) are collinear.

A. −6
B. −5
C. −1
D. 0

11. Which of the following points lies on the perpendicular bisector of the line segment joining the points A(−3, 4) and B(3, −4)?

A. (0, 4)
B. (−3, 2)
C. (0, 0)
D. (−1.5, 2)

12. Which of the following represents the path of a point P(x, y), which is equidistant from A(3, 2) and B(−7, −2)?

A. $x + y = 2$
B. $5x + 10y = 4$
C. $5x + 2y + 10 = 0$
D. $x + y + 10 = 0$

13. If the distance between P(−7, −3) and Q(y, 4) is 7 units, find the value of y.

A. 7
B. 4
C. ±7
D. −7

14. Which of the following represents the centre of a circle with the endpoints of diameter as A(−6, 5) and B(2, −3)?

A. (−3, 5)
B. (−2, 1)
C. (2, −1)
D. (−4, 4)

15. Which of the following represents the coordinates of the point P, which divides the line segment joining the points (2, −2) and (−7, 4) in the ratio 1 : 2?

A. (−1, 1)
B. (−1, 0)
C. $\left(\frac{-4}{3}, \frac{1}{3}\right)$
D. (−2, 7)

16. Find the ratio in which the point (3, −2) divides the line segment joining the points (8, 3) and (1, −4).

A. 5 : 2
B. 2 : 5
C. 3 : 2
D. 5 : 1

17. If A(5, 2), B(3, 4), C(a, 7) and D(6, 5) are the vertices of a parallelogram taken in an order, then find the value of a.

A. 9
B. 5
C. 4
D. 3

18. Which of the following points divides the line segment joining A($x + y$, $x - y$) and B($y - x$, $y + x$) in the ratio 1 : 1?

A. (x, y)
B. (y, x)
C. $\left(\frac{x+y}{2}, \frac{y-x}{2}\right)$
D. $\left(\frac{y}{2}, \frac{x}{2}\right)$

19. Find the area of triangle PQR, with the vertices P($a + 1$, $b + 2$), Q(a, $b + 2$) and R(a, $b - 4$).

A. 3 square units
B. $\frac{3a+b}{2}$ square units
C. $\frac{3a-2b}{2}$ square units
D. 6 square units

20. Find the ratio in which x-axis divides P(2, −2) and Q(8, 1).

A. 3 : 1
B. 2 : 1
C. 3 : 2
D. 5 : 3

21. Which of the following statements holds true for the collinear points X(−5, −8), Y(4, −5) and Z(7, −4)?

A. $YZ = \frac{1}{2}XY$
B. $YZ = \frac{1}{4}XZ$
C. $XY = 2YZ$
D. $XY = \frac{1}{3}XZ$

22. In a rhombus PQRS, with vertices P(−3, −3), Q(0, 1) and R(3, −3), find the coordinates of S.

A. (1, −3) B. (3, −7)

C. (0, −7) D. (−3, 0)

23. Find the point of trisection of the line segment joining A(1, 6) and B(7, 3).

A. (5, 4); (3, 5) B. (3, 4); (5, 4)

C. (4, 5); (2, 1) D. (5, 3); (4, 3)

24. Find the coordinates of the point where the perpendicular bisector of the line segment joining the points A(−2, 3) and B(−7, −2) intersects the *x*-axis.

A. (4, 0) B. (0, 5)

C. (−4, 0) D. (0, −4)

25. Find the coordinates of the centroid of triangle ABC, with A(−3, 2), B(7, 3) and C(2, 1).

A. (2, 2) B. (−1, 1)

C. (3, 1) D. (0, 0)

SELF-ASSESSMENT 2

Choose the correct option.

26. What is the distance of the point A(–60, 11) from the origin?
    A. 40 units B. $50\sqrt{3}$ units
    C. $48\sqrt{11}$ units D. 61 units

27. What is the distance between the points A(–7, 8) and B(–2, –4)?
    A. $9\sqrt{7}$ units B. 13 units
    C. $11\sqrt{3}$ units D. 14 units

28. A triangle with vertices (3, 1), (–1, –1) and (1, –5) can be classified as ________.
    A. scalene triangle
    B. isosceles triangle
    C. isosceles right-angled triangle
    D. equilateral triangle

29. Identify the type of quadrilateral whose vertices are (6, 1), (8, –1), (6, –3) and (4, –1).
    A. Rectangle
    B. Rhombus
    C. Square
    D. Parallelogram

30. Find the perimeter of the triangle formed by the points (7, –2), (1, 6) and (1, –2).
    A. 18 units
    B. 24 units
    C. $12 + \sqrt{17}$ units
    D. $6\sqrt{3}$ units

31. ABCD is a rectangle with three vertices, A(1, – 8), B(–2, –5), and C(2, – 1). Find the coordinates of the fourth vertex of the rectangle.
    A. (5, –4) B. (4, 5)
    C. (3, –5) D. (–5, 2)

32. If A(–7, –3), B(–4, 2), C(0,–2) and D(–4, –6) are the vertices of a quadrilateral, then find the area of the quadrilateral ABCD.
    A. 22.5 square units
    B. 24 square units
    C. 28 square units
    D. 36 square units

33. Find the coordinates of the midpoint of the line segment joining A(–4, –9) and B(6, 7).
    A. (1, –1)
    B. (5, 8)
    C. (–2, 3)
    D. (3, –2)

34. Which of the following represents the path of a point M(*x*, *y*) which is equidistant from R(–5, –2) and S(7, 6)?
    A. $3x - 2y + 7 = 0$
    B. $2x + 3y = 7$
    C. $3x + 2y - 7 = 0$
    D. $6x - 4y = 14$

35. Find the value of x for which $A(x + 3, -2)$, $B(x - 1, 6)$ and $C\left(\frac{x}{2}, 7\right)$ are collinear.

A. 4 B. 3

C. −3 D. −4

36. How many points are equidistant from E(−1, −5) and F(−2, −6)?

A. 1 B. 2

C. 3 D. Infinite

37. If the distance between A(−2, −3) and $B\left(\frac{2t}{3}, 4\right)$ is 25 units, find the value of t.

A. 33 B. 39

C. ±24 D. −26

38. On a 14 ft × 14 ft wall, the wall clock is mounted at the centre of the wall at a height of 6 ft. Find the distance of the clock from the corner of the wall.

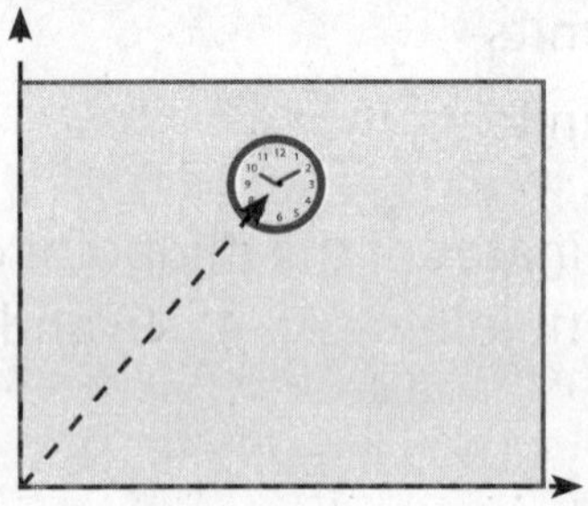

A. $\sqrt{69}$ ft B. $\sqrt{85}$ ft

C. 7 ft D. $7\sqrt{3}$ ft

39. Triangle ABC, right-angled at B, is circumscribed in a circle with centre O. Which of the following represents the centre of a circle if the coordinates of A, B and C are A(2, −5), B(−6, 3) and C(−1, 7)?

A. (0, 1) B. $\left(\frac{1}{2}, 1\right)$

C. (2, −1) D. (−4, 4)

40. Which of the following represents the coordinates of the point P, which divides the line segment joining the points M(−7, 5) and N(1, −3), such that $MP = \frac{5}{8} MN$?

A. (−2, 0) B. (0, −2)

C. $\left(\frac{-3}{2}, \frac{1}{2}\right)$ D. (−4, 2)

41. Find the ratio in which the origin divides the line segment joining the points (−8, −8) and (5, 5).

A. 8 : 5 B. 8 : 13

C. 5 : 4 D. 3 : 2

42. Find the ratio in which the line segment $x + 3y = 4$ divides the line segment joining A(−5, 1) and B(7, 6).

A. 2 : 7 B. 3 : 21

C. 19 : 9 D. 4 : 9

43. Find the area of triangle PQR, with the vertices P(1, 2), Q(−7, 5) and R(−7, −4).

A. 81 square units

B. 56 square units

C. 42.5 square units

D. 36 square units

44. Find the value of a, such that the midpoint of the line segment joining A(12, −3) and B (6, a) lies on the line segment $3x - 2y = 10$.

A. 9 B. 14

C. −12 D. 20

45. If A(−3, 5), B(−4, −8), C(−8, 10) are the vertices of a triangle, then find the length of the median AD.

A. $\sqrt{167}$ units B. 5 units

C. $4\sqrt{85}$ units D. $5\sqrt{2}$ units

46. Which of the following points lies inside a circle passing through the origin with centre at (3, −2)?

A. (5, −5) B. (2, 2)

C. (1, −4) D. (6, 0)

47. Which of the following points lies on the perpendicular bisector of the line segment joining the points A(−7, −3) and B(−3, −7)?

A. (0, 1) B. (−2, −2)

C. (−6, −4) D. (−4, −6)

48. In the triangle ABC with vertices $A(x_1, y_1)$, $B(x_2, y_2)$ and $C(x_3, y_3)$, find the coordinates of the centroid of the triangle.

A. $\left(\frac{x_1+x_2+x_3}{3}, \frac{y_1+y_2+y_3}{3}\right)$

B. $\left(\frac{x_1+x_2+x_3}{2}, \frac{y_1+y_2+y_2}{2}\right)$

C. $\left(\frac{x_1+x_2+2x_3}{6}, \frac{y_1+y_2+2y_3}{6}\right)$

D. $\left(\frac{x_1+x_2}{3}, \frac{y_1+y_2}{3}\right)$

49. The line segment AB is trisected by two points, X and Y. If the coordinates of A are (−4, 5) and the coordinates of Y are (8, −3), then find the coordinate of X.

A. (2, 1) B. (6, −1)

C. (−1, 2) D. $\left(\frac{14}{3}, \frac{-1}{3}\right)$

50. In the triangle ABC with vertices, A(2, −5) and B(4, 4) and centroid O(3, 1), find the third vertex of the triangle.

A. (3, 4) B. (2, −1)

C. (0, 3) D. (1, 2)

CHAPTER 8

Introduction to Trigonometry

PRIOR KNOWLEDGE TEST

Choose the correct option.

1. Each side of a square is 18 cm. Find the length of its diagonal.
   A. 18 cm B. $18\sqrt{2}$ cm
   C. 36 cm D. $36\sqrt{2}$ cm

2. The height of an isosceles right-angled triangle is 15 cm. Find the perimeter of the triangle.
   A. 45 cm B. $30 + 15\sqrt{2}$ cm
   C. $(15 + 30\sqrt{2})$ cm D. Insufficient data

3. Which of the following measurements does not form a right-angled triangle?
   A. 18, 24, 30 B. 5, 12, 13
   C. 8, 15, 17 D. 15, 20, 24

4. If the complement of an angle is 6° more than twice the angle, find the angle.
   A. 28° B. 56° C. 58° D. 62°

5. Two complementary angles are in the ratio 7 : 8. Find the greatest angle.
   A. 80° B. 70° C. 48° D. 42°

KEYWORDS

Trigonometric ratios: Ratios of the sides of a right-angled triangle with respect to its acute angles

Trigonometric ratios of angle A in triangle ABC right-angled at B:

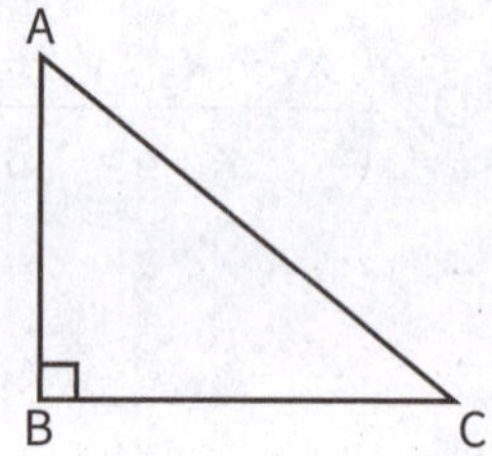

- sine of $\angle A = \dfrac{\text{side opposite to angle A}}{\text{hypotenuse}} = \dfrac{BC}{AC}$
- cosine of $\angle A = \dfrac{\text{side adjacent to angle A}}{\text{hypotenuse}} = \dfrac{AB}{AC}$
- tangent of $\angle A = \dfrac{\text{side opposite to angle A}}{\text{side adjacent to angle A}} = \dfrac{BC}{AB}$
- cosecant of $\angle A = \dfrac{\text{hypotenuse}}{\text{side oppoosite to angle A}} = \dfrac{AC}{BC}$
- secant of $\angle A = \dfrac{\text{hypotenuse}}{\text{side adjacent to angle A}} = \dfrac{AC}{AB}$
- cotangent of $\angle A = \dfrac{\text{side adjacent to angle A}}{\text{side opposite to angle A}} = \dfrac{AB}{BC}$

Trigonometric identities: An equation involving the trigonometric ratios of an angle (if it is true for all values of the angle(s) involved)

CONCEPT MAP

Trigonometry

derived from:
- 'Tri' - three
- 'Gon' - sides
- 'Metron' - measure

deals with: Study of the relationship between sides and angles of a right-angled triangle

includes:

Trigonometric Ratios

- $\sin A = \dfrac{\text{side opposite to angle A}}{\text{hypotenuse}} = \dfrac{BC}{AC}$
- $\cos A = \dfrac{\text{side adjacent to angle A}}{\text{hypotenuse}} = \dfrac{AB}{AC}$
- $\tan A = \dfrac{\text{side opposite to angle A}}{\text{side adjacent to angle A}} = \dfrac{BC}{AB}$
- $\text{cosec } A = \dfrac{\text{hypotenuse}}{\text{side opposite to angle A}} = \dfrac{1}{\sin A} = \dfrac{AC}{BC}$
- $\sec A = \dfrac{\text{hypotenuse}}{\text{side adjacent to angle A}} = \dfrac{1}{\cos A} = \dfrac{AC}{AB}$
- $\cot A = \dfrac{\text{side adjacent to angle A}}{\text{side opposite to angle A}} = \dfrac{1}{\tan A} = \dfrac{AB}{BC}$

of

Specific Angles are

∠A	0°	30°	45°	60°	90°
sin A	0	$\frac{1}{2}$	$\frac{1}{\sqrt{2}}$	$\frac{\sqrt{3}}{2}$	1
cos A	1	$\frac{\sqrt{3}}{2}$	$\frac{1}{\sqrt{2}}$	$\frac{1}{2}$	0
tan A	0	$\frac{1}{\sqrt{3}}$	1	$\sqrt{3}$	Not defined
cosec A	Not defined	2	$\sqrt{2}$	$\frac{2}{\sqrt{3}}$	1
sec A	1	$\frac{2}{\sqrt{3}}$	$\sqrt{2}$	2	Not defined
cot A	Not defined	$\sqrt{3}$	1	$\frac{1}{\sqrt{3}}$	0

Complimentary Angles are

- $\sin(90° - A) = \cos A$
- $\cos(90° - A) = \sin A$
- $\tan(90° - A) = \cot A$
- $\cot(90° - A) = \tan A$
- $\sec(90° - A) = \text{cosec } A$
- $\text{cosec}(90° - A) = \sec A$

Trigonometric Identities include

- $\sin^2 A + \cos^2 A = 1$
- $\sec^2 A - \tan^2 A = 1$ for $0° \le A < 90°$
- $\text{cosec}^2 A = 1 + \cot^2 A$ for $0° < A \le 90°$

PART 1

CHAPTER 8: Introduction to Trigonometry

SELF-ASSESSMENT 1

Choose the correct option.

1. Which of the following is true?
   A. cos A is the ratio of sin A and tan A.
   B. The value of sin A is always less than 1.
   C. cosec A is the reciprocal of secant A.
   D. The short form of cosecant of angle A is cos A.

2. If $\sin\theta = \frac{1}{\sqrt{2}}$, what is the value of $\sec\theta$?
   A. $\frac{1}{\sqrt{2}}$ B. $\sqrt{2}$
   C. 1 D. $\frac{\sqrt{3}}{2}$

3. If cosec A = $\sqrt{6}$, find the value of tan A.
   A. $\frac{1}{\sqrt{6}}$ B. $\frac{1}{\sqrt{5}}$
   C. $\sqrt{5}$ D. $\sqrt{6}$

4. If $\tan\theta = \frac{3}{4}$, find the value of $\frac{1-\sin\theta}{1+\sin\theta}$.
   A. 4 B. 1
   C. $\frac{1}{4}$ D. 2

5. If $\sqrt{5}\tan\theta = 5\sin\theta$, find the value of $4\cos^2\theta - \sin^2\theta$.
   A. 5 B. 1
   C. $\frac{1}{5}$ D. 0

6. If $\sin\theta = \frac{3}{\sqrt{10}}$, find the value of $\frac{\text{cosec}^2\theta + \cot^2\theta}{\text{cosec}^2\theta - \cot^2\theta}$.
   A. 1 B. $\frac{1}{9}$
   C. $\frac{5}{9}$ D. $\frac{11}{9}$

7. If $\sec\theta = \frac{13}{12}$, what is the value of $\frac{2\cos\theta - 3\sin\theta}{4\cos\theta - 9\sin\theta}$?
   A. 1 B. 3
   C. 9 D. $\frac{12}{13}$

8. If $\cot\theta = \frac{b}{a}$, find the value of $\frac{a\sin\theta - b\cos\theta}{\sin\theta + \cos\theta}$.
   A. $a + b$ B. $a - b$
   C. $2a + b$ D. $2a - b$

9. If $\cos A = \frac{2\sqrt{2}}{3}$, what is the value of cosec A cos A + cot A sin A?
   A. $\frac{4\sqrt{2}}{3}$ B. $\frac{8\sqrt{2}}{3}$
   C. $2\sqrt{2}$ D. $4\sqrt{2}$

10. If $\tan A = \sqrt{3} - 1$, find the value of cosec A cos A.

A. $\sqrt{3} - 1$
B. $\frac{1}{\sqrt{3} - 1}$
C. $\sqrt{3}$
D. $\sqrt{3} + 1$

11. If $\sin (2A + B) = 1$ and $\cos (2A - B) = \frac{\sqrt{3}}{2}$, $0° < A + B \leq 90°$, which of the following is true?

A. $2B = A$
B. $A = B$
C. $2A = B$
D. Insufficient data

12. If $\tan \theta + \frac{1}{\tan \theta} = 2$ and θ is an acute angle, find the value of $5 \tan^9 \theta$.

A. 1
B. 5
C. 10
D. 14

13. An equilateral triangle of 8 cm is inscribed in a circle. Find the radius of the circle.

A. $\frac{8}{\sqrt{2}}$ cm
B. $\frac{8}{\sqrt{3}}$ cm
C. $8\sqrt{3}$ cm
D. $4\sqrt{3}$ cm

14. Find the value of $\sin 60° \cos 30° + \sin 30° \cos 60°$.

A. 1
B. 2
C. $\frac{2}{\sqrt{3}}$
D. $\frac{\sqrt{3}}{2}$

15. Find the value of $2 \sin^2 30° + 4 \cos^2 60° - \tan 45°$.

A. 1
B. 2
C. $\frac{5}{2}$
D. $\frac{1}{2}$

16. Find the value of A, if $\sin A = \sqrt{3} \cos A$.

A. 30°
B. 45°
C. 60°
D. 90°

17. Find the value of $\sin 18° \cos 72° + \cos 18° \sin 72° + \sin 60° + \cos 30°$.

A. 1
B. 2
C. 3
D. $1 + \sqrt{3}$

18. Which of the following is equal to $\frac{2}{3}$?

A. $\sin 68° \cos 22° + \cos 68° \sin 22° + \tan^2 60°$
B. $\frac{\sin^2 30°}{\cos 60°} + \cot 30°$
C. $\tan 45° + \sin 30° - \cos 30°$
D. $\sin 80° \cos 10° + \cos 80° \sin 10° - \cot^2 60°$

19. Find the value of $\sec \theta \sqrt{1 - \sin^2 \theta}$.

A. $\frac{1}{4}$
B. 1
C. 2
D. 4

20. If $a = x \cos \theta$ and $b = y \cot \theta$, find the value of $\frac{y^2}{b^2} - \frac{x^2}{a^2}$.

A. –1
B. 1
C. 2
D. 0

21. Simplify the given expression.
$(\text{cosec } \theta + \cot \theta - 1)(\text{cosec } \theta - \cot \theta + 1)$

A. 0
B. $2 \cot \theta$
C. $2 \cot \theta + 2$
D. 2

22. If $\cos A + \cos^2 A = 1$, find $\frac{\sin^2 A + \sin^4 A}{\cos A}$.

A. $\frac{1 + \sin A}{\cos A}$
B. $\cos A$
C. $1 + \cos A$
D. $\sin A \cos A$

23. Find the value of
$\operatorname{cosec}^4 \theta\left(1 - \cos^4 \theta\right) - 2 \cot^2 \theta$.

A. 0 B. 1

C. –1 D. 2

24. If $1 + \cos^2 \theta = 3 \sin \theta \cos \theta$, find the value of $\cot \theta$.

A. 1 and $\frac{1}{2}$ B. 1 and $\frac{-1}{2}$

C. –1 and $\frac{-1}{2}$ D. –1 and $\frac{1}{2}$

25. Find the value of $\frac{\cos A - 3\cos^3 A}{3 \sin^3 A - 2 \sin A}$.

A. tan A B. cot A

C. sin A D. cos A

SELF-ASSESSMENT 2

Choose the correct option.

26. If cosec θ = $\frac{29}{21}$, what is the value of cot θ?

A. $\frac{20}{21}$ B. $\frac{29}{20}$

C. $\frac{21}{20}$ D. $\frac{20}{29}$

27. In a right-angled triangle ABC, right angled at C, if AB = 17 cm, BC = 15 cm, find sin B.

A. $\frac{8}{15}$ B. $\frac{8}{17}$

C. $\frac{15}{17}$ D. $\frac{17}{15}$

28. If cot θ = $\frac{12}{16}$, find the value of $\frac{1+\cos\theta}{1-\cos\theta}$.

A. 1

B. 2

C. 4

D. $\frac{1}{4}$

29. If 9 tan x − 12 = 0, find the value of $\frac{3\sin x+5\cos x}{3\sin x-5\cos x}$.

A. 9

B. −9

C. 81

D. −81

30. If cos θ = $\frac{2}{\sqrt{5}}$, find the value of $\frac{\sec^2\theta-\tan^2\theta}{\sec^2\theta}$.

A. $\frac{4}{5}$ B. 1

C. 0 D. $\frac{16}{25}$

31. If cosec θ = $\frac{17}{15}$, what is the value of $\frac{\sec\theta+\tan\theta}{\sec\theta-\tan\theta}$?

A. 4 B. 8

C. 12 D. 16

32. If $\sqrt{3}$ tan A = 3, what is the value of sec A sin A + cos A cosec A?

A. $\frac{4}{3}$ B. $\frac{8}{3}$

C. $\frac{4}{\sqrt{3}}$ D. $\frac{\sqrt{3}}{4}$

33. If 3 cos A = $\sqrt{2}$, find the value of cot A sin A.

A. $\frac{2}{\sqrt{3}}$ B. $\frac{\sqrt{2}}{3}$

C. 1 D. 2

34. If cot A = $\frac{x}{y}$, find $\frac{x\cos A+y\sin A}{x\cos A-y\sin A}$.

A. x^2-y^2 B. x^2+y^2

C. $\frac{x^2+y^2}{x^2-y^2}$ D. $\frac{x^2-y^2}{x^2+y^2}$

35. In a right-angled triangle XYZ, right angled at X, XY = 18 cm and $\angle Z = 30°$. Find YZ.

A. 24 cm B. 30 cm
C. 32 cm D. 36 cm

36. If $\sin\theta + \frac{1}{\sin\theta} = 2$ and $\theta \le 90°$, find the value of $\sin\theta - \cos\theta$.

A. 0 B. 1
C. $\frac{1}{2}$ D. $\frac{\sqrt{3}}{2}$

37. An equilateral triangle is inscribed in a circle of diameter $16\sqrt{3}$ cm. Find the height of the triangle.

A. 12 cm
B. $6\sqrt{3}$ cm
C. $12\sqrt{3}$ cm
D. 24 cm

38. Find the value of $\tan 30° \cot 30° + \tan 60° \cot 60°$.

A. $2\sqrt{3}$
B. 1
C. $\frac{2}{\sqrt{3}}$
D. 2

39. Find the value of $3\operatorname{cosec}^2 30° - 4\sec^2 60° + 2\cot 45° + 3\tan 45°$.

A. 0 B. 1
C. 2 D. 4

40. Find the value of θ, if $\tan\theta = \frac{1}{2}\sec\theta$.

A. 30° B. 45°
C. 60° D. 90°

41. Find the value of $\cot 35° \tan 55° - \operatorname{cosec} 35° \sec 55° + \sin 10° \cos 80° + \sin 80° \cos 10°$.

A. 0 B. 1
C. 2 D. 3

42. What is the value of $\cot 1° \times \cot 2° \times \cot 3 \times \ldots\ldots \times \cot 89°$?

A. 0 B. 1
C. $\frac{1}{2}$ D. Not defined

43. Find the value of $4(\sin^6 A + \cos^6 A) - 6(\sin^4 A + \cos^4 A)$.

A. 1
B. $-2(\sin^2 A + \cos^2 A)$
C. –1
D. –2

44. If $x = a\sec\theta + b\tan\theta$ and $y = a\tan\theta + b\sec\theta$, find the value of $x^2 - y^2$.

A. $a^2 - b^2$
B. $a^2 + b^2$
C. $b^2 - a^2$
D. $2(a^2 - b^2)$

45. Find the value of $\frac{\sin^2\theta}{\cos\theta} - \sec\theta + \cos\theta$.

A. 0 B. $\frac{2}{\cos\theta}$
C. 1 D. 2

46. Which of the following is equal to $\cot^2\theta - \cos^2\theta$?

A. $2\cot\theta\cos\theta$
B. $\cot^2\theta - \cos^2\theta$
C. $\cot^2\theta\cos^2\theta$
D. $\cot\theta\cos\theta$

47. Which of the following is equal to

$$\sqrt{\frac{1+\sin\theta}{1-\sin\theta}}+\sqrt{\frac{1-\sin\theta}{1+\sin\theta}}?$$

A. $2\sin\theta$

B. $2\cos\theta$

C. $2\sec\theta$

D. $2\operatorname{cosec}\theta$

48. $\sec A - \tan A =$ ______________.

A. $\dfrac{\cos A}{1+\sin A}$ B. $\dfrac{1-\sin A}{\cos A}$

C. $\sqrt{\dfrac{1-\sin A}{1+\sin A}}$ D. All of these

49. Which of the following is equal to

$$\frac{5}{\sin^2\theta}-5\cot^2\theta?$$

A. 0 B. 5

C. 1 D. -5

50. Find the value of $\dfrac{\sec^2 A-\tan^2 A}{\cot^2 A-\operatorname{cosec}^2 A}$.

A. 2 B. 1

C. 0 D. -1

CHAPTER 9

Some Applications of Trigonometry

PRIOR KNOWLEDGE TEST

Choose the correct option.

1. If sec A = $\frac{5}{3}$, what is the value of tan A?

   A. $\frac{3}{4}$ B. $\frac{3}{5}$

   C. $\frac{4}{3}$ D. $\frac{4}{5}$

2. In a triangle ABC, right angled at B, if AB = 7 cm and AC = 25 cm, find the length of BC.

   A. 26 cm

   B. 24 cm

   C. 20 cm

   D. 15 cm

3. Find the value of tan 60° cot 30° + cot 60° tan 30°.

   A. $\frac{8}{3}$ B. 1

   C. 2 D. $\frac{10}{3}$

4. Which of the following is equal to sin 35° cos 55° + sin 55° cos 35°?

   A. 1 B. 2

   C. $\frac{1}{2}$ D. $\frac{1}{4}$

5. Find the value of $\sec^4 A + \tan^4 A - 2\sec^2 A \tan^2 A$.

   A. 1 B. 2

   C. 4 D. 0

KEYWORDS

Line of sight: A line drawn from the eye of an observer to the point in an object viewed by the observer

Angle of elevation: An angle formed by the line of sight with the horizontal when the line of sight is above the horizontal level, that is, the case when we raise our head to look at an object

Angle of depression: An angle formed by the line of sight with the horizontal when the line of sight is below the horizontal level, that is, the case when we lower our head to look at an object

CONCEPT MAP

Applications of Trigonometry → in finding → Heights and distances → of → Objects

Objects → when viewed by an observer forms → Line of sight

Line of sight → is → A line drawn from the eye of an observer to the point in an object viewed by the observer

Line of sight → forms → **Angle of elevation** and **Angle of depression**

Angle of elevation → is → An angle formed by the line of sight with the horizontal when the line of sight is above the horizontal level, that is, the case when we raise our head to look at an object

→ example

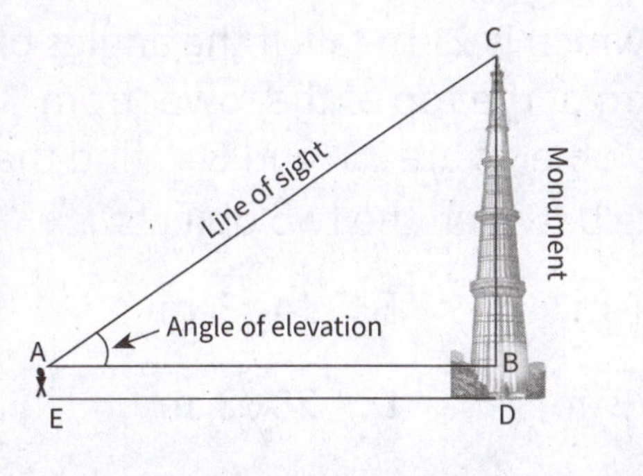

Angle of depression → is → An angle formed by the line of sight with the horizontal when the line of sight is below the horizontal level, that is, the case when we lower our head to look at an object

→ example

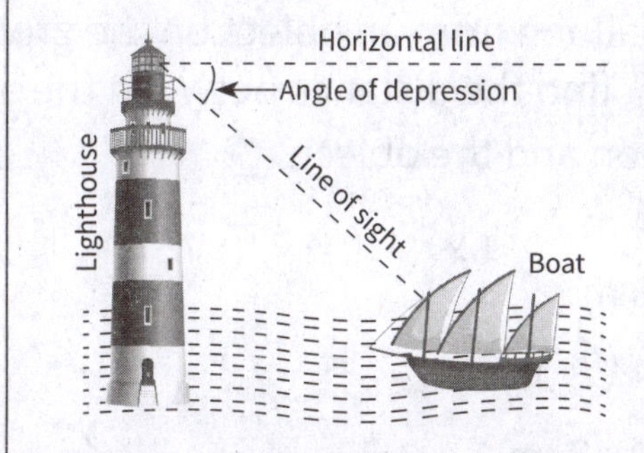

PART 1

CHAPTER 9: Some Applications of Trigonometry

SELF-ASSESSMENT 1

Choose the correct option.

1. The ratio of the lengths of an object placed vertically and its shadow is $\sqrt{3} : 1$. Find the angle of elevation of the sun.
   A. 30° B. 45°
   C. 60° D. 90°

2. If the angle of elevation of the tip of a building from a distance of 60 m from its foot is 30°, find the height of the building.
   A. 20 m B. $20\sqrt{3}$ m
   C. $\frac{20}{\sqrt{3}}$ m D. $\frac{40}{\sqrt{3}}$ m

3. A ladder is leaning against a wall at an angle of 30°, and the distance between the foot of the ladder and the wall is 12 m. Find the length of the ladder.
   A. 12 m B. $12\sqrt{3}$ m
   C. 24 m D. $8\sqrt{3}$ m

4. An air balloon is allowed to fly in the sky for some advertisement purpose. It is flying at a height of 42 m from the ground level. If the angle of elevation of the balloon from an object on the ground is 60°, find the distance between the air balloon and the object.
   A. 14 m
   B. 28 m
   C. $14\sqrt{3}$ m
   D. $28\sqrt{3}$ m

5. The angle of depression of an object from the top of a building is 45°. If the object is 16 m away from the building, find the height of the building.
   A. 8 m B. 16 m
   C. 32 m D. $16\sqrt{3}$ m

6. From a lighthouse, the angles of depression of two ships on the opposite sides of the lighthouse are 30° and 45°. If the height of the lighthouse is 30 m, find the distance between the two ships.
   A. 30 m B. $30\sqrt{3}$ m
   C. $30(1+\sqrt{3})$ m D. $60\sqrt{3}$ m

7. A man, 1.7 m tall, finds the angle of elevation of the topmost part of a tree to be 30°. If the distance between the man and the tree is 24 m, find the height of the tree. (Take $\sqrt{3} = 1.7$)
   A. 11.9 m B. 13.6 m
   C. 13.7 m D. 15. 3 m

8. Two objects are on the same side of a tower, which is 21 m tall. If the angles of elevation of the top of the tower from the two objects are 30° and 60°, find the distance between the two objects.
   A. $7\sqrt{3}$ m B. $14\sqrt{3}$ m
   C. $21\sqrt{3}$ m D. $28\sqrt{3}$ m

9. A girl is standing $9\sqrt{3}$ m away from a tower. The angle of elevation of the tower from the eyes of the girl is 45°. If the height of the tower is $10\sqrt{3}$ m, find the height of the girl (to the nearest 10th digit).

A. 1.5 m B. 1.72 m
C. 1.7 m D. 1. 6 m

10. From the top of a building which is 80 m high, the angle of depression of an object is 30°. If the object moves x m towards the building, the angle of depression changes to 45°. Find x to the nearest metre.

A. 58 m B. 60 m
C. 80 m D. 138 m

11. The angle of depression of a truck parked on the road from the top of a 120 m high building is 60°. What is the distance of the truck from the building?

A. 120 m B. $120\sqrt{3}$ m
C. $40\sqrt{3}$ m D. 40 m

12. Two electric poles of heights 42 m and 36 m are connected by an electric wire, which makes an angle of 30° with the horizontal. Find the length of the wire.

A. 6 m B. 12 m
C. $4\sqrt{3}$ m D. $3\sqrt{2}$ m

13. The angle of elevation of a $200\sqrt{3}$ m high tower from a car is 60°. If the car moves 400 m away from the tower, find the change in the angle of elevation.

A. 30° B. 60°
C. 45° D. No change

14. The angle of elevation of two towers from a point is 30°. If the heights of the towers are x m and $2x$ m, find the distance between the two towers in terms of x.

A. $\frac{x}{\sqrt{3}}$ m B. $\frac{2x}{\sqrt{3}}$ m
C. $x\sqrt{3}$ m D. $2x\sqrt{3}$ m

15. The angles of elevation of the tip of a tower from the top and the bottom of a building are 30° and 60°, respectively. Find the ratio of the height of the tower and the height of the building.

A. 1 : 2 B. 1 : 4
C. 3 : 2 D. $1 : \sqrt{3}$

16. The angle of depression of the topmost part of a ship from a lighthouse is 45°. If the ship is 90 m away from the lighthouse and the ratio of their heights is 1 : 5, find the height of the lighthouse.

A. 90 m B. 108 m
C. 112. 5 m D. 120 m

17. Two pillars of heights x m and $4x$ m are 200 m apart. If the angles of depression of an object in between them from the two pillars are 30° and 60°, find the distance of the object from the longer pillar to the nearest metre.

A. 120 m B. 114 m
C. 86 m D. 80 m

18. The angles of elevation of the top of a tower from points A and B, at a distance of 16 m and 36 m, respectively, from the base of the tower are complementary. Find the height of the tower.

A. 48 m B. 36 m
C. 24 m D. 16 m

19. An ant observes extreme tip of a flagpole inclined at an angle of 30°. If the ant moves 30 m towards the pole, the angle of elevation changes to 60°. Find the height of the flagpole.

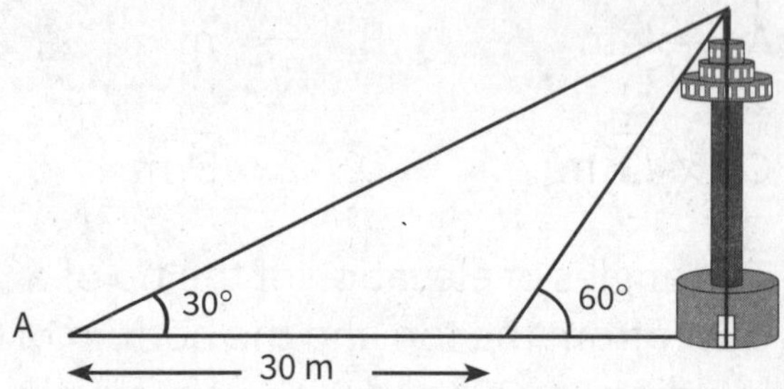

A. 15 m

B. $15\sqrt{3}$ m

C. 30 m

D. $30\sqrt{3}$ m

20. The angle of elevation from an observer's eyes to the tip of a monument is 30°. If the monument is 200 ft away from the observer, find the height of the monument.

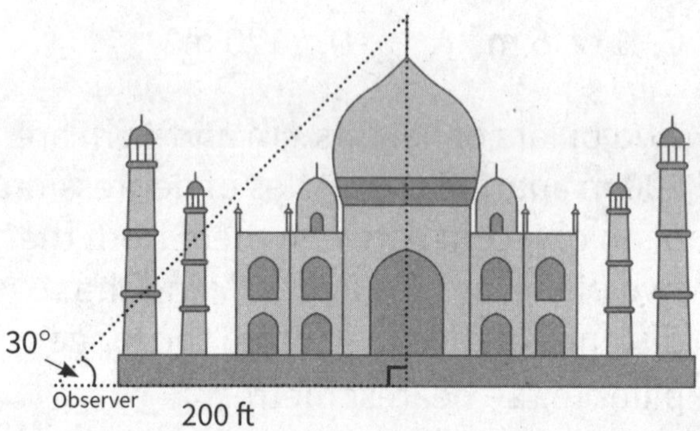

A. 100 ft

B. $\frac{200}{\sqrt{3}}$ ft

C. $100\sqrt{3}$ ft

D. $200\sqrt{3}$ ft

21. The driver of a car observes the angle of elevation of the topmost part of a building to be 30°. After travelling for 4 seconds towards the building, he finds the angle of elevation to be 60°. If the height of the building is 60 m, find the speed of the car.

A. $36\sqrt{3}$ km/h

B. $45\sqrt{3}$ km/h

C. $24\sqrt{3}$ km/h

D. $60\sqrt{3}$ km/h

22. There is a small island in the middle of a $120\sqrt{3}$ m wide river, and a tall tree stands on the island. Two persons are standing directly opposite to each other on the two banks and are in-line with the tree. If the height of each of them is 1.8 m and the angles of elevation of the top of the tree from the eyes of the two persons are 30° and 60°, respectively, find the height of the tree.

A. 90 m

B. 91.8 m

C. 92.6 m

D. 120 m

23. An electric pole $12\sqrt{3}$ m high breaks due to heavy winds, and the broken part bends in a way that the top of the pole touches the ground, making an angle of 30°. Find the distance between the foot of the pole and the point at which the top of the pole touches the ground.

A. $4\sqrt{3}$ m

B. 8 m

C. 12 m

D. $9\sqrt{3}$ m

24. A water tank is mounted on a building, and the angle of elevation of the water tank and the top of the building from a point is 60° and 45°, respectively. If the height of the building is 15 m, find the length of the water tank to the nearest metre. (Take $\sqrt{3} = 1.732$)

A. 10 m

B. 11 m

C. 12 m

D. 14 m

25. From an aeroplane vertically above a straight horizontal road, the angles of depression of two consecutive milestones on the opposite sides of the road are $x°$ and $y°$. Find the height in miles at which the aeroplane is flying in terms of x and y.

A. $\dfrac{\tan x + \tan y}{\tan x - \tan y}$

B. $\dfrac{\tan x - \tan y}{\tan x \tan y}$

C. $\dfrac{\tan x \tan y}{\tan x + \tan y}$

D. $\dfrac{\tan x + \tan y}{\tan x \tan y}$

CHAPTER 10

Circles

PRIOR KNOWLEDGE TEST

Choose the correct option.

1. A line segment joining any two points on a circle is called a __________.
   A. sector B. chord
   C. arc D. segment

2. Find the value of x in the given figure.

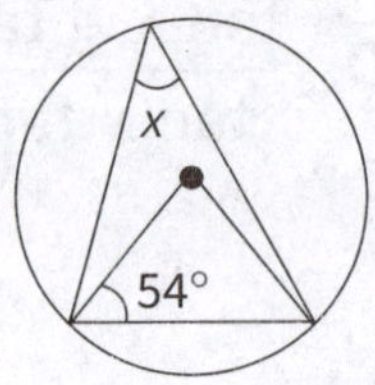

   A. 27°
   B. 54°
   C. 36°
   D. 72°

3. Find the value of ∠BXD, if the length of the chord AB = BD.

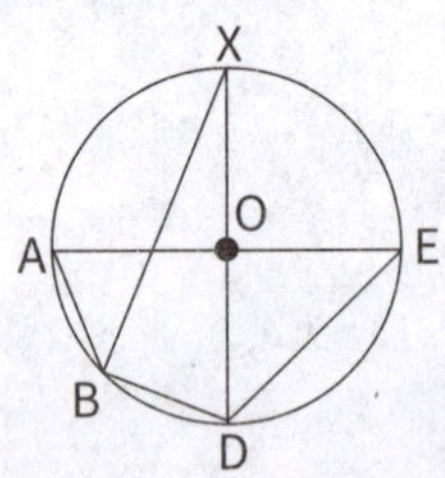

   A. 21°
   B. 22.5°
   C. 25°
   D. 27°

4. In the given figure, the chord XZ subtends an angle of 112° at the centre. Find ∠XYZ.

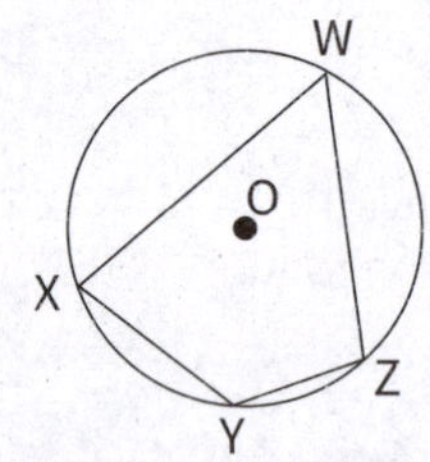

   A. 56°
   B. 112°
   C. 160°
   D. 124°

5. Find the length of a chord which is at a distance of 8 cm from the centre of a circle of radius 10 cm.
   A. 6 cm B. 8 cm
   C. 12 cm D. 16 cm

KEYWORDS

Circle: A collection of all the points in a plane, which are equidistant from a fixed point on the plane
Radius: The distance of any point on a circle from its centre
Secant: A line intersecting a circle in exactly two points
Chord: A line segment joining any two points on a circle
Circumference: The length of a circle, which is also known as the perimeter of the circle
Segment: The region between a chord and either of its arcs of a circle
Sector: The region between an arc and the two radii, joining the centre to the endpoints of the arc
Tangent: A line that intersects the circle at only one point
Point of contact: The point where a tangent touches the circle
Normal of a circle: The line perpendicular from the centre to the point of contact of a tangent

CONCEPT MAP

- **Circle**
  - is: A collection of all the points in a plane, which are equidistant from a fixed point
  - parts:
    - **Centre**: Fixed point
    - **Radius**: Fixed distance from the centre
      - **Diameter**: Longest chord that passes through centre (is twice the radius)
    - **Chord**: A line segment whose endpoints lie on the circle
      - properties:
        - Equal chords of a circle subtend equal angles at the centre.
        - The perpendicular from the centre of a circle to a chord bisects the chord.
        - Equal chords of a circle are equidistant from the centre.
    - **Tangent**: A line that intersects the circle at only one point
      - properties:
        - Only one tangent can be drawn through a point on a circle.
        - Only two tangents can be drawn to a circle from an external point.
        - A tangent is perpendicular to the radius through the point of contact.
        - Lengths of tangents from an external point to a circle are equal.
    - **Normal of a circle**: The line perpendicular from the centre to the point of contact of a tangent
    - **Point of contact**: The point where a tangent touches the circle
    - **Arc**: The part of a circle between any two points
      - property: The angle subtended by an arc at the centre is double the angle subtended by it at any point on the remaining part of the circle.
      - **Major arc**
      - **Minor arc**
      - **Semicircle**
        - property: Angle in a semicircle is a right angle.

PART 1

CHAPTER 10: Circles

SELF-ASSESSMENT 1

Choose the correct option.

1. A circle with centre O has a radius of 25 cm. How many tangents can be drawn from a point P, which is 24 cm away from the centre?
   A. 0
   B. 1
   C. 2 equal tangents
   D. 2 unequal tangents

2. Find the distance between two parallel tangents drawn to a circle of radius 4.5 cm.
   A. 4.5 cm B. $4.5\sqrt{2}$ cm
   C. 9 cm D. 10 cm

3. Find the length of the tangent drawn from a point, which is 13 cm away from the centre of a circle of diameter 10 cm.
   A. $2\sqrt{11}$ cm B. $2\sqrt{61}$ cm
   C. 12 cm D. 13 cm

4. Tangents from a point P to a circle with centre O intersect it at A and B. Find the measure of ∠APB, if the chord AB subtends an angle of 67° at the centre.
   A. 33.5°
   B. 67°
   C. 113°
   D. 134°

5. Find the radius of the given circle if the length of the tangent XY = 16 cm and OY = 20 cm.
   A. $8\sqrt{5}$ cm B. 10 cm
   C. 12 cm D. 16 cm

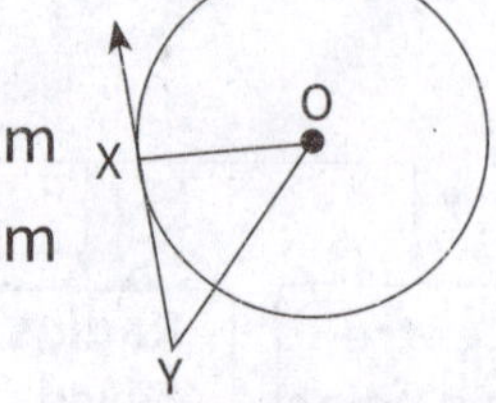

6. In the given figure, find the measure of ∠BAC.
   A. 151° B. 122°
   C. 111° D. 90°

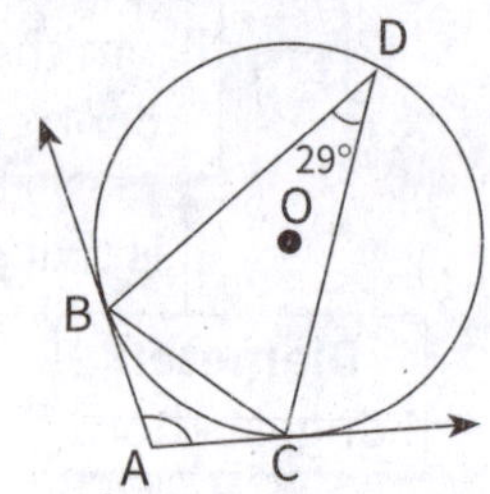

7. Two concentric circles C_1 and C_2 with centre O have radii 15 cm and 17 cm, respectively. Find the length of the longest chord of C_2, which is tangent to C_1.
   A. 30 cm B. 17 cm
   C. 16 cm D. 8 cm

8. Tangents from a point A to a circle with centre O intersect it at X and Y. Find the area of AXOY, if AO = 15 cm and OY = 9 cm.
   A. 135 cm² B. 124 cm²
   C. 108 cm² D. 54 cm²

9. In the given figure, find the measure of ∠AXY.
   A. 22° B. 44°
   C. 68° D. 90°

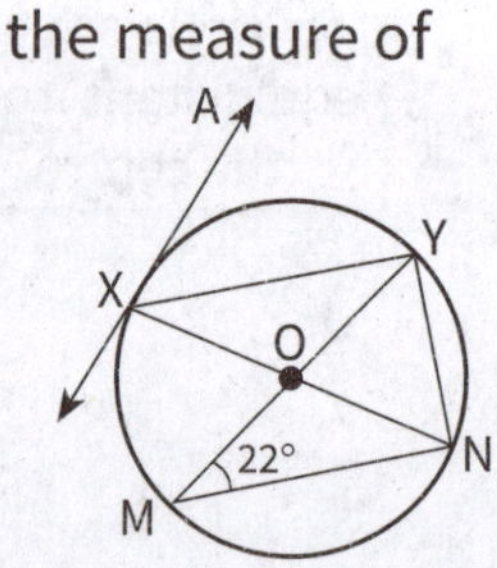

10. Find the radius of the circle given below, if point X is at a distance of 26 cm from the centre.

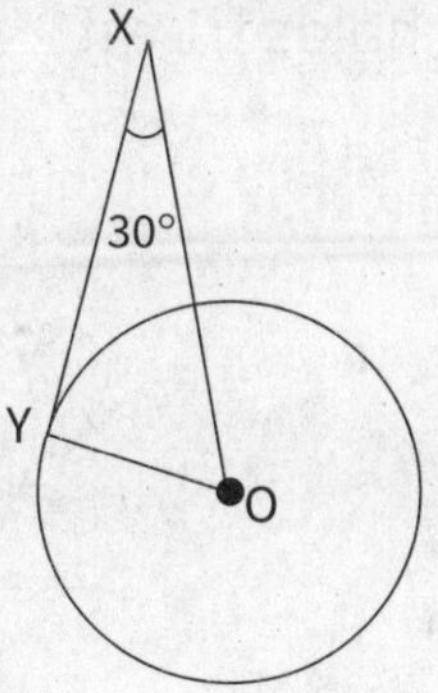

A. $13\sqrt{3}$ cm

B. 13 cm

C. $\frac{26}{\sqrt{3}}$ cm

D. $\frac{52}{\sqrt{3}}$ cm

11. Find the length of ZY, if the radius of the circle given below is 6 cm.

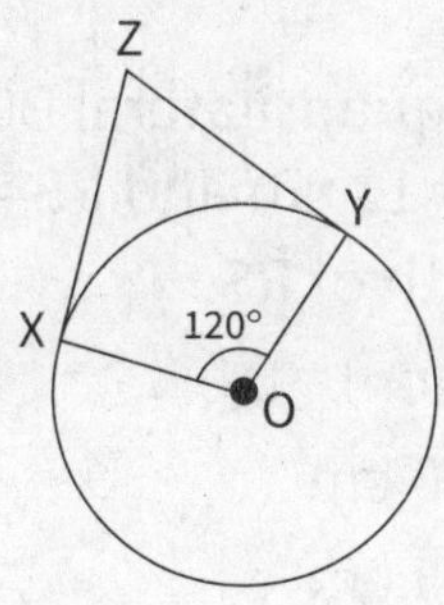

A. $6\sqrt{3}$ cm

B. 6 cm

C. $\frac{12}{\sqrt{3}}$ cm

D. $\frac{24}{\sqrt{3}}$ cm

12. Find the measure of $\angle BDC$, if $\angle ABC = 43°$.

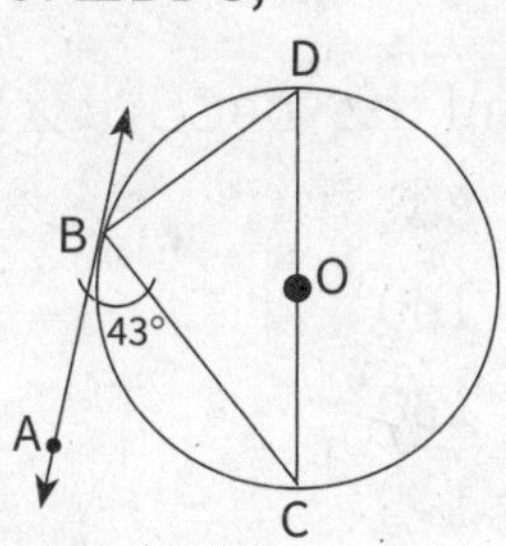

A. 43°

B. 47°

C. 86°

D. 90°

13. Which of the following holds true for the given figure?

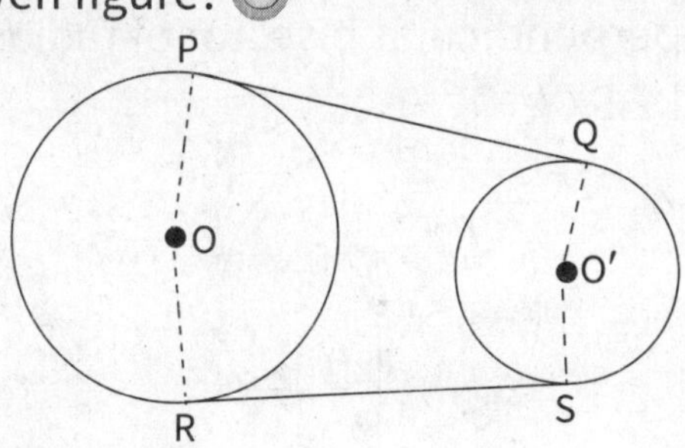

A. OP = 2O′S

B. PS = QR

C. PQ = RS

D. Both B and C

14. Two circles with radii in the ratio 4 : 3 are given below. Find the ratio of the tangents PQ and PS.

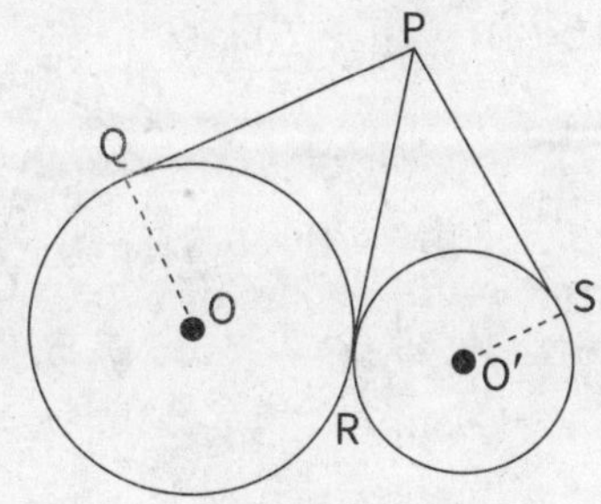

A. 4 : 3 B. 1 : 1

C. 2 : 1 D. 3 : 4

15. In the triangle ABC, AB = 8 cm and BC = 12 cm. Find the length of AC.

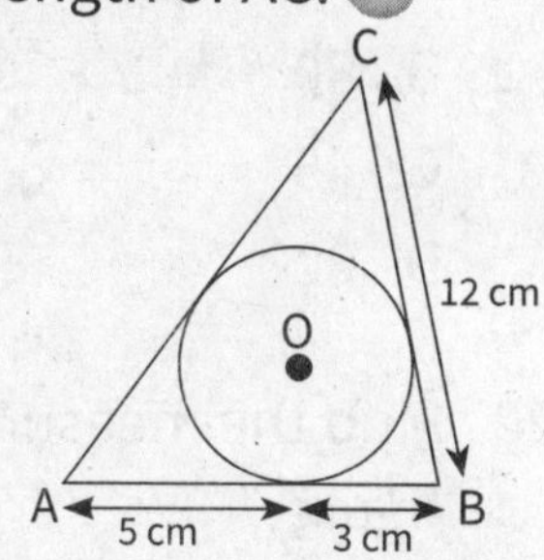

A. 14 cm

B. 12 cm

C. 8 cm

D. 5 cm

16. In the figure given below, find the length of AC if $\angle BAC = 90°$.

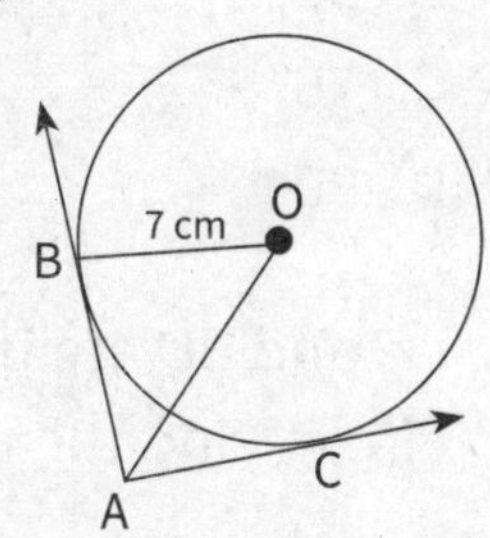

A. 3.5 cm

B. $\frac{7}{\sqrt{2}}$ cm

C. 7 cm

D. $7\sqrt{2}$ cm

17. QP and QR are the two tangents to the given circle. Find the length of QR if the length of PR is equal to the radius (*r* units) of the circle.

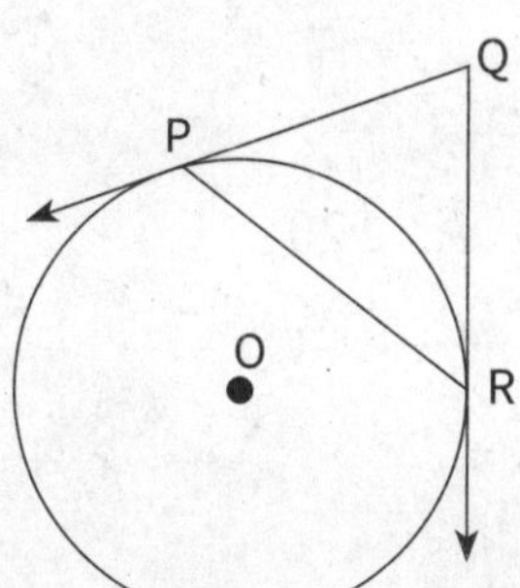

A. $\frac{2r}{\sqrt{3}}$ units

B. $\frac{r}{\sqrt{3}}$ units

C. $\frac{\sqrt{3}r}{2}$ units

D. $r\sqrt{3}$ units

18. QP, QR and XY are the tangents to the given circle with centre O. Find the perimeter of the triangle QXY, if QP = 15 cm.

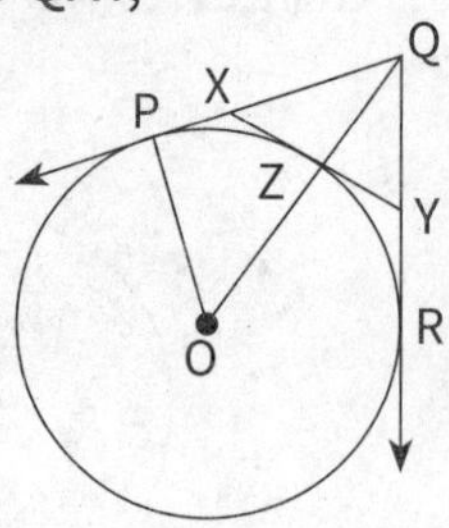

A. 15 cm
B. 22.5 cm
C. 30 cm
D. 45 cm

19. In the figure given below, the chord BC is parallel to the tangent drawn through the point A. Find the measure of ∠CAB.

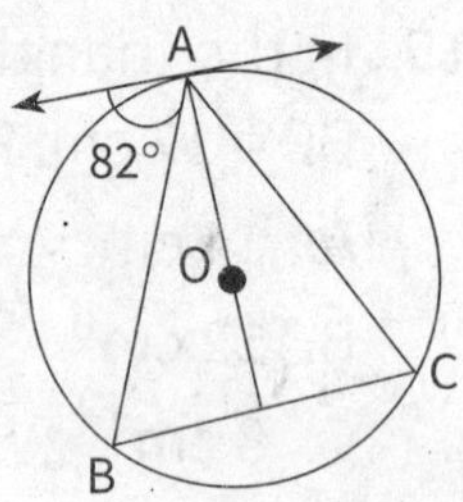

A. 16°
B. 30°
C. 45°
D. 82°

20. Find the measure of *x* in the given figure.

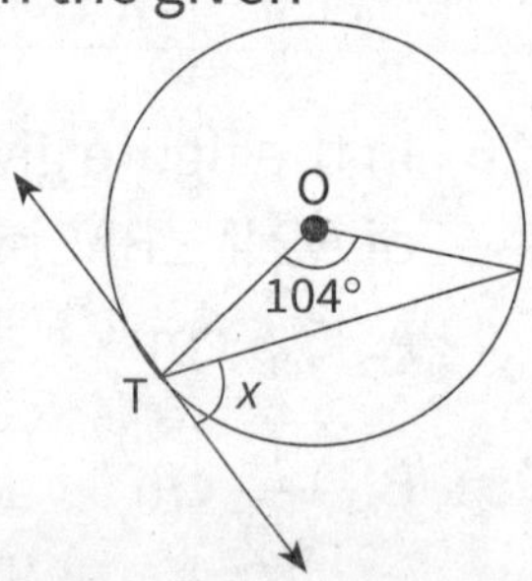

A. 38°
B. 52°
C. 76°
D. 90°

21. AC and BD are the diameters of the given circle. Find the measure of ∠AXB.

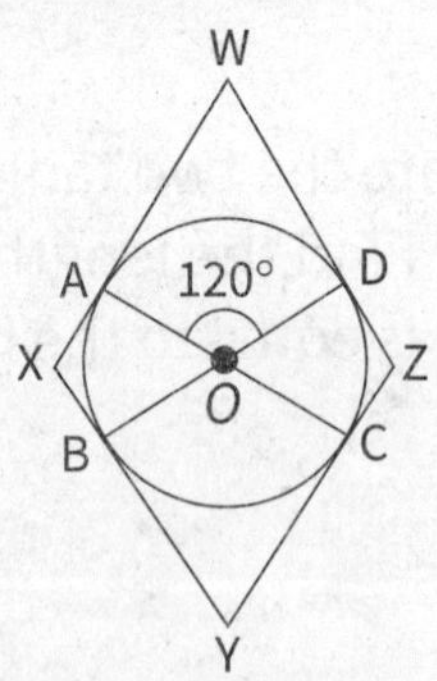

A. 120° B. 90°
C. 70° D. 60°

22. AC and BD are the diameters of the given circle. Which of the following statements holds true if ∠AOD = 120°?

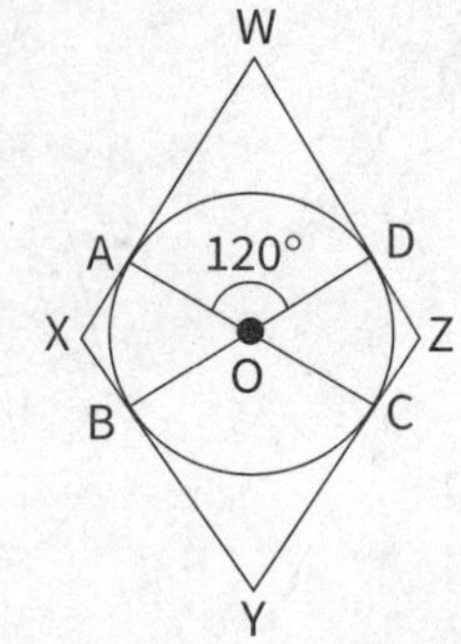

A. AX = AB B. WA = YB
C. AB = BC D. AD = WD

23. In a quadrilateral PQRS, PQ = 8 cm, QR = 12 cm and PS = 5 cm. Find the length of RS.

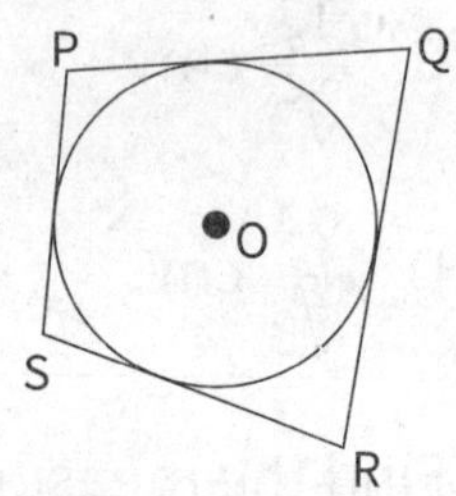

A. 9 cm
B. 10 cm
C. 15 cm
D. 16 cm

24. Find the ∠ACB, if ∠DAB = 50°.

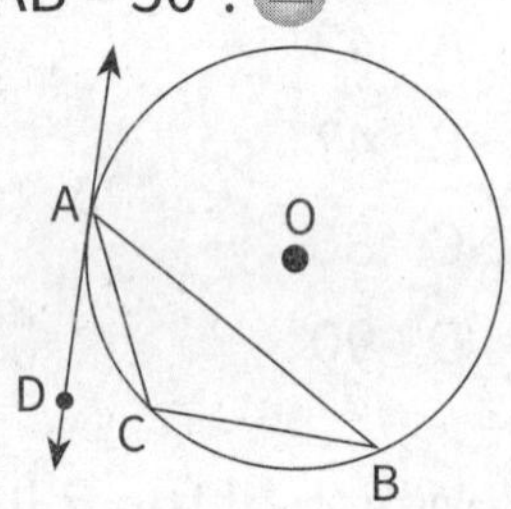

A. 80°
B. 100°
C. 130°
D. 145°

25. In the figure given below, the chord SR is the perpendicular bisector of radius OX. Find ∠SXY.

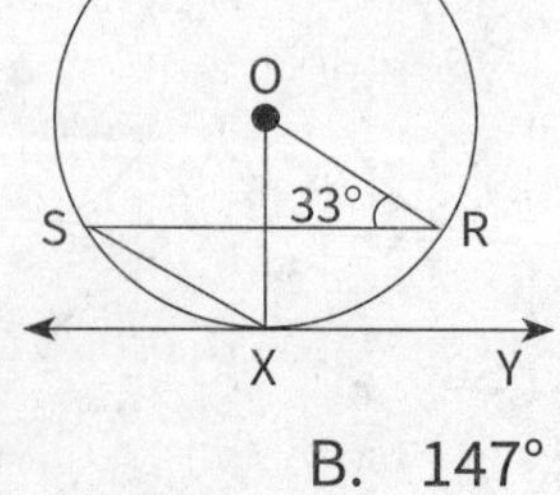

A. 127° B. 147°
C. 153° D. 157°

SELF-ASSESSMENT 2

Choose the correct option.

26. A circle with centre O has a diameter of 30 cm. How many tangents can be drawn from a point P, which is 24 cm away from the centre?
    A. 0
    B. 1
    C. 2 equal tangents
    D. 2 unequal tangents

27. Tangents drawn at the ends of the diameter of a circle are ___________.
    A. parallel
    B. perpendicular
    C. equal
    D. Both B and C

28. Find the distance of a point from the centre of a circle of radius 18 cm. The length of the tangent drawn from the point to the circle is 24 cm.
    A. $9\sqrt{2}$ cm   B. $15\sqrt{3}$ cm
    C. 30 cm   D. 32 cm

29. Tangents from a point X to a circle with centre O intersect it at A and B. Find the angle subtended by the chord AB at the centre, if $\angle AXB = 108°$.
    A. 36°
    B. 72°
    C. 90°
    D. 108°

30. Find the length of the tangent XY, if the diameter of the given circle is 22 cm and OY = 61 cm.
    A. 60 cm
    B. 56.89 cm
    C. $52\sqrt{3}$ cm
    D. 24 cm

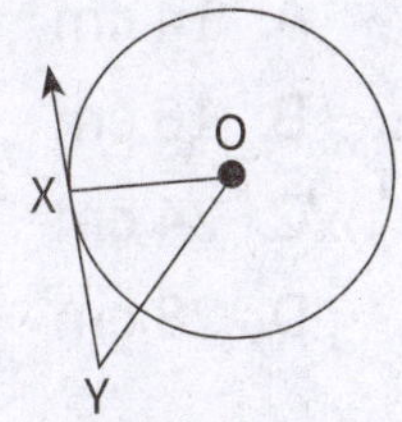

31. A line perpendicular to the tangent to a circle and passing through the point of contact is called the ________ to the circle.
    A. chord   B. segment
    C. normal   D. sector

32. Two concentric circles, C_1 and C_2, are given below. Find the radius of the bigger circle, if OM = 35 cm and the length of the chord XY = 24 cm.
    A. 42.43 cm
    B. 37 cm
    C. 33 cm
    D. 25.64 cm

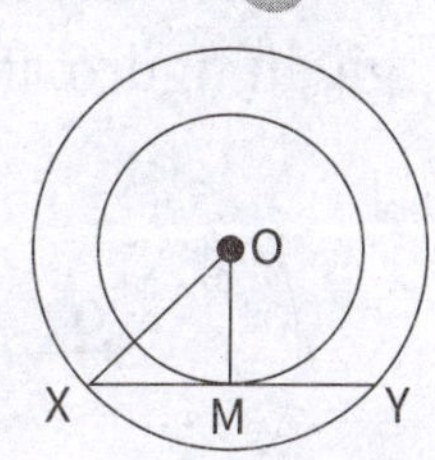

33. Tangents from a point P to a circle with centre O intersect it at X and Y. Find the area of PXOY, if PY = 13 cm and $\angle XPY = 90°$.
    A. 338 cm^2
    B. 169 cm^2
    C. 139 cm^2
    D. 120 cm^2

34. In the figure given below, find the measure of $\angle AXY$.

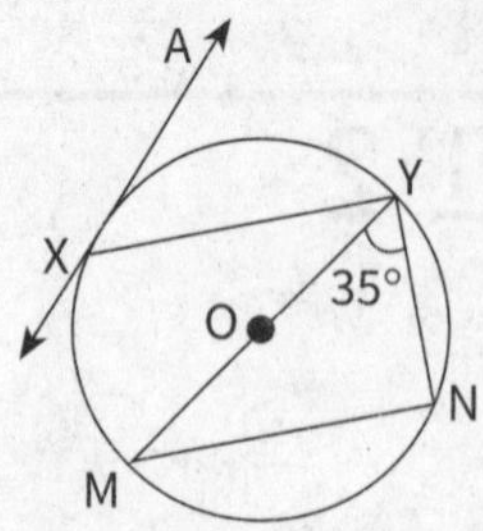

A. 35°

B. 45°

C. 55°

D. 70°

35. Find the distance between two parallel tangents of a circle if its area is 616 cm^2.

A. 14 cm

B. 16 cm

C. 24 cm

D. 28 cm

36. Find the distance of the point Z from the centre, if the length of the tangent ZY = 5 cm.

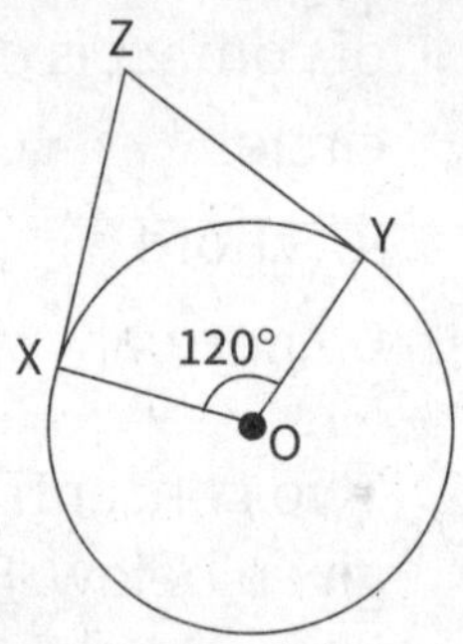

A. $10\sqrt{3}$ cm

B. 10 cm

C. $\frac{10}{\sqrt{3}}$ cm

D. $5\sqrt{3}$ cm

37. Which of the following holds true for the given figure, if OP : O′Q = 2 : 1?

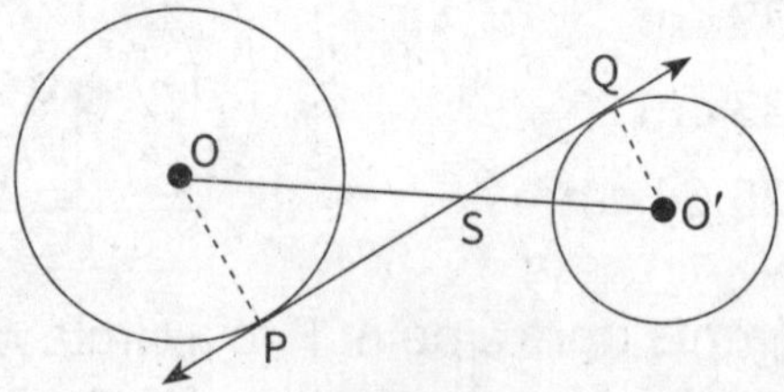

A. PS = 2OS

B. SO′ = 2SO

C. $QS = \frac{PS}{2}$

D. PS = QS

38. Find the length of SQ, if AB = 8 cm and the length of the tangent from the point S to the circle with centre O is 3.8 cm.

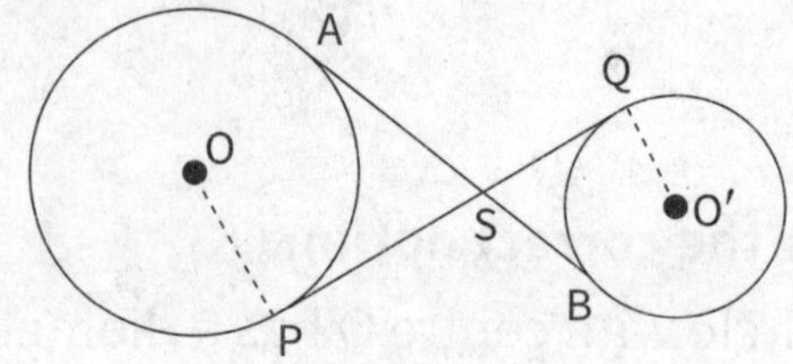

A. 3.8 cm B. 4.2 cm

C. 8 cm D. 11.8 cm

39. In the figure given below, QP and QR are the two tangents to the circle with centre O. Find the measure of $\angle ORP$ if $\angle PQR = 56°$.

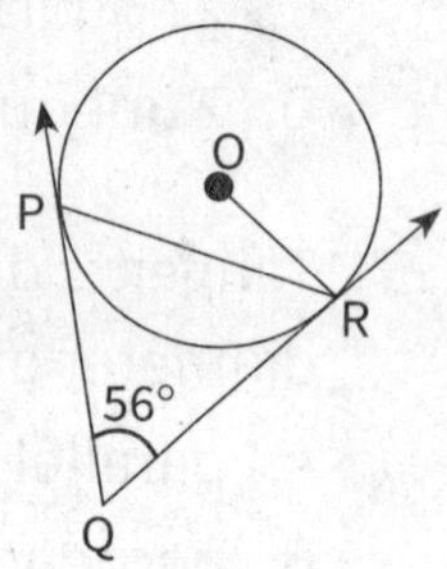

A. 23°

B. 28°

C. 62°

D. 128°

40. In the figure given below, the perimeter of the triangle ABC is 46 cm. The length of the tangent from the point C to the circle is 12 cm, and the length of the tangent from the point A to the circle is 7 cm. Find the length of side BC.

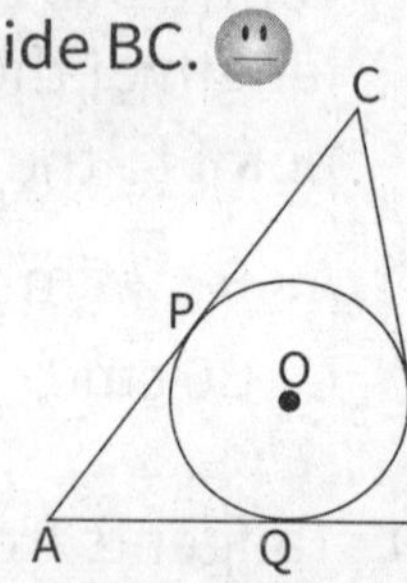

A. 8 cm

B. 11 cm

C. 14 cm

D. 16 cm

41. In the figure given below, find the length of AC, if $\angle BAC = 60°$ and the diameter of the circle is 8 cm.

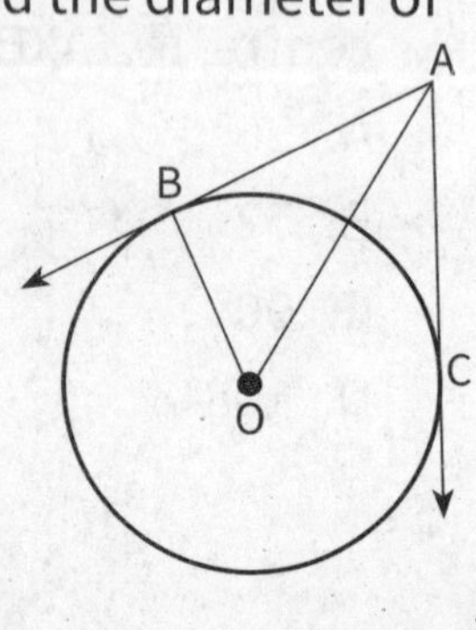

A. 2 cm

B. $\frac{4}{\sqrt{2}}$ cm

C. 4 cm

D. $4\sqrt{3}$ cm

42. OP and OQ are the two radii of a circle with centre O. Find the angle between the tangents drawn at P and Q, if $\angle POQ$ is 75°.

A. 75° B. 90°

C. 105° D. 150°

43. QP, QR and XY are the tangents to the circle with centre O. Find the length of the tangent QR, if the perimeter of the triangle QXY is 45 cm.

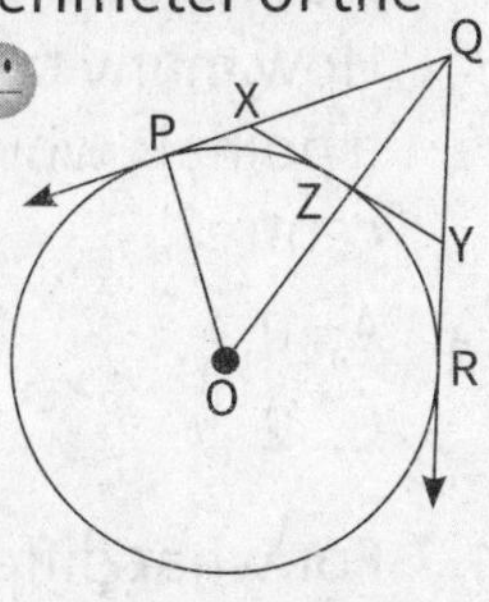

A. 20 cm

B. 22.5 cm

C. 32 cm

D. 45 cm

44. In the figure given below, the chord QR is parallel to the tangent drawn through the point P. Find the measure of $\angle XPR$.

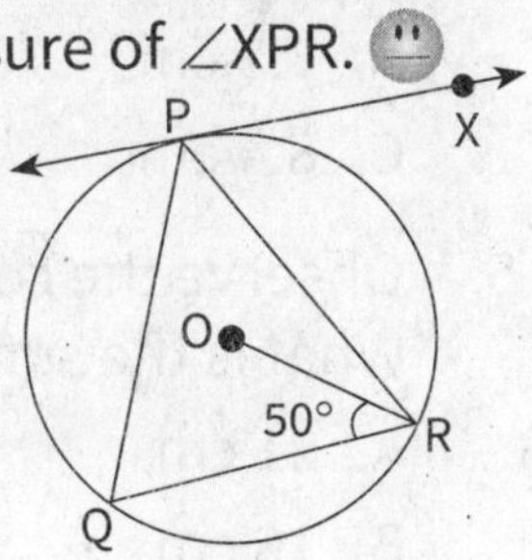

A. 25°

B. 55°

C. 65°

D. 70°

45. Find the measure of x in the figure given below.

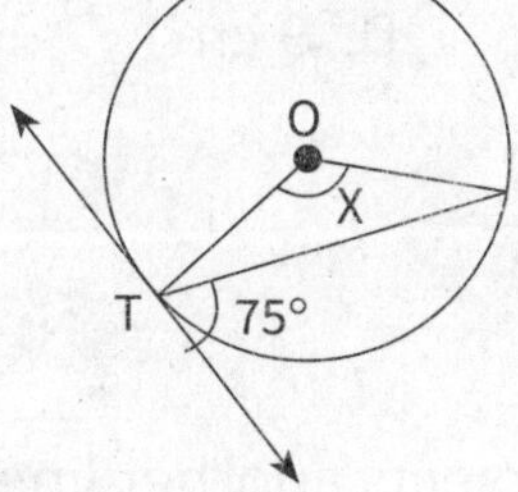

A. 150°

B. 120°

C. 105°

D. 90°

46. Find the measure of $\angle MAB$ in the figure given below.

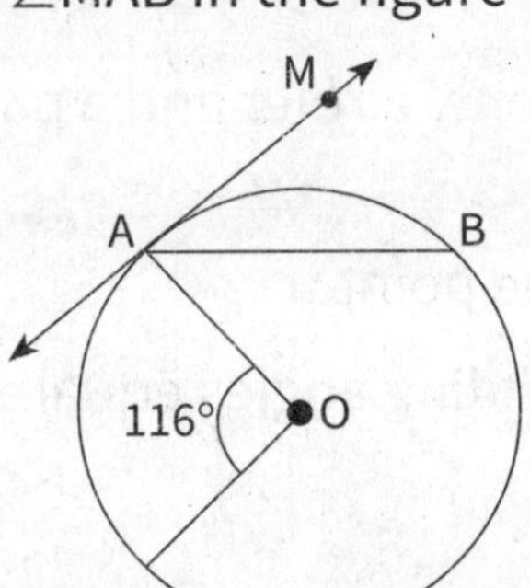

A. 64°

B. 58°

C. 32°

D. 30°

47. In the figure given below, BC and CD are the two chords of the circle with centre O, and AB and ED are the two tangents. Find the value of $\angle BOD$ if $\angle ABC = 25°$ and $\angle EDC = 45°$.

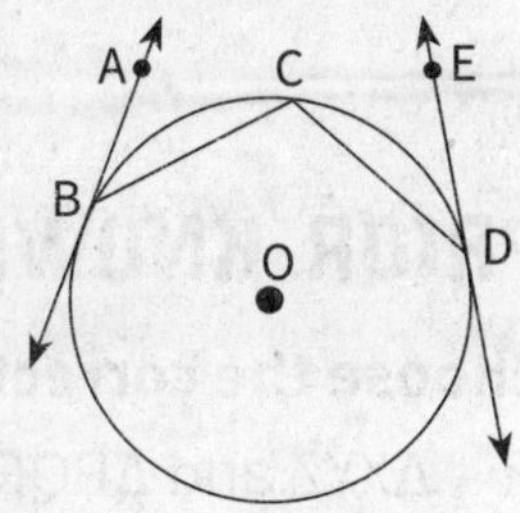

A. $\angle BOD = 100°$

B. $\angle BOD = 110°$

C. $\angle BOD = 140°$

D. $\angle BOD = 160°$

48. In the figure given below, find $\angle PQR$, if $\angle PRS = 125°$.

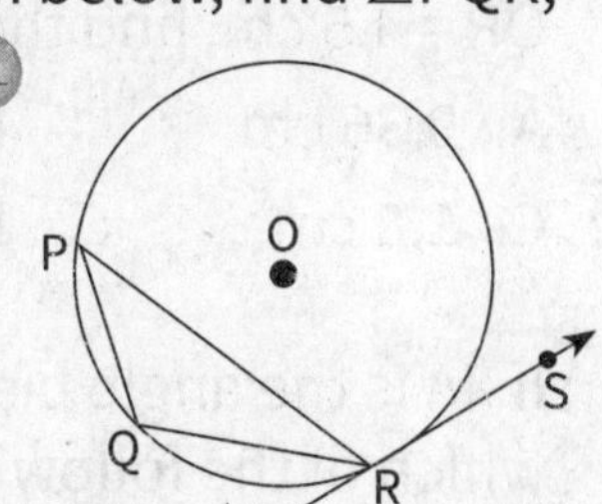

A. 110°

B. 125°

C. 135°

D. 145°

49. In the figure given below, QR is the chord and PS is the tangent to the circle. Find $\angle PSQ$, if $\angle ORS = 150°$.

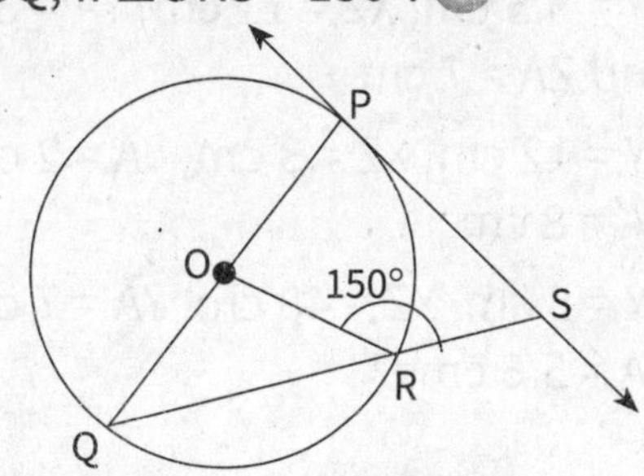

A. 60° B. 70°

C. 80° D. 85°

50. AB and CD are the two perpendicular diameters of a circle with centre O. Identify the shape formed by the tangents drawn at the points A, B, C and D.

A. Rhombus B. Parallelogram

C. Square D. Quadrilateral

CHAPTER 11

Constructions

PRIOR KNOWLEDGE TEST

Choose the correct option.

1. ΔXYZ and ΔPQR are similar. If their areas are 4 cm^2 and 25 cm^2, respectively, and QR = 4.5 cm, find the measurement of YZ.
   A. 0.36 cm B. 1.38 cm
   C. 1.8 cm D. 2.2 cm

2. If XA is the angle bisector of $\angle YXZ$, then which of the following cannot be the measurements of ΔXYZ?
   A. XY = 2 cm, XZ = 4 cm, YA = 1.2 cm and ZA = 2.4 cm
   B. XY = 5.5 cm, XZ = 11 cm, YA = 3.5 cm and ZA = 7 cm
   C. XY = 12 cm, XZ = 3 cm, YA = 2 cm and ZA = 8 cm
   D. XY = 8 cm, XZ = 48 cm, YA = 7 cm and ZA = 5.6 cm

3. A circle with centre O has a radius of 8 cm. How many tangent(s) can be drawn from a point P, which is 8 cm away from the centre?
   A. 0 B. 1
   C. 2 D. Infinite

4. For what difference of XY and XZ, the construction of ΔXYZ is not possible when YZ = 8.5 cm and $\angle Y = 75°$.
   A. 7.5 cm B. 7.9 cm
   C. 8.4 cm D. 8.7 cm

5. Observe the construction given below. What is the sum of the sides AB and AC?
   A. 21 cm
   B. 16 cm
   C. 12 cm
   D. 9 cm

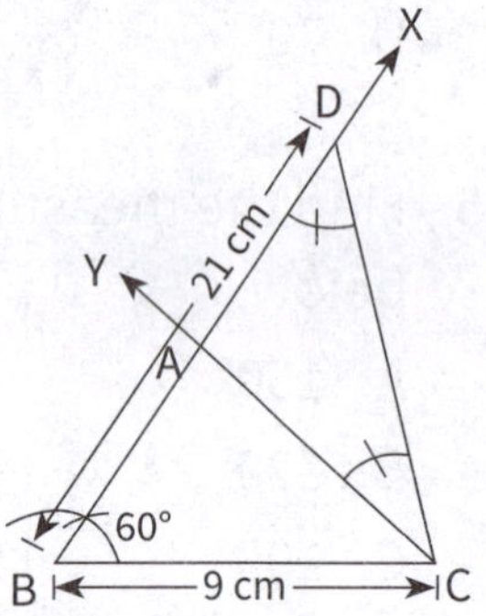

KEYWORDS

Perpendicular bisector: A line segment that intersects another line segment at a right angle and divides it into two equal parts

Geometrical constructions: Constructions using only a ruler and a pair of compasses as geometrical instruments

Tangent: A line that intersects the circle at only one point

Similar triangles: Triangles having their corresponding angles equal and their corresponding sides in the same ratio or proportion

CONCEPT MAP

Construction

of

- Division of a line segment in a given ratio internally
- Similar triangles
- Tangents to a circle

Division of a line segment in a given ratio internally → steps

To divide a line segment PQ in the ratio $a : b$ internally

1. Draw any ray PX, making an acute angle with PQ.
2. Locate $(a + b)$ equidistant points P_1, P_2, ...P_{a+b} on PX.
3. Join QP_{a+b}.
4. Draw a line parallel to QP_{a+b} (by making an angle equal to $\angle PP_{a+b}Q$) through P_a intersecting PQ at the point R.
5. R is the required point so that PR : RQ = $a : b$.

→ example

To divide PQ in the ratio of 5 : 4 internally

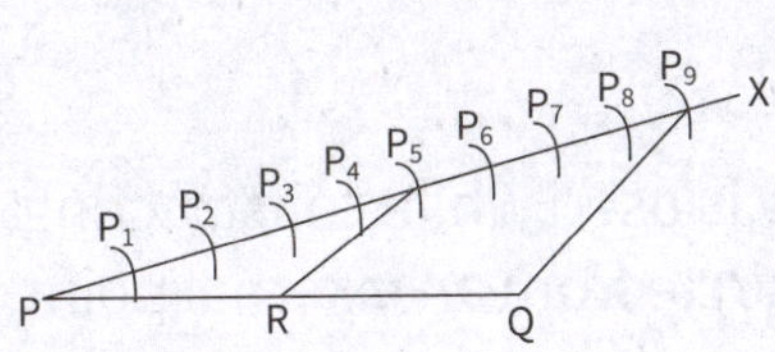

Similar triangles → steps

To construst a $\triangle XY'Z'$ similar to $\triangle XYZ$ with a scale factor $\frac{7}{4}$

1. Draw any ray XP making an acute angle with XZ on the side opposite to the vertex Y.
2. Locate 7 (the greater of 4 and 7 in $\frac{7}{4}$) equidistant points on XP. Join X_4 to Z.
3. Draw a line parallel to X_4Z through X_7 to intersect XR at Z′.
4. Draw a line through Z′ parallel to the line ZY to intersect XQ at Y′.
5. Then, $\triangle XY'Z'$ is the required triangle.

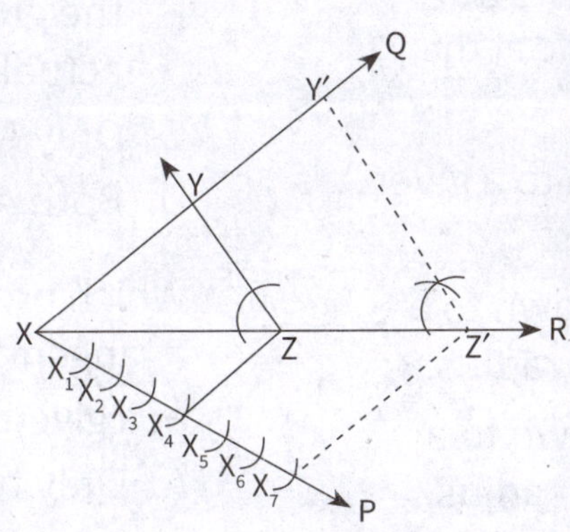

Tangents to a circle → steps

To draw tangents to a given circle from an external point A

1. Join AO and draw a perpendicular bisector to AO such that it intersects AO at X.
2. Taking X as centre and XO as radius, draw a circle to intersect the given circle. Mark the points of intersection as B and C.
3. Join AB and AC, which are the required tangents to the circle.

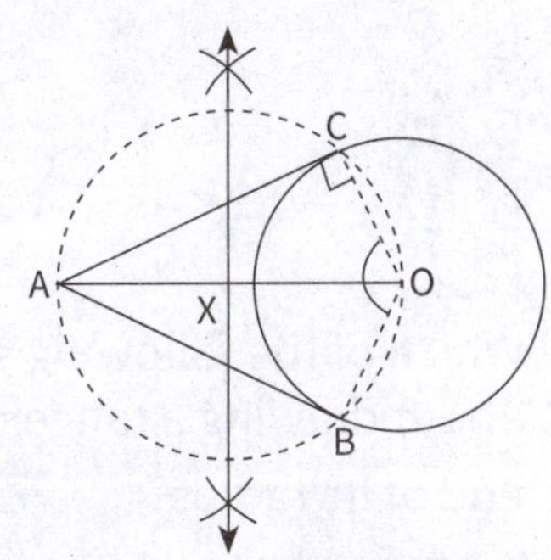

SELF-ASSESSMENT 1

Choose the correct option.

1. We have to divide a line segment XY in the ratio 6 : 7. What will be the next step after drawing the line segment XY?
   A. Make a perpendicular bisector to XY.
   B. Cut equidistant arcs on XY.
   C. Draw a ray making an acute angle of any measure with XY.
   D. Draw a perpendicular to XY at Y.

2. To divide a line segment MN in the ratio 4 : 9, a ray MX is drawn so that ∠NMX is an acute angle, and then, at equal distances, points are marked on the ray MX. Find the minimum number of points marked.
   A. 5
   B. 9
   C. 13
   D. 14

3. Which of the following statements is true about drawing a tangent to a circle at the end of its radius?
   A. Two tangents can be drawn to a given circle at the end of its radius.
   B. Only one tangent can be drawn to a given circle at the end of its radius.
   C. Infinite tangents can be drawn to a given circle at the end of its radius.
   D. No tangents can be drawn to a circle at the end of its radius.

4. If the centre of a circle is not given, which of the following methods can be used to locate the centre?
   A. Draw any two chords and their point of intersection is the centre.
   B. Draw a diameter and a chord, and their point of intersection is the centre.
   C. Locate the centre approximately by measuring the diameter.
   D. Draw perpendicular bisectors of any two non-parallel chords, and their point of intersection gives the required centre of that circle.

5. Which of the following is true about dividing a line segment in a given ratio?
   A. A line segment can be divided in the given ratio by measuring the length of it.
   B. A line segment can also be divided in the given ratio without measuring its actual length.
   C. Only A
   D. Both A and B

6. Which property is used while constructing a tangent to a circle from an external point at a given distance from the centre?
   A. Only two tangents can be drawn from a point external to the circle.
   B. A diameter subtends a right angle at any point on the circle.
   C. A radius of the circle is perpendicular to the tangent.
   D. Both B and C

7. Name the main principle used in the construction of division of a line segment in a given ratio internally.
   A. Perpendicular bisectors are equidistant from both the ends
   B. Basic proportionality theorem for triangles
   C. Congruency of triangles
   D. Angle sum property of triangles

8. Select the odd one out with respect to constructions.
   A. Equilateral triangles with lengths of the sides as 2 cm and 6 cm
   B. Circles with radii as 2 cm and 6 cm
   C. Rhombuses with lengths of the sides as 2 cm and 6 cm
   D. Squares with lengths of the sides as 2 cm and 6 cm

9. To construct a pair of tangents to a circle which are inclined to each other at an angle of 75°, first two radii are drawn. Which of the following could be the angle between them?
   A. 75° B. 90°
   C. 105° D. 150°

10. What is the ratio in which the point P divides the line segment AB?

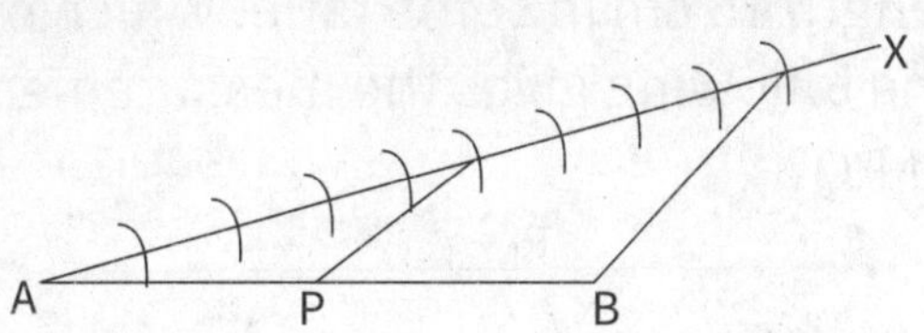

   A. 6 : 9
   B. 5 : 4
   C. 4 : 5
   D. 1 : 1

11. The line segment XY is divided into seven equal parts by the points A, B, C, D, E and F. Find the value of *a* for which XY = *a* × YD.
   A. $\frac{4}{7}$ B. $\frac{3}{4}$
   C. $\frac{3}{7}$ D. $\frac{7}{3}$

12. To divide a line segment MN in the ratio $\sqrt{9+5}:\frac{3}{\sqrt{11+3}}$, a ray MX is drawn so that ∠NMX is an acute angle and then at equal distances, points are marked on the ray MX. Find the minimum number of such points.
   A. 9
   B. 11
   C. 17
   D. Construction is not possible

13. Select the ratio for which the division of a line segment is not possible with the help of a ruler and a compass.
   A. $\sqrt{9}:\frac{3}{4}$
   B. $\sqrt{5}+1:\frac{1}{\sqrt{5}-1}$
   C. 1 : 5
   D. $\sqrt{4+3}:\frac{1}{7}$

14. PQRS is a rhombus with the length of each side as 6 cm. Find the length of the sides of the rhombus constructed with a scale factor of $\frac{2}{3}$.
   A. 4 cm B. 6 cm
   C. 10 cm D. 12 cm

15. A triangle ADE is constructed similar to another triangle ABC such that $AE = \frac{4}{7} AC$. Which of the following represents the correct ratio to divide the line segment AB?

A. 4 : 7 B. 7 : 4
C. 4 : 13 D. 4 : 3

16. The triangle XY′Z′ is constructed similar to the triangle XYZ. Find the scale factor for this construction.

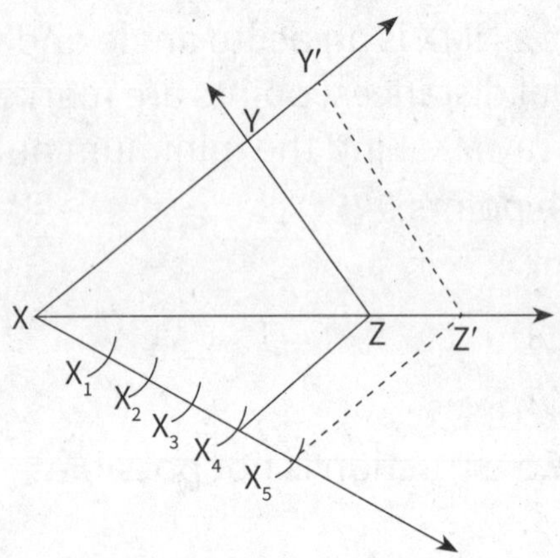

A. $\frac{4}{5}$ B. $\frac{4}{1}$
C. $\frac{5}{4}$ D. $\frac{6}{4}$

17. In the construction given below, what could be the angle of inclination of the tangents?

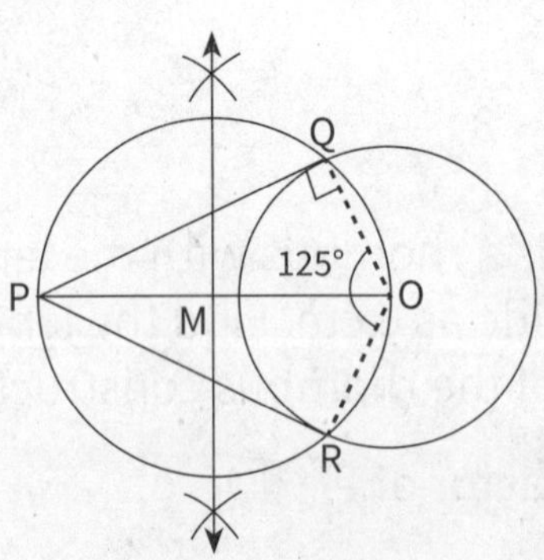

A. 55° B. 65°
C. 75° D. 125°

18. If the sides of a ΔABC are enlarged in the ratio 2 : 5 to get a similar ΔA′B′C′, then the ratio of their respective areas is ________.

A. 2 : 5
B. 4 : 10
C. 4 : 25
D. 5 : 2

19. The figure given below shows the construction of the triangle XY′Z′, which is constructed similar to the triangle XYZ. Which of the following relations holds true?

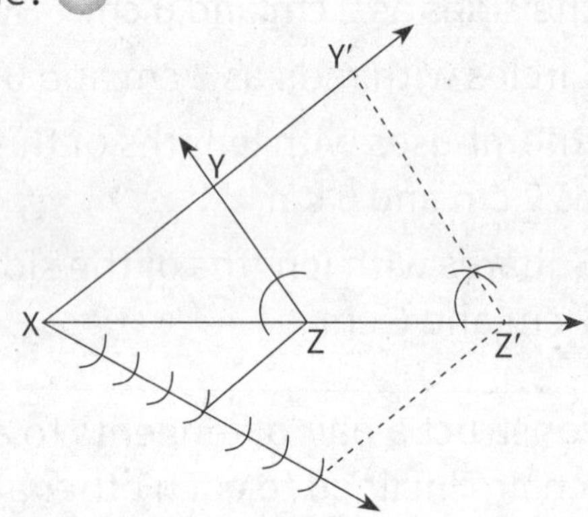

A. $\frac{XY}{XY'} = \frac{XZ}{XZ'} = \frac{4}{3}$ B. $\frac{XY'}{XY} = \frac{XZ'}{XZ} = \frac{7}{4}$

C. $\frac{XY}{XY'} = \frac{XZ}{XZ'} = \frac{3}{4}$ D. $\frac{XY'}{XY} = \frac{XZ'}{XZ} = \frac{4}{7}$

20. The figure given below shows the division of the line segment PQ of length 16 cm in some ratio. Which of the following gives the measurements of RQ?

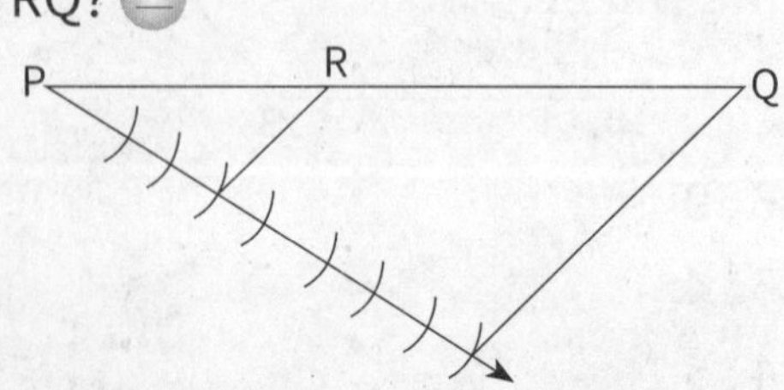

A. 10 cm B. 9.6 cm
C. 8 cm D. 6 cm

21. A pair of tangents is constructed to a circle of radius 4 cm, and the angle between the radii from the two points of contact is 120°. Find the length of the tangents formed.

A. $4\sqrt{3}$ cm
B. $\frac{8}{\sqrt{3}}$ cm
C. 8 cm
D. 2 cm

22. Observe the construction given below and select the correct relation.

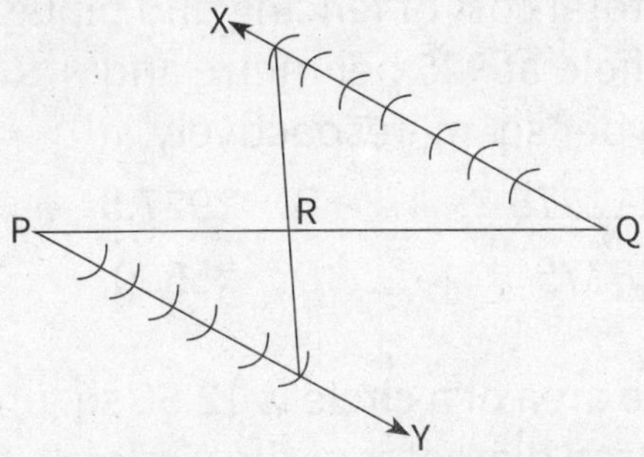

A. PR = RQ
B. $\frac{PR}{RQ} = \frac{6}{7}$
C. $\frac{PR}{PQ} = \frac{1}{2}$
D. $\frac{RQ}{PR} = \frac{6}{7}$

23. To construct a triangle XY′Z′ similar to another triangle XYZ such that $Y'Z' = \frac{11}{5}$ YZ, first draw a ray XP such that ∠YXP is an acute angle and X lies on the opposite side of Z with respect to XY. Then, mark equidistant points X_1, X_2, ... on XP. How many such equidistant points will be marked on XP?

A. 5
B. 6
C. 11
D. 17

24. While constructing a pair of tangents to a circle of radius 5 cm from a point 9 cm away from the centre, Ziyad first drew a circle C_1 with centre O of radius 5 cm. Then, he marked a point P, 9 cm away from O. Next, he drew a perpendicular bisector to OP, which intersected OP at M. Find the length of OM.

A. 9.5 cm
B. 9 cm
C. 5 cm
D. 4.5 cm

25. Read the steps and answer the question that follows:

- Draw a line segment AB = 9 cm.
- With A as centre, draw a circle of radius 5 cm and with B as centre, draw a circle of radius 4 cm.
- Draw a perpendicular bisector to AB, and mark the point of intersection as X.

How many tangents can be drawn from the point X to both the circles altogether?

A. 0
B. 2
C. 3
D. 4

CHAPTER 12

Areas Related to Circles

PRIOR KNOWLEDGE TEST

Choose the correct option.

1. Find the area of a circle with diameter 14 cm.
   A. 616 sq. cm B. 308 sq. cm
   C. 154 sq. cm D. 72 sq. cm

2. If the perimeter of a circle is 66 cm, find its radius.
   A. 7 cm B. 21 cm
   C. 14 cm D. 10.5 cm

3. A wire of length 176 m is bent in the form of a circle. Find the area of the circle.
   A. 17248 sq. m B. 8624 sq. m
   C. 4928 sq. m D. 2464 sq. m

4. The radius of a circular field is 35 m. Find the total cost of fencing and ploughing the field at ₹25 per metre and ₹1.5 per sq. m, respectively.
   A. ₹11275 B. ₹927.5
   C. ₹5775 D. ₹5500

5. If the area of a circle is 12.56 sq. units, find the diameter of the circle. (Take $\pi = 3.14$)
   A. 2 units B. 4 units
   C. 6 units D. 7 units

KEYWORDS

Area of a circle: The part of a plane enclosed by a circle

Circumference: The perimeter of a circle

Arc: A portion of the circumference of a circle

Sector: A portion of the circular region enclosed by two radii and the corresponding arc of a circle

Segment: A portion of the circular region enclosed between a chord and the corresponding arc of a circle

CONCEPT MAP

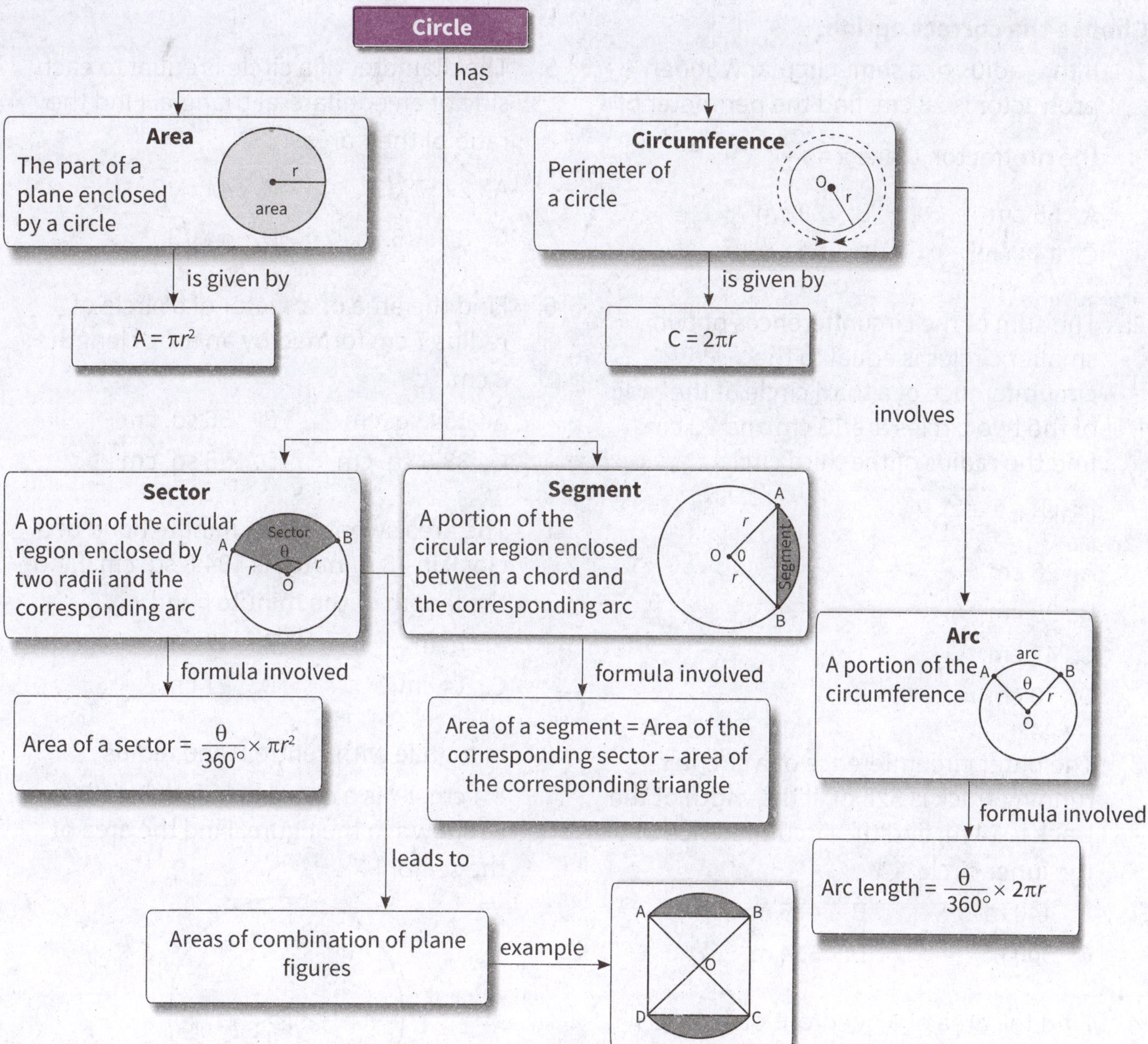

Circle
has
Area
The part of a plane enclosed by a circle
r
area
is given by
$A = \pi r^2$
Circumference
Perimeter of a circle
O
r
is given by
$C = 2\pi r$
involves
Sector
A portion of the circular region enclosed by two radii and the corresponding arc
Sector
A
B
θ
r
r
O
formula involved
Area of a sector = $\frac{\theta}{360^\circ} \times \pi r^2$
Segment
A portion of the circular region enclosed between a chord and the corresponding arc
A
r
O
θ
r
Segment
B
formula involved
Area of a segment = Area of the corresponding sector – area of the corresponding triangle
Arc
A portion of the circumference
arc
A
B
θ
r
r
O
formula involved
Arc length = $\frac{\theta}{360^\circ} \times 2\pi r$
leads to
Areas of combination of plane figures
example
A
B
O
D
C

PART 1

CHAPTER 12: Areas Related to Circles

SELF-ASSESSMENT 1

Choose the correct option.

1. If the radius of a semi-circular wooden protractor is 28 cm, find the perimeter of the protractor. (Take $\pi = \frac{22}{7}$)

   A. 56 cm B. 88 cm
   C. 144 cm D. 232 cm

2. The sum of the circumferences of two smaller circles is equal to the circumference of a third circle. If the radii of the two circles are 13 cm and 22 cm, find the radius of the third circle.

   (Take $\pi = \frac{22}{7}$)

   A. 28 cm
   B. 35 cm
   C. 42 cm
   D. 70 cm

3. The outer circumference of a circular running track is 528 m. If the width of the track is 14 m, find the circumference of the inner circle.

   A. 440 m B. 475 m
   C. 500 m D. 514 m

4. Find the area of a quadrant of a circle whose circumference is 44 cm.

   A. 77 sq. cm
   B. 154 sq. cm
   C. 38.5 sq. cm
   D. 19.25 sq. cm

5. The diameter of a circle is equal to each side of an equilateral triangle. Find the ratio of their areas.

   A. $22 : 7\sqrt{3}$ B. $4\pi : \sqrt{3}$
   C. $8\pi : \sqrt{3}$ D. $\pi : \sqrt{3}$

6. Find the area of a sector of a circle of radius 7 cm formed by an arc of length 8 cm.

   A. 154 sq. cm B. 56 sq. cm
   C. 38.5 sq. cm D. 28 sq. cm

7. The area swept by the minute hand of a clock in 18 minutes is 184.8 sq. cm. Find the length of the minute hand.

   A. 7 cm B. 12 cm
   C. 14 cm D. 21 cm

8. In a circle with centre P and radius 8.4 cm, XY is a chord of length $8.4\sqrt{3}$ cm, as shown in the figure. Find the area of the sector PXY.

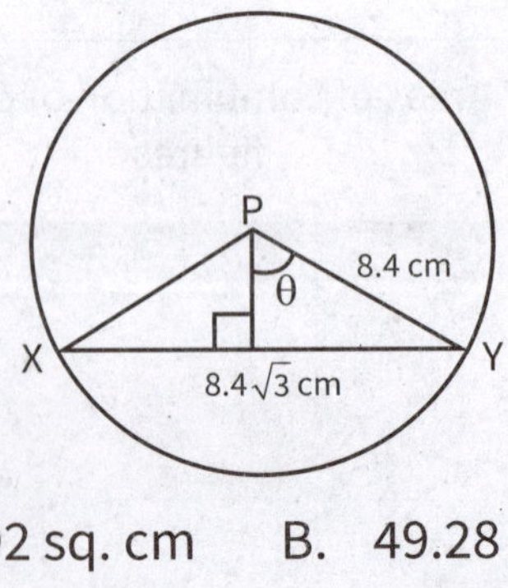

   A. 73.92 sq. cm B. 49.28 sq. cm
   C. 98.56 sq. cm D. 112. 4 sq. cm

9. The area of a sector with central angle 150° is 23.1 sq. cm. Find the radius of the sector.

A. 2.8 cm   B. 3.5 cm
C. 4.2 cm   D. 8.4 cm

10. The area of a sector of a circle is 0.3 times the area of the circle. Find the angle of the sector.

A. 116°   B. 124°
C. 120°   D. 108°

11. In a circle of radius $10\sqrt{2}$ cm, a chord of length 20 cm long is drawn to divide the circle into two segments. Find the area of the minor segment. (Take $\pi = 3.14$)

A. 28.5 cm   B. 47 sq. cm
C. 57 sq. cm   D. 117.75 sq. cm

12. The chord of a circle of radius 14 cm makes a right angle at the centre of the circle. Find the area of the major segment.

A. 560 sq. cm   B. 462 sq. cm
C. 280 sq. cm   D. 154 sq. cm

13. If the area of a circle is numerically equal to its circumference, find the radius of the circle.

A. 1 unit   B. 2 units
C. 4 units   D. $\frac{1}{4}$ unit

14. A wire is bent in the form of a square whose area is 3969 sq. m. If the same wire is bent in the form of a semicircle, find the area of the semicircle.

A. 7546 sq. m   B. 3773 sq. m
C. 5035.4 sq. m   D. 10070.8 sq. m

15. Find the area of the largest triangle which can be inscribed in a semicircle of radius 35 cm.

A. 1225 sq. cm
B. 612.5 sq. cm
C. 961.6 sq. cm
D. 625 sq. cm

16. A chord of length 12 cm subtends an angle of 90° at the centre of a circle. Find the difference of the areas of two segments formed. (Take $\pi = 3.14$)

A. 226 sq. cm
B. 206 sq. cm
C. 185 sq. cm
D. 170 sq. cm

17. If the arc length of a sector of a circle of radius 17.5 cm is 44 cm, find the area of the sector.

A. 770 sq. cm
B. 385 sq. cm
C. 424 sq. cm
D. 532 sq. cm

18. A hand fan is in the form of a sector of a circle where the angle at the centre is 150°. If the area covered by the hand fan is 577.5 sq. cm, find the arc length of the fan.

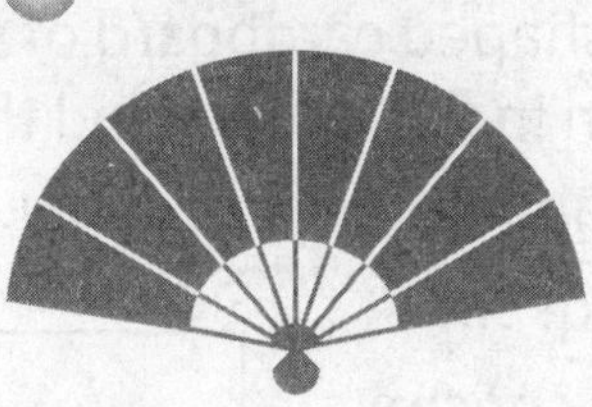

A. 21 cm
B. 42 cm
C. 55 cm
D. 110 cm

19. A large pizza of diameter 10 inches is divided equally into 8 sectors, a medium pizza of diameter 8 inches is divided equally into 5 pieces and a small pizza of diameter 6 inches is cut into 3 equal pieces. Assuming all the pizzas to be of the same thickness, which piece of pizza occupies more area?
   A. Large pizza
   B. Medium pizza
   C. Small pizza
   D. All of them occupy the same area

20. Four cows are tied at the corners of a square-shaped grass field of side 10 m. They are tied by the ropes of equal length of 3.5 m. Assuming that the cows graze all the field available to them, find the area of the field not grazed by them.
   A. 22 sq. m   B. 38.5 sq. m
   C. 42.25 sq. m   D. 61.5 sq. m

21. An equilateral triangle is inscribed in a circle. What is the ratio of their areas?
   A. $4\pi : \sqrt{3}$ B. $16\pi : 3\sqrt{3}$
   C. $\pi : 3\sqrt{3}$ D. $4\pi : 3\sqrt{3}$

22. Two quadrants of radii 14 cm and two quadrants of radii 7 cm are cut from a square-shaped cardboard of side 24 cm as shown in the figure. Find the area of the remaining sheet of paper.
   A. 385 sq. cm
   B. 192.5 sq. cm
   C. 191 sq. cm
   D. 144 sq. cm

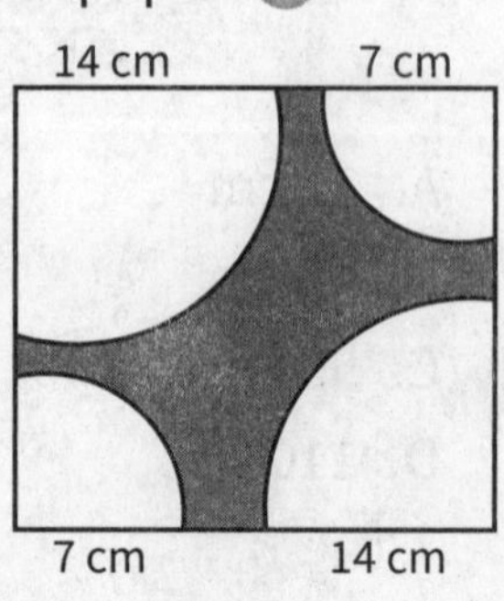

23. Find the area of the unshaded region, if the radius of each circle and each semicircle is 10 cm.

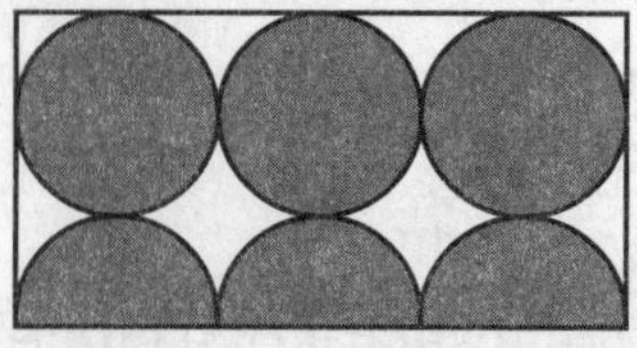

   A. 1413 sq. cm   B. 765 sq. cm
   C. 387 sq. cm   D. 285 sq. cm

24. Find the area of the shaded region, if the radius of the circle is 21 cm (to the nearest sq. cm).

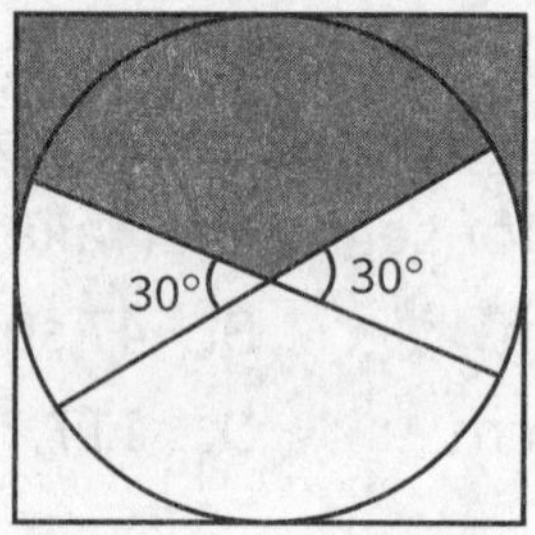

   A. 336 sq. cm   B. 672 sq. cm
   C. 767 sq. cm   D. 1363 sq. cm

25. Two concentric circles of radii 21 cm and 28 cm are divided into 8 equal sectors as shown in the figure. Find the area of the shaded region.

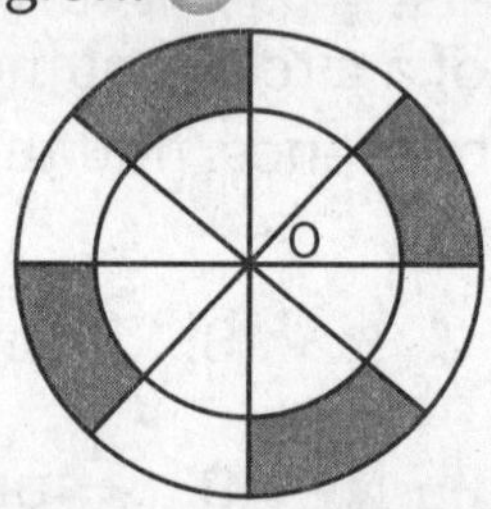

   A. 539 sq. cm   B. 436 sq. cm
   C. 246 sq. cm   D. 126.6 sq. cm

CHAPTER 12: Areas Related to Circles

SELF-ASSESSMENT 2

Choose the correct option.

26. If the perimeter of a circle is 57.2 cm, what is the area of the circle to its nearest sq. cm? (Take $\pi = \frac{22}{7}$)
    A. 260 sq. cm B. 130 sq. cm
    C. 195 sq. cm D. 261 sq. cm

27. The sum of the areas of two smaller circles is equal to the area of a third circle. If the radii of the two circles are 12 cm and 16 cm, find the radius of the third circle. (Take $\pi = \frac{22}{7}$)
    A. 20 cm B. 28 cm
    C. 40 cm D. 56 cm

28. The circumference of a circle is four more than six times its radius. What is the radius of the circle? (Take $\pi = \frac{22}{7}$)
    A. 7 cm B. 14 cm
    C. 21 cm D. 28 cm

29. Find the number of rotations made by a wheel of radius 56 cm to cover a distance of 528 m.
    A. 75 B. 150
    C. 250 D. 300

30. If the area of a quadrant of a circle is 346.5 sq. cm, find its circumference.
    A. 156 cm B. 144 cm
    C. 132 cm D. 128 cm

31. The circumference of a circle is equal to the perimeter of a square. Find the ratio of their areas.
    A. 14 : 11 B. 7 : 22
    C. 7 : 11 D. 7 : 44

32. The area of a sector of a circle is $\frac{7}{12}$ of the area of the circle. If the radius of the circle is 12.6 cm, find the arc length of the sector. (Take $\pi = \frac{22}{7}$)
    A. 33 cm B. 42 cm
    C. 44.6 cm D. 46.2 cm

33. A wiper of a car has a blade sweeping through an angle of 135°. If the area cleaned by each wiper at each sweep of the blade is 924 sq. cm, find the length of the blade.
    A. 14 cm B. 22 cm
    C. 26 cm D. 28 cm

34. A chord of length 21 cm is drawn in a circle of radius $7\sqrt{3}$ cm, as shown in the figure. Find the area of the minor segment to its nearest sq. m. (Take $\pi = \frac{22}{7}, \sqrt{3} = 1.73$)
    A. 113 sq. cm
    B. 90 sq. cm
    C. 132 sq. cm
    D. 166 sq. cm

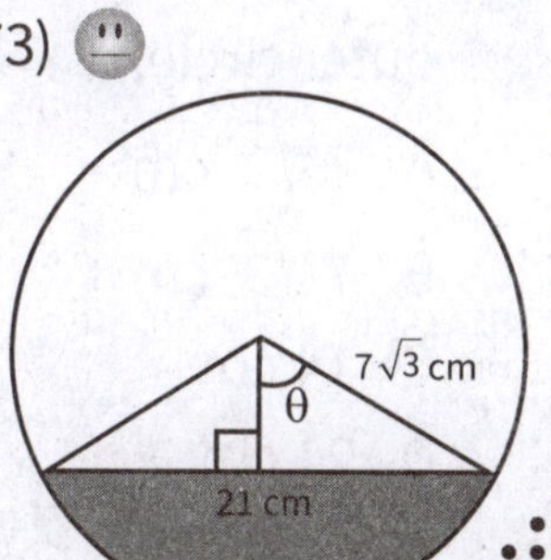

35. Find the arc length of a sector of a circle of radius 17 cm, if the area of the sector is 85 sq. cm.

A. 10 cm B. 12 cm

C. 14 cm D. 17 cm

36. Find the angle of the sector of a circle of radius 28 cm, if the area of the sector is 616 sq. cm.

A. 90° B. 120°

C. 115° D. 135°

37. In a circle, a chord of length 28 cm is drawn to divide the circle into two segments such that the sector angle is 90°. Find the radius of the circle.

A. 7 cm

B. $7\sqrt{2}$ cm

C. 14 cm

D. $14\sqrt{2}$ cm

38. The chord of a circle of radius 21 cm makes an angle of 120° at the centre of the circle. Find the length of the chord.

A. 14 cm

B. $10.5\sqrt{3}$ cm

C. $21\sqrt{3}$ cm

D. 42 cm

39. A circle is divided into three parts of equal areas by drawing two concentric circles as shown in the figure. If the radius of the inner circle is 7 cm, find the radius of the outer circle.

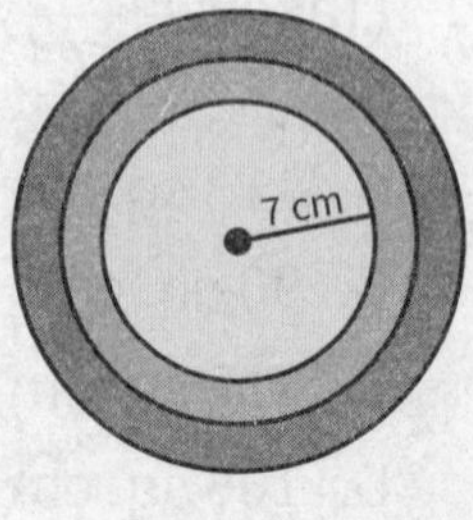

A. $7\sqrt{2}$ cm

B. $7\sqrt{3}$ cm

C. 14 cm

D. 21 cm

40. The available length of a wire is 132 cm. It is bent in the form of a square, circle and a semicircle. Which of the following occupies the least area?

A. Square

B. Circle

C. Semicircle

D. All of them have the same area

41. In a rectangular sheet of a paper ABCD, AB = 42 cm and BC = 35 cm. A semi-circular region with diameter CD is cut-off. Find the area of the remaining sheet of paper.

A. 693 sq. cm

B. 777 sq. cm

C. 958.75 sq. cm

D. 1225 sq. cm

42. Two sectors of sector angles 50° and 150° of a circle of radius 16.8 cm are shaded as shown in the figure. Find the area of the unshaded region to its nearest sq. cm.

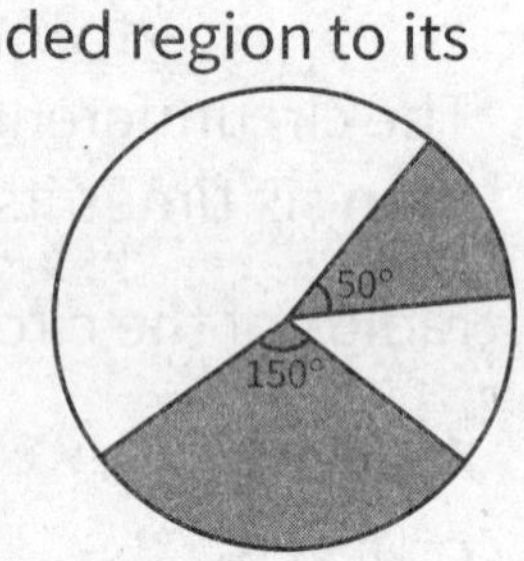

A. 123 sq. cm

B. 370 sq. cm

C. 394 sq. cm

D. 493 sq. cm

43. A square-shaped lawn of side 35 cm is inside a circular park. If the area of the circular park excluding the square-shaped lawn is 2625 sq. cm, find the radius of the circular park.

A. 35 cm

B. 42 cm

C. 49 cm

D. 56 cm

44. Find the area of the unshaded region to its nearest sq. cm in the given figure. (Use $\pi = 3.14$)

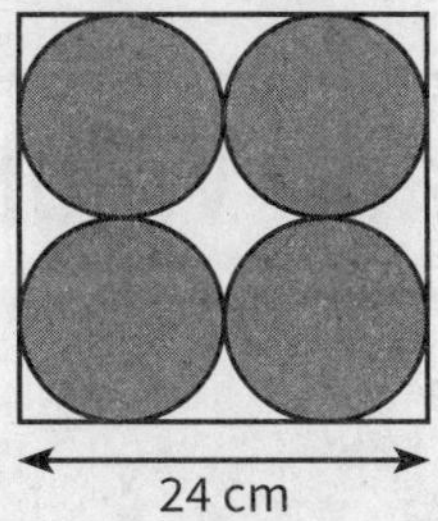

A. 576 sq. cm
B. 452 sq. cm
C. 113 sq. cm
D. 124 sq. cm

45. ABDC is a sector of a circle of radius 21 cm. A semicircle BEC is drawn with BC as diameter. Find the area of the shaded region.

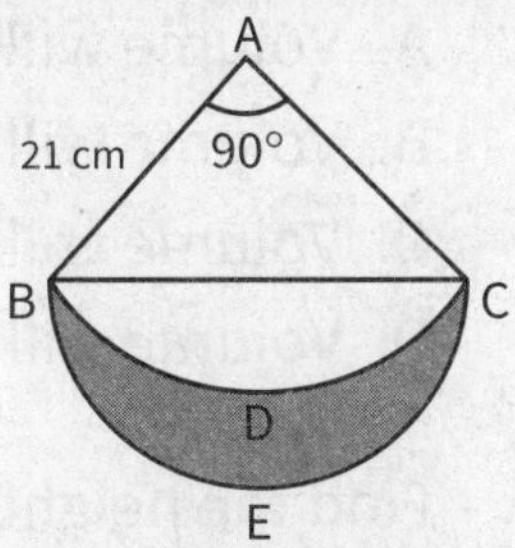

A. 126 sq. cm
B. 220.5 sq. cm
C. 346.5 sq. cm
D. 441 sq. cm

46. An equilateral triangle is inscribed in a square of side 36 cm. A circle is inscribed in the triangle as shown in the figure. Find the area of the shaded region to the nearest sq. cm. (Take $\pi = 3.14$, $\sqrt{3} = 1.73$)

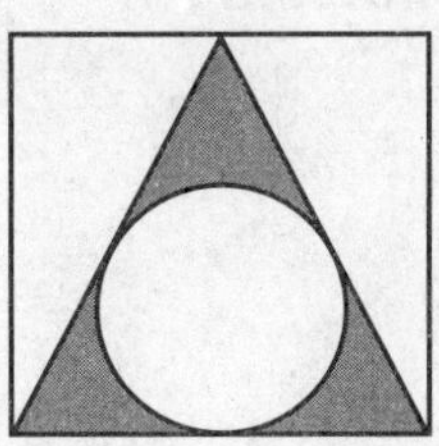

A. 221 sq. cm
B. 220 sq. cm
C. 339 sq. cm
D. 561 sq. cm

47. Two semicircles of radius 21 cm each and three semicircles of radius 14 cm each are joined as shown in the figure. Find the area of the figure.

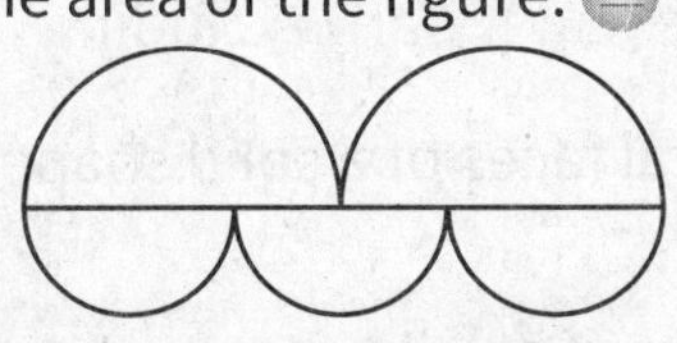

A. 2002 sq. cm B. 2310 sq. cm
C. 1386 sq. cm D. 924 sq. cm

48. XYZ is a right-angled triangle, right-angled at Z, such that XZ = 12 cm, YZ = 16 cm. If I is the incentre of triangle XYZ as given in the figure, find the radius of the circle.

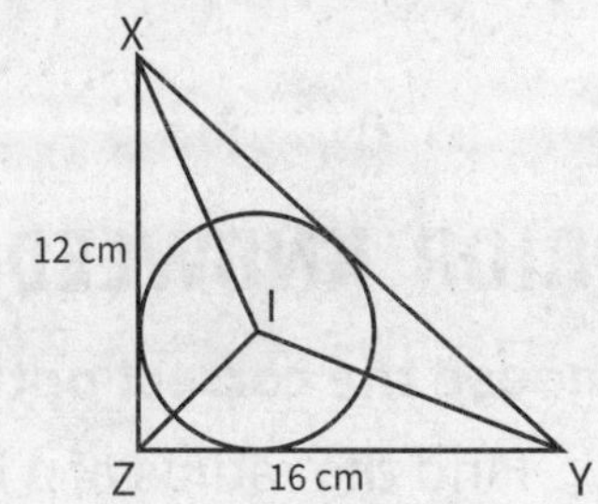

A. 2 cm
B. 3 cm
C. 4 cm
D. 6 cm

49. Three sectors of radii 4 cm, 5 cm and 6 cm are shaded in an equilateral triangle of side 14 cm as shown in the figure. Find the area of the shaded portion.

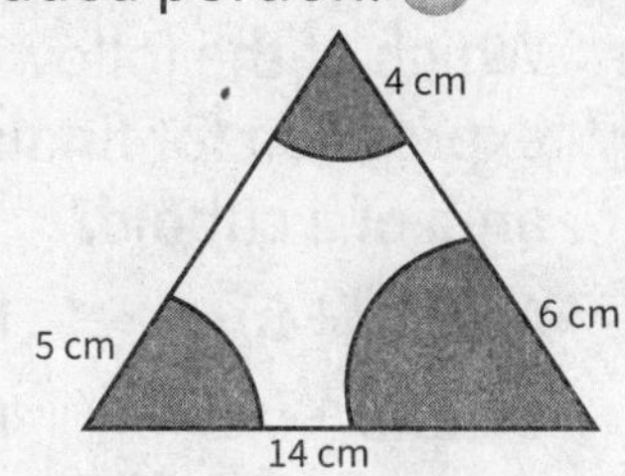

A. 121 sq. cm
B. 40.3 sq. cm
C. 85 sq. cm
D. 25 sq. cm

50. What is the area of the square which can be inscribed in a circle of radius 21 cm?

A. 882 sq. cm
B. 441 sq. cm
C. 1764 sq. cm
D. 220.5 sq. cm

CHAPTER 13

Surface Areas and Volumes

PRIOR KNOWLEDGE TEST

Choose the correct option.

1. Find the radius of a hemispherical solid whose total surface area is 462 cm^2.
   A. 7 cm B. 12 cm
   C. 14 cm D. 21 cm

2. Which of the following is the correct expression for finding the total surface area of a cuboid?
   A. $2h(l + b)$ B. $2h(lb + bh)$
   C. $2(lb + bh + lh)$ D. $2l(lb + bh + lh)$

3. The curved surface area of a cylinder with height $2a$ cm and radius a cm is equal to the ______________________.
   A. surface area of a cone of radius a cm and height $2a$ cm
   B. lateral surface area of a cube with length of the side as a cm
   C. total surface area of a hemisphere with radius a cm
   D. surface area of a sphere of radius a cm

4. Find the change in volume of a cone if its height is halved and radius is doubled.
   A. Volume will be halved
   B. Volume will be doubled
   C. Volume will be same
   D. Volume will be four times

5. Find the height of the right circular cone formed by a semicircle of radius 7 cm.
   A. 14 cm
   B. $3.5\sqrt{3}$ cm
   C. 7 cm
   D. 3.5 cm

KEYWORDS

Lateral Surface Area (LSA): The sum of the areas of the lateral faces of a solid shape; also called curved surface area (CSA)

Total Surface Area (TSA): The sum of the areas of all the faces of a solid shape

Volume: The space occupied by an object

Frustum of a cone: Formed by cutting the top of the cone parallel to the base of the cone; has upper and lower circular parallel bases

CONCEPT MAP

3-D Shapes have:

- **Surface area** is:
  - **Lateral surface area:** The sum of the areas of all the faces of an object excluding the area of the top and the base
  - **Total surface area:** The sum of the areas of all the faces of an object including the area of the top and the base
- **Volume** is: Space occupied by an object

3-D Shapes include:

Cube — formulae involved
- **Lateral surface area of a cube** = $4a^2$ sq. units
- **Total surface area of a cube** = $6a^2$ sq. units
- **Volume of a cube** = $(\text{side})^3 = a^3$ cubic units

Cuboid — formulae involved
- **Lateral surface area of a cuboid** = $2h(l + b)$ sq. units
- **Total surface area of a cuboid** = $2(lb + bh + lh)$ sq. units
- **Volume of a cuboid** = $(l \times b \times h)$ cubic units

Cylinder — formulae involved
- **Curved surface area of a cylinder** = $2\pi rh$ sq. units
- **Total surface area of a cylinder** = $2\pi r(r + h)$ sq. units
- **Volume of a cylinder** = πr^2h cubic units

Frustum — formulae involved

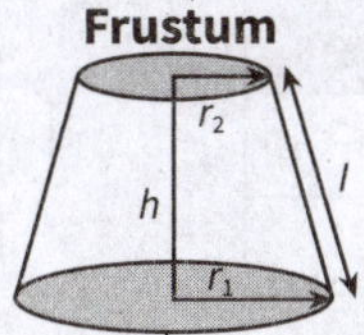

- **Slant height,** $l = \sqrt{(r_1 - r_2)^2 + h^2}$
- **Curved surface area of a frustum** = $\pi(r_1 + r_2)l$ sq. units
- **Total surface area of a frustum** = $\pi l(r_1 + r_2) + \pi r_1^2 + \pi r_2^2$ sq. units
- **Volume of a frustum** = $\frac{1}{3}\pi h[r_1^2 + r_2^2 + r_1r_2]$ cubic units

Cone — formulae involved
- **Slant height,** $l = \sqrt{(r^2 + h^2)}$
- **Curved surface area of a cone** = πrl sq. units
- **Total surface area of a right circular cone** = $\pi r(l + r)$ sq. units
- **Volume of a cone** = $\frac{1}{3}\pi r^2h$ cubic units

Sphere — formulae involved
- **Surface area of a sphere of radius** r = $4\pi r^2$ sq. units
- **Volume of sphere of radius** r = $\frac{4}{3}\pi r^3$ cubic units

Hemisphere — formulae involved
- **Curved surface area of a hemisphere** = $2\pi r^2$ sq. units
- **Total surface area of a hemisphere** = $3\pi r^2$ sq. units
- **Volume of a hemisphere** = $\frac{2}{3}\pi r^3$ cubic units

PART 1

CHAPTER 13: Surface Areas and Volumes

SELF-ASSESSMENT 1

Choose the correct option.

1. The shape of a medicine capsule is generally a combination of ________.
   A. a cylinder and a cone
   B. a cuboid and a hemisphere
   C. a cylinder and a sphere
   D. a cylinder and a hemisphere

2. Match the following.

Volume	Solid Shape
a. $\pi r^2 h$	i. Cone
b. $\frac{1}{3}\pi r^2 h$	ii. Hemisphere
c. $\frac{4}{3}\pi r^3$	iii. Cylinder
d. $\frac{1}{3}\pi h[r_1^2 + r_2^2 + r_1 r_2]$	iv. Sphere
e. $\frac{2}{3}\pi r^3$	v. Frustum

   A. a – i; b – ii; c – iii; d – iv; e – v
   B. a – iii; b – i; c – iv; d – v; e – ii
   C. a – iii; b – iv; c – ii; d – v; e – i
   D. a – i; b – ii; c – iii; d – v; e – iv

3. If a rectangle of length 12 cm and breadth 8 cm is rolled along its length to form a cylinder, then the base radius of the cylinder is ________.
   A. 8π cm
   B. $\frac{6}{\pi}$ cm
   C. 4π cm
   D. $\frac{12}{\pi}$ cm

4. Six cubes of edge 6 cm are joined end to end. Find the total surface area of the resulting shape.
   A. 936 cm^2
   B. 996 cm^2
   C. 1008 cm^2
   D. 1296 cm^2

5. Find the total surface area of the shape formed by mounting a cone on a hemisphere, if the slant height of the cone is equal to its radius and the diameter of the cone is 7 cm.
   A. 115.5 cm^2
   B. 221 cm^2
   C. 246 cm^2
   D. 616 cm^2

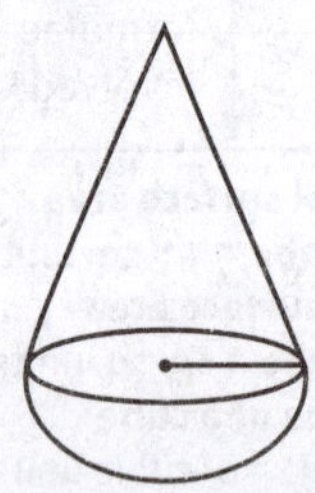

6. A rattle is a toy with a cylindrical handle and spherical ball on the top. Find the total surface area of the toy if the radius of the sphere is r, height of the handle is twice the radius of sphere and radius of the handle is one-fourth the radius of the sphere.
   A. $\frac{25}{4}\pi r^2$ cm^2
   B. $4\pi r^2$ cm^2
   C. $5\pi r^2$ cm^2
   D. $\frac{15}{2}\pi r^2$ cm^2

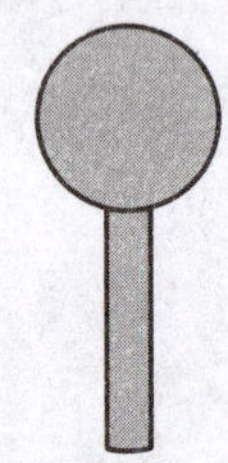

7. A carpenter cuts a conical depression from one face of a cubical wooden block of edge 14 cm such that the diameter of the cone is equal to the edge of the cube and the depth of the cone is half of its radius. If he wants to paint all the open surfaces, find the area to be painted. [Use $\sqrt{5} = 2.2$]

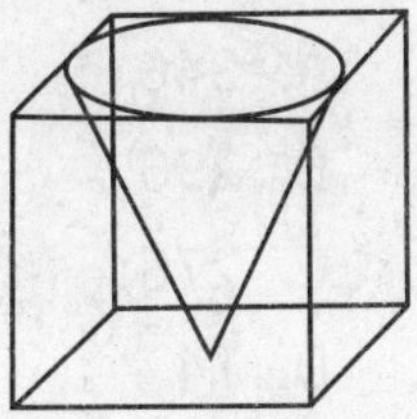

A. 852.6 cm^2
B. 952.6 cm^2
C. 1022 cm^2
D. 1191.4 cm^2

8. Which of the following has the greatest total surface area if all the given options have a radius of 7 cm?
A. Hemisphere
B. Cone with slant height equal to twice the radius
C. Cylinder with height equal to twice the radius
D. Sphere

9. A cylindrical block with its height equal to twice its radius is cut into two equal halves along the height of the cylinder. Find the total surface area of the new shapes formed altogether.
A. $8\pi r^2$, where r is the radius of the cylinder
B. $2r^2(3\pi + 4)$, where r is the radius of the cylinder
C. $4r^2(\pi + 3)$, where r is the radius of the cylinder
D. $6\pi r^2$, where r is the radius of the cylinder

10. Find the ratio of surface area to volume of the hemisphere with radius 1 cm.
A. 9 : 2 B. 3 : 2
C. 3 : 1 D. 1 : 2

11. Sumit has a cubical block. On each face, he painted a parallelogram formed by joining the midpoints of the adjacent edges. Find the total surface area of the unpainted region if the area of one painted parallelogram is 9 cm^2.
A. 54 cm^2 B. 62 cm^2
C. 81 cm^2 D. 108 cm^2

12. A cube of side a is cut into 27 equal cubes. The total surface area of all the smaller cubes is ________.
A. equal to the bigger cube
B. half of the bigger cube
C. three times the bigger cube
D. double the bigger cube

13. Find the volume of the water tank given here.

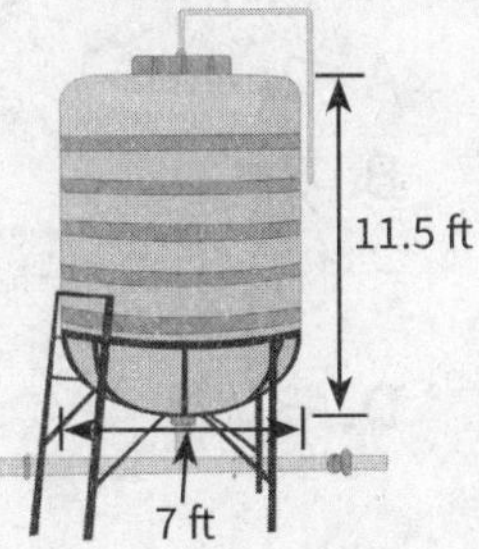

A. 389 ft^3
B. 397.83 ft^3
C. 1232 ft^3
D. 1950.6 ft^3

14. Three spherical metal balls have radius 3 cm, 4 cm and 5 cm, respectively. Find the surface area of the spherical metal ball formed by melting all three smaller balls into one. (Take $\pi = 3.14$)
A. 308.4 cm^2
B. 314 cm^2
C. 452.16 cm^2
D. 468 cm^2

15. Find the ratio of the volumes of a cylinder and a cone of equal radius if the ratio of their heights is 5 : 6.
A. 5 : 6 B. 18 : 5
C. 5 : 2 D. 2 : 15

16. A cone is mounted on the top of a hemisphere. If the total height of the solid is equal to diameter of the hemisphere, which of the following represents the volume of the solid?

A. πr^3

B. $\frac{4}{3}\pi r^3$

C. $\frac{1}{2}\pi r^3$

D. $2\pi r^3$

17. A cone of height equal to its radius (r) is truncated from the top of a bigger cone, such that the volume of the new cone is $\frac{1}{27}$th of the original cone. Which of the following represents the slant height of the remaining part of the cone?

A. $2r$

B. $3r$

C. $2\sqrt{2}r$

D. $3\sqrt{2}r$

18. The volume of the bucket shown in the figure is given by __________.

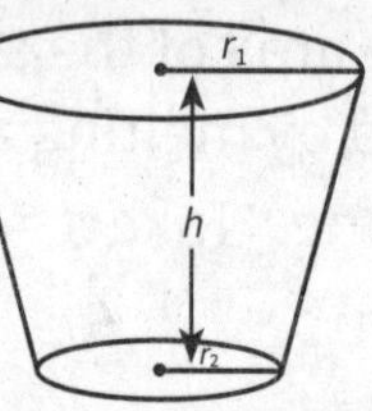

A. $\frac{1}{3}\pi h[r_1^2 + r_2^2 - r_1 r_2]$ cubic units

B. $\frac{1}{3}\pi h[r_2^2 - r_1^2 + r_1 r_2]$ cubic units

C. $\frac{1}{3}\pi h[r_2^2 - r_1^2 - r_1 r_2]$ cubic units

D. $\frac{1}{3}\pi h[r_1^2 + r_2^2 + r_1 r_2]$ cubic units

19. A bucket full of water is in the shape of a frustum having a height of 42 cm and the two radii being 15 cm and 20 cm respectively. How many cylindrical glasses of diameter 5 cm and height 7 cm can be filled with the water from the bucket?

A. 346

B. 296

C. 276

D. 74

20. Find the height of a frustum of a cone if its slant height is 3.7 cm and the radius of both the bases are 2.2 cm and 5.7 cm, respectively.

A. 1.2 cm

B. 1.24 cm

C. 2.2 cm

D. 3.5 cm

21. A fire bucket in the shape of a frustum, with slant height 40 cm and the two radii 14 cm and 21 cm, needs to be painted red from outside. Find the surface area to be painted.

A. 6446 cm^2

B. 6602 cm^2

C. 5242 cm^2

D. 5016 cm^2

22. Find the volume of the largest possible cylinder that can be enclosed in a cuboidal block of dimension 21 cm × 9 cm × 9 cm.

A. 1336.5 cm^3

B. 1536.5 cm^3

C. 4576 cm^3

D. 5346 cm^3

23. Find the ratio of volume of the largest possible cone and sphere which can be enclosed inside a cube of side 9 cm.

A. 1 : 4

B. 4 : 9

C. 1 : 2

D. 3 : 4

24. What can be concluded about the volume of a right circular cone if its radius is halved and the height is doubled?

A. Volume will be halved

B. Volume will increase by four times

C. Volume will remain the same

D. Volume will be doubled

25. Rita bought 16 cylindrical-shaped juice cans of radius 7 cm and height 15 cm. The glasses used for serving the drink are frustum in shape with height 5 cm and the radii 6 cm and 3 cm. How many more juice cans she should buy if she wants to fill 140 such glasses?

A. 0

B. 2

C. 4

D. 5

PART 1

CHAPTER 13: Surface Areas and Volumes

SELF-ASSESSMENT 2

Choose the correct option.

26. Match the following.

Solid	Curved surface area
a. Frustum of a cone	i. $2\pi r^2$
b. Hemisphere	ii. $2\pi rh$
c. Cylinder	iii. $\pi l(r_1 + r_2)$
d. Cone	iv. $\pi r(l + r)$
	v. $\pi l(r_1 + r_2) + \pi r_1^2 + \pi r_2^2$
	vi. πrl

A. a – v; b – i; c – iv; d – iii
B. a – iii; b –i; c – ii; d – vi
C. a – v; b – i; c – iv; d – Iii
D. a – iii; b – i; c – ii; d – iv

27. Find the volume of a cube whose lateral surface area is 784 cm^2?
A. 1728 cm^3
B. 1946 cm^3
C. 2644 cm^3
D. 2744 cm^3

28. Find the length of the longest rod that can fit into a cuboidal box of dimensions 12 cm × 3 cm × 4 cm.
A. 13 cm
B. 12 cm
C. 8 cm
D. 6 cm

29. At a play area, one huge model of a Lego block was installed and painted blue. Find the cost of painting at the rate of ₹30 per m^2? (Use $\pi = 3.14$)

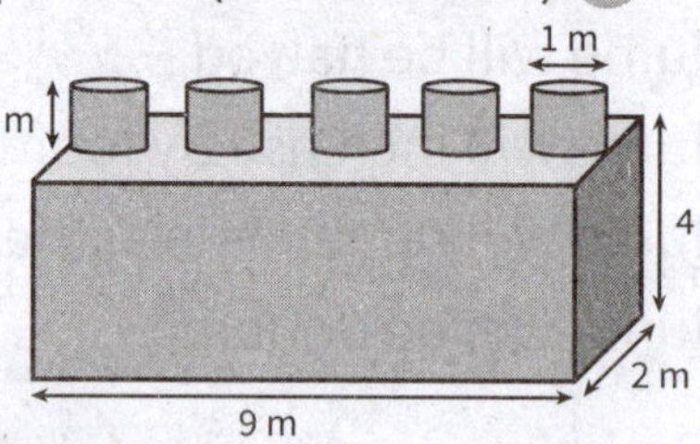

A. ₹3651
B. ₹3665
C. ₹4671
D. ₹4771

30. Find the volume of a cylinder formed by rolling a rectangular sheet which is 24 cm long and 22 cm wide when rolled along its width.
A. 997.5 cm^3
B. 924 cm^3
C. 616 cm^3
D. 132 cm^3

31. A right-angled triangle PQR with sides 24 cm, 7 cm and 25 cm is revolved about the side 24 cm. Find the curved surface area of the solid so obtained. (Use $\pi = 3.14$)
A. 528 cm^2
B. 550 cm^2
C. 1100 cm^2
D. 1884 cm^2

32. A dome-shaped trunk is a combination of half cylinder mounted on a cuboidal box. The dimension of the base of the trunk is 14 ft × 7 ft and the total height of the trunk is 11.5 ft. Find the total surface area of the trunk.

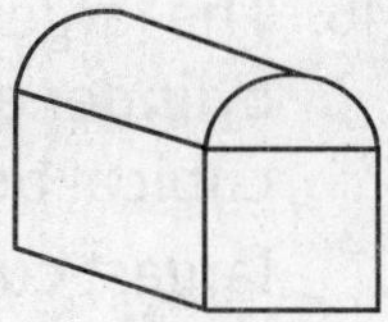

A. 385 cm^2

B. 532 cm^2

C. 626.5 cm^2

D. 716 cm^2

33. Let C be the largest possible cube that can be enclosed in the sphere S of radius r. Find the ratio of total surface area of the cube C to sphere S.

A. $2 : \pi$

B. $3 : 2\sqrt{3}\,\pi$

C. $3 : 2$

D. $1 : \pi$

34. A paper tree is made by mounting a cone on top of a cylinder. The height and the radius of the cone is double than that of the cylinder. Find the curved surface area of the paper tree if the radius of the cone is 5 cm and height is 12 cm.

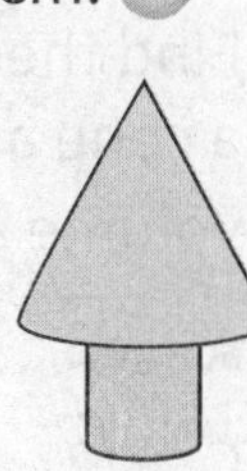

A. 65π cm^2

B. 85π cm^2

C. 90π cm^2

D. 95π cm^2

35. The surface areas of two spheres are in the ratio 16 : 81. Find the ratio of their volumes.

A. 729 : 64

B. 64 : 729

C. 12 : 27

D. 27 : 12

36. A shape is made with a combination of three solid shapes: a frustum of cone and cones on both the sides. Which of the following represents the volume of the solid?

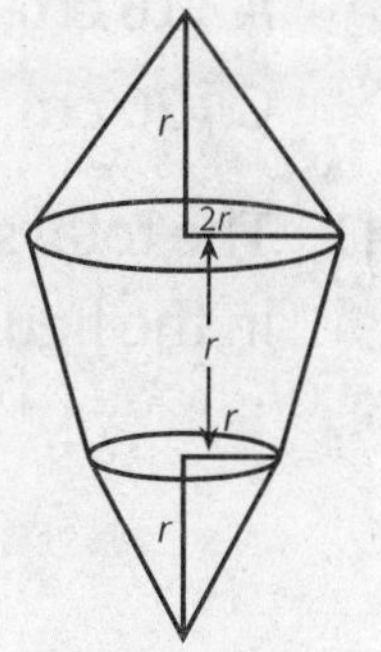

A. $4\pi r^3$

B. $\frac{7}{3}\pi r^3$

C. $\frac{11}{3}\pi r^3$

D. $6\pi r^3$

37. A cuboidal truck trolley, with dimension 28 ft × 11 ft × 7 ft, is full of sand. When the sand is emptied from the truck, it forms a heap similar to a right circular cone of diameter 28 ft. Find the height of the heap.

A. 77 ft B. 21 ft

C. 10.5 ft D. 7 ft

38. A hemispherical metal container has inner and outer radii as 6 cm and 9 cm, respectively. Find the weight of the container, if the density of the metal is 8.05 g per cm^3.

A. 9.4 kg

B. 8.6 kg

C. 8.4 kg

D. 7.5 kg

39. The water filled in a conical vessel is transferred into a cylindrical flask with the same radius. Find the minimum height of the flask so that it can be filled without overflow if the height of conical vessel is 18 cm.

A. 6 cm B. 6.25 cm

C. 8 cm D. 9 cm

40. Find the slant height of the frustum of a cone whose height is 15 cm and the radii of the ends are 29 cm and 21 cm, respectively.

A. 16 cm B. 17 cm
C. 20 cm D. 23 cm

41. The total surface area of the bucket shown in the figure is given by __________.

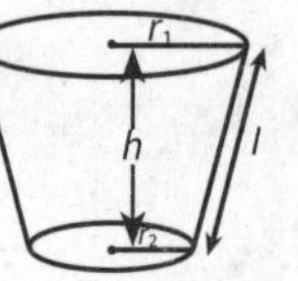

A. $\frac{1}{3}\pi h[r_1^2 + r_2^2 - r_1 r_2]$ cubic units
B. $\pi h(r_1 + r_2) + \pi r_1^2 + \pi r_2^2$ sq. units
C. $\pi l(r_1 + r_2) + \pi r_1^2 + \pi r_2^2$ sq. units
D. $\pi l(r_1 + r_2) + \pi r_1^2 - \pi r_2^2$ sq. units

42. Find the height of a frustum of a cone if its slant height is 25 cm and the circumference of both the bases is 176 cm and 132 cm, respectively.

A. 23 cm B. 24 cm
C. 25 cm D. 27 cm

43. Geeta is making a lamp shade with a cloth which is in the shape of frustum with slant height 35 cm and two radii 7 cm and 28 cm. Find the measurement of the cloth required to make the lamp. (Approximately 150 square cm of cloth is used in pasting the edges.)

A. 6480 cm²
B. 6468 cm²
C. 4000 cm²
D. 3850 cm²

44. Find the volume of the largest possible frustum of a cone that can be enclosed in a cube of side 6 cm, if the radii of the frustum are in the ratio of 2 : 1.

A. 99 cm³ B. 74.25 cm³
C. 69 cm³ D. 49.5 cm³

45. Find the volume of a frustum of a cone, if its height is 14 cm, the sum of its radii is 12 cm and their product is 27 cm².

A. 2508 cm³ B. 1716 cm³
C. 1647 cm³ D. 1536 cm³

46. The largest possible cone, sphere and cylinder are enclosed in three identical cubical boxes. Which one will have the largest curved surface area?

A. Cone B. Sphere
C. Cylinder D. Both B and C

47. A spherical clay ball of radius 6 cm is flattened into a cuboidal sheet of dimensions 12 cm × 4 cm. Find the height of the sheet.

A. 6 cm B. 12.14 cm
C. 17 cm D. 18.84 cm

48. One litre of water is poured into a cuboidal jug of base dimensions 20 cm × 5 cm. Find the height of the jug if the water level is 4 cm below the top?

A. 4.001 cm B. 5 cm
C. 10 cm D. 14 cm

49. Find the ratio of the radius of a cylinder, a cone and a hemisphere having same volume and same height.

A. $\sqrt{3} : \sqrt{2} : 1$ B. $1 : 3 : 2$
C. $\sqrt{2} : \sqrt{6} : \sqrt{3}$ D. $2 : 6 : 3$

50. Find the slant height of the frustum of a cone whose height is 35 cm and the radii of the ends are 42 cm and 30 cm.

A. 33 cm B. 37 cm
C. 43 cm D. 47 cm

CHAPTER 14

Statistics

PRIOR KNOWLEDGE TEST

Choose the correct option.

1. What is the median of the following data?

15	10	3	8	9	6

A. 8 B. 8.5 C. 9 D. 9.5

2. The given data is about the number of fishes being caught by different people.

3	4	7	3	5	2	6	10

What is the average number of fishes caught by them?

A. 2 B. 4 C. 5 D. 10

3. The heights of different soft dolls are given below in cm.

108	99	112	111	108

What is the height of the middlemost doll?

A. 111 B. 112 C. 108 D. 99

4. The following is the strength of different classes in a senior secondary school.

29	24	24	26	27	26	30	24
29	24	27					

What is the most common strength of the class?

A. 29 B. 27
C. 26 D. 24

5. The average score of a cricketer in three matches is 55 runs. What is his score in the fourth match if the average falls to 52 runs?

A. 43 B. 45
C. 53 D. 55

KEYWORDS

Statistics: The area of study dealing with the presentation, analysis and interpretation of data

Data: Facts or figures, collected with a definite purpose

Class interval: A small group of large amount of data

Class width: The size of each class interval

Class limit: The least and the largest value of each class interval

Cumulative frequency: Obtained by adding the frequencies of all the classes preceding the given class

Ogive: Graphical representation of a cumulative frequency distribution as a cumulative frequency curve; Ogive can be of less than type or more than type

Mean: Average values of the observations; denoted by $\overline{x}$

Sigma: The Greek symbol (Σ) used to denote the summation of value of observations

Median: Value of the middlemost observation

Mode: The most frequently occurring observation

CONCEPT MAP

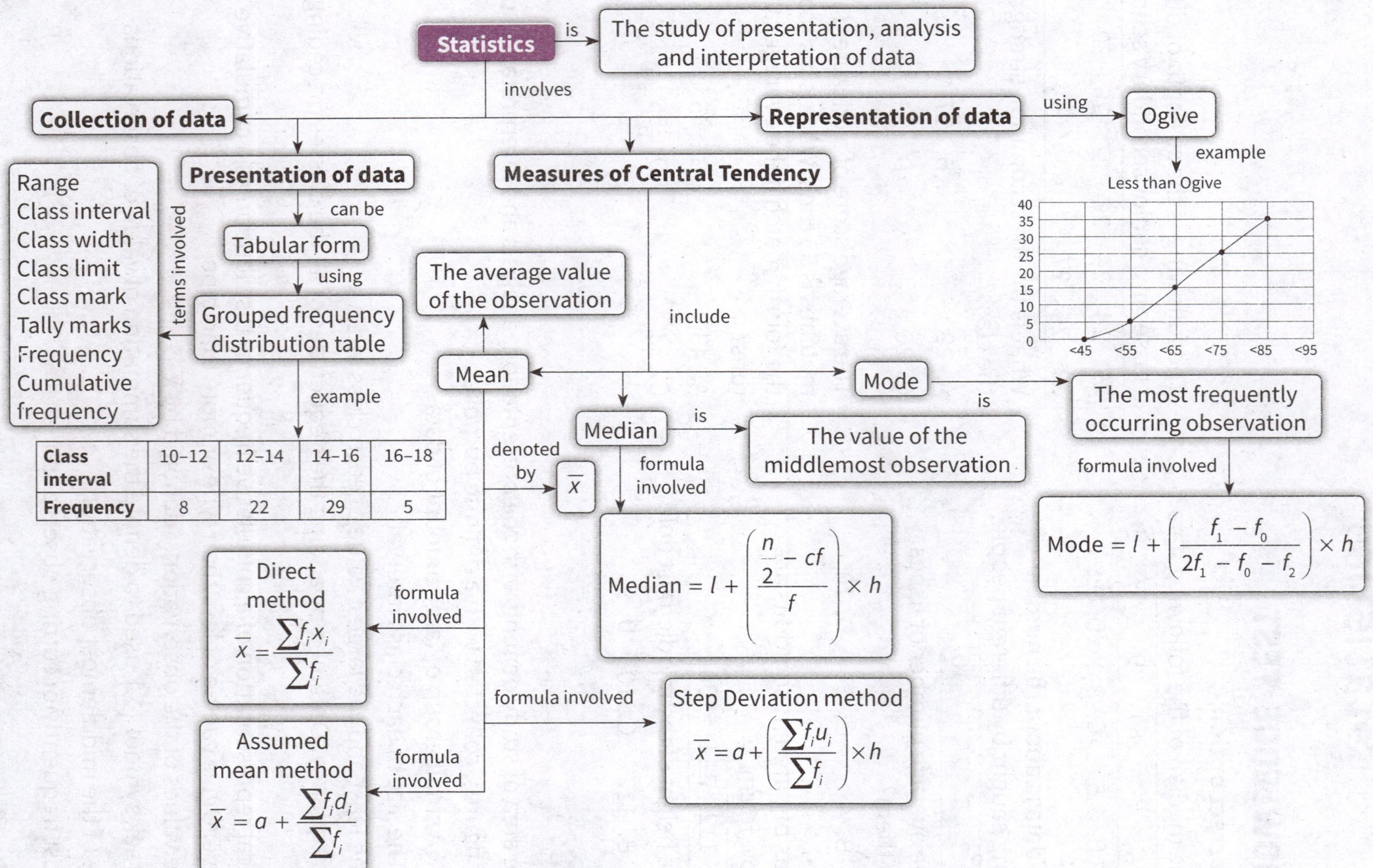

Statistics
is
The study of presentation, analysis and interpretation of data
involves
Collection of data
Representation of data
using
Ogive
example
Less than Ogive
40
35
30
25
20
15
10
5
0
<45
<55
<65
<75
<85
<95
Presentation of data
can be
Tabular form
using
Grouped frequency distribution table
terms involved
Range
Class interval
Class width
Class limit
Class mark
Tally marks
Frequency
Cumulative frequency
example
Class interval | 10–12 | 12–14 | 14–16 | 16–18
Frequency | 8 | 22 | 29 | 5
Measures of Central Tendency
include
Mean
The average value of the observation
denoted by
$\overline{x}$
formula involved
Direct method
$\overline{x} = \frac{\sum f_i x_i}{\sum f_i}$
formula involved
Assumed mean method
$\overline{x} = a + \frac{\sum f_i d_i}{\sum f_i}$
formula involved
Step Deviation method
$\overline{x} = a + \left(\frac{\sum f_i u_i}{\sum f_i}\right) \times h$
Median
is
The value of the middlemost observation
formula involved
$\text{Median} = l + \left(\frac{\frac{n}{2} - cf}{f}\right) \times h$
Mode
is
The most frequently occurring observation
formula involved
$\text{Mode} = l + \left(\frac{f_1 - f_0}{2f_1 - f_0 - f_2}\right) \times h$

SELF-ASSESSMENT 1

Choose the correct option.

1. What does f_2 stand for in the given formula?

$$\text{Mode} = l + \left(\frac{f_1 - f_0}{2f_1 - f_0 - f_2}\right) \times h$$

A. Sum of the frequency

B. Frequency of modal class

C. Frequency of class succeeding the modal class

D. Frequency of class preceding the modal class

2. What is the formula used to find the mean in the assumed mean method?

A. $\overline{x} = \frac{\sum f}{N}$ B. $\overline{x} = \frac{\sum f_i x_i}{\sum f_i}$

C. $\overline{x} = a + \frac{\sum f_i d_i}{\sum f_i}$ D. $\overline{x} = a + \left(\frac{\sum f_i u_i}{\sum f_i}\right) \times h$

3. What does the letter f stand for in the given formula?

$$\text{Median} = l + \left(\frac{\frac{n}{2} - cf}{f}\right) \times h$$

A. Frequency of the median class

B. Frequency of class succeeding the median class

C. Frequency of class preceding the median class

D. Sum of frequency

4. What is f_1 in the given data, if 40–50 is the modal class?

Marks	10–20	20–30	30–40	40–50	50–60
Frequency	3	12	27	80	57

A. 12

B. 27

C. 80

D. 57

5. What is the empirical relationship between the three measures of central tendency?

A. 3 Median = Mode + Mean

B. 3 Median = 2 Mode + 2 Mean

C. 3 Median = 2 Mode + Mean

D. 3 Median = Mode + 2 Mean

6. The following table shows the number of students of different age group in a primary school.

Age group (in years)	2–5	5–8	8–11	11–14
Number of students	19	20	18	23

What is the average age group of students?

A. 8.1 B. 8.18

C. 8.8 D. 8.81

7. What is the average of the data, if the class interval of the assumed mean is 30–40, and $\sum f_i d_i$ and $\sum f_i$ are 2100 and 210, respectively?

A. 30 B. 35

C. 40 D. 45

8. What is the average of the data, if the continuous class interval of the assumed mean is 21–30, and $\sum f_i u_i$ and $\sum f_i$ are 100 and 180, respectively?

A. 21

B. 26

C. 28

D. 30.5

9. What is the average of the following data?

Class interval	50–54	54–58	58–62	62–66
Frequency	2	7	8	3

A. 54.4

B. 58.4

C. 62.4

D. 64.4

10. Find the missing frequency in the given table, if the average is 5.2.

Class interval	2–4	4–6	6–8	8–10
Frequency	3	4	x	1

A. 1

B. 2

C. 3

D. 4

11. Find the missing frequency for the given data, if the average is 23.3.

Class interval	0–10	10–20	20–30	30–40
Frequency	7	x	3	12

A. 0

B. 1

C. 2

D. 3

12. Find the median for the given data by taking 20–30 as the median class.

Class interval	0–10	10–20	20–30	30–40	40–50
Frequency	3	8	25	40	24

A. 15.6

B. 25.6

C. 35.6

D. 45.6

13. Find the median for the following data.

Class interval	0–10	10–20	20–30	30–40	40–50
Frequency	8	14	12	9	7

A. 22.5

B. 24.5

C. 26.5

D. 28.5

14. Find the median for the following data.

Class interval	5–10	10–15	15–20	20–25	25–30	30–35
Frequency	2	6	2	2	6	2

A. 18

B. 19

C. 20

D. 21

15. Find the median for the following data.

Class interval	0–10	10–20	20–30	30–40	40–50	50–60
Frequency	1	2	3	7	4	3

A. 34.71

B. 35.71

C. 36.71

D. 37.71

16. Find the mode for the given data by taking 20–30 as the modal class.

Class interval	0–10	10–20	20–30	30–40	40–50
Frequency	14	23	27	21	15

A. 20
B. 24
C. 27
D. 30

17. What is the modal score of the students in the class?

Score	10–12	12–14	14–16	16–18	18–20
Frequency	4	6	12	9	8

A. 14.33
B. 15.33
C. 16.33
D. 18.33

18. What is the modal marks of the students in the class?

Marks	4–8	8–12	12–16	16–20	20–24
Frequency	13	8	12	11	6

A. 13.88
B. 11.88
C. 8.88
D. 6.88

19. What is the modal score of the students in the class?

Score	2–4	4–6	6–8	8–10	10–12
Frequency	2	3	6	2	1

A. 5.85
B. 6.85
C. 7.85
D. 8.85

20. What will be the mode of the data if the mean and the median are 3.4 and 3.5, respectively?

A. 3.4
B. 3.5
C. 3.6
D. 3.7

21. The table given below shows the marks of 50 students in the class. If the median of the data is 21, find the missing value in the given data.

Marks	0–10	10–20	20–30	30–40	40–50
Number of students	10	14	y	6	10

A. $y=10$
B. $y=11$
C. $y=12$
D. $y=13$

22. The table given below shows the number of visitors spending time in the library. Compare the average number of people spending time in the library for two different days.

Time (in hours)	0–2	2–4	4–6	6–8	8–10
Day 1	6	3	2	4	5
Day 2	7	3	5	6	4

A. The average number of visitors on day 1 is less than those who visited on day 2.
B. The average number of visitors on day 1 is same as those who visited on day 2.
C. The average number of visitors on day 1 is more than those who visited on day 2.
D. None of the above

23. The table given below shows the area of cultivation land owned by different families in a village. Find the missing number if the average land area owned by different families is 9 acres.

Land (in acres)	0–5	5–10	10–15	15–20	20–25
No of families	8	$2x$	4	x	2

A. $x = 1$ and $2x = 2$

B. $x = 2$ and $2x = 4$

C. $x = 3$ and $2x = 6$

D. $x = 4$ and $2x = 8$

24. The following table shows the electricity consumption of different families in an apartment. Find the average consumption and the consumption range of the maximum number of customers.

Electricity consumptions	60–80	80–100	100–120	120–140	140–160
Number of consumers	2	5	10	9	4

A. Mean = 115.67 and Mode = 116.33

B. Mean = 115.67 and Mode = 116.67

C. Mean = 115.33 and Mode = 116.33

D. Mean = 115.33 and Mode = 116.67

25. What is the mode for the given ogive?

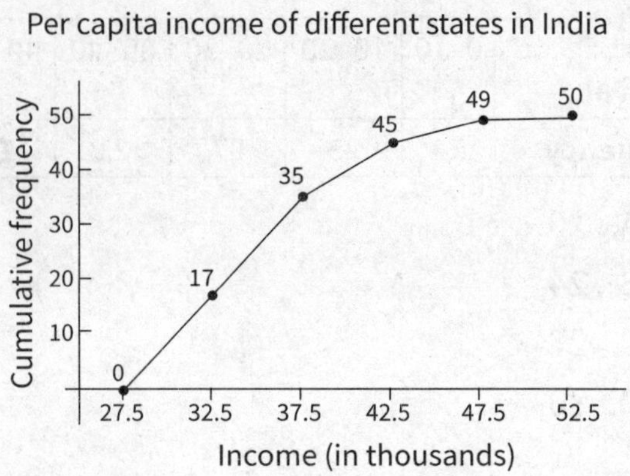

A. 33.05

B. 33.5

C. 33.55

D. 33.75

PART 1

CHAPTER 14: Statistics

SELF-ASSESSMENT 2

Choose the correct option.

26. What is l of the modal class for the given data?

Class	0–10	10–20	20–30	30–40	40–50	50–60
Frequency	5	6	13	38	30	4

A. 20
B. 30
C. 40
D. 50

27. What is the formula used to find the mean in the step deviation method?

A. $\overline{x} = \frac{\sum f}{N}$

B. $\overline{x} = \frac{\sum f_i x_i}{\sum f_i}$

C. $\overline{x} = a + \frac{\sum f_i d_i}{\sum f_i}$

D. $\overline{x} = a + \left(\frac{\sum f_i u_i}{\sum f_i}\right) \times h$

28. What is cf of the median class for the given data?

Marks	10–20	20–30	30–40	40–50	50–60
Frequency	3	12	27	80	57

A. 15
B. 42
C. 122
D. 179

29. What does the letter f_0 stand for in the given formula?

$$\text{Mode} = l + \left(\frac{f_1 - f_0}{2f_1 - f_0 - f_2}\right) \times h$$

A. Frequency
B. Frequency of the modal class
C. Frequency of the class preceding the modal class
D. Frequency of the class succeeding the modal class

30. What is obtained graphically as the x-coordinate of the point of intersection of the two ogives for a given data?

A. Mean
B. Median
C. Mode
D. All the above

31. The following table shows the late entries of spectators in a cinema hall.

Time (in minutes)	5–10	10–15	15–20	20–24
Number of people	2	8	4	1

What is the average time of the late entries?

A. 12.83
B. 13.83
C. 14.83
D. 15.83

32. What is the average of the data, if the class interval of the assumed mean is 15–25, and $\sum f_i d_i$ and $\sum f_i$ are 1188 and 540, respectively?

A. 15.2

B. 17.2

C. 19.2

D. 22.2

33. What is the average of the data, if the continuous class interval of the assumed mean is 20–30, and $\sum f_i u_i$ and $\sum f_i$ are 75 and 75, respectively?

A. 20

B. 25

C. 30

D. 35

34. Find the missing frequency in the given table, if the average is 14.7.

Class interval	10–12	12–14	14–16	16–18
Frequency	4	12	x	14

A. 10

B. 12

C. 14

D. 16

35. What is the average of the following data?

Class interval	30–36	36–42	42–48	48–54
Frequency	3	8	7	2

A. 36.4

B. 38.4

C. 41.4

D. 44.4

36. Find the missing frequency for the given data, if the average is 27.6.

Class interval	5–15	15–25	25–35	35–45
Frequency	6	x	7	9

A. 0

B. 1

C. 2

D. 3

37. Find the median for the given data by taking 30–40 as the median class.

Class interval	10–20	20–30	30–40	40–50	50–60	60–70
Frequency	4	12	20	8	4	2

A. 32.5

B. 34.5

C. 36.5

D. 38.5

38. Find the median for the following data.

Class interval	1–5	5–9	9–13	13–17	17–21
Frequency	12	11	10	4	3

A. 6.9

B. 7.9

C. 8.9

D. 9.9

39. Find the median for the following data.

Class interval	3–7	7–11	11–15	15–19	19–23	23–27
Frequency	2	1	3	7	6	1

A. 15.28

B. 16.28

C. 17.28

D. 18.28

40. Find the median for the following data.

Class interval	1-9	9–17	17–25	25–33	33–41	41–49
Frequency	2	1	6	4	3	4

A. 26
B. 27
C. 29
D. 32

41. Find the mode for the given data by taking 35–40 as the modal class.

Class interval	20–25	25–30	30–35	35–40	40–45	45–50
Frequency	1	3	8	12	7	5

A. 27.22
B. 32.22
C. 37.22
D. 42.22

42. Find the mode for the given data by taking 30–40 as the modal class.

Class interval	0–10	10–20	20–30	30–40	40–50
Frequency	3	8	24	60	21

A. 32.8
B. 34.8
C. 36.8
D. 38.8

43. What is the modal marks of the students in the class?

Marks	4–6	6–8	8–10	10–12	12–14
Frequency	3	6	4	5	2

A. 6.2
B. 7.2
C. 8.2
D. 9.2

44. What is the modal score of the players in the field?

Score	0–4	4–8	8–12	12–16	16–20
Frequency	5	6	10	7	2

A. 8.28 B. 9.28
C. 10.28 D. 11.28

45. What will be the median of a data, if the mean and the mode are 5.2 and 6, respectively?

A. 5.2 B. 5.4
C. 5.6 D. 5.8

46. The given table shows 20 people of different age group walking/sitting in a park. If the median of the data is 27.5, find the missing values in the given data.

Age group	0–10	10–20	20–30	30–40	40–50
Number of people	2	5	x	6	y

A. $x = 3$ and $y = 4$
B. $x = 4$ and $y = 4$
C. $x = 3$ and $y = 3$
D. $x = 4$ and $y = 3$

47. The given table shows the marks of students in a class in two consecutive tests. Compare the average test marks scored by the students.

Marks	40–50	50–60	60–70	70–80	80–90
Test 1	6	4	2	3	5
Test 2	2	3	5	6	4

A. The average score of students in test 1 is better than test 2.
B. The average score of students in test 1 is same as test 2.
C. The average score of students in test 2 is better than test 1.
D. None of the above

48. The table given below shows the number of hours spent by different people in a library in a week. Find the value of x, if the average time spent in the library is 4.2 hours.

Time (hours)	0–2	2–4	4–6	6–8	8–10
Number of students	10	$3x$	6	$2x$	4

A. $x = 12$

B. $x = 8$ and $y = 4$

C. $x = 20$

D. $x = 4$

49. The table given below shows the water consumption of different people in a day. Find the average consumption of water and the consumption range of the maximum number of people.

Water consumption (litres)	0–50	50–100	100–150	150–200	200–250
Number of people	3	4	8	7	3

A. Mean = 131 and Mode = 140

B. Mean = 131 and Mode = 131

C. Mean = 140 and Mode = 131

D. Mean = 140 and Mode = 131

50. What is the mode for the given ogive?

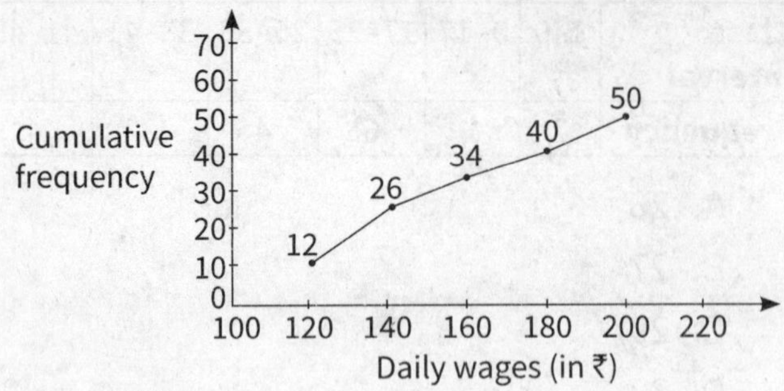

A. 140

B. 125

C. 160

D. 170

CHAPTER 15

Probability

PRIOR KNOWLEDGE TEST

Choose the correct option.

1. What is the probability of getting at least one head when two coins are tossed simultaneously?

   A. $\frac{1}{4}$ B. $\frac{1}{2}$ C. $\frac{3}{4}$ D. 1

2. What is the probability of getting number 0 by rolling a die?

   A. 0 B. $\frac{1}{2}$ C. $\frac{1}{3}$ D. $\frac{1}{6}$

3. What is the numerical measurement of probability of a possible event?

   A. 0 B. < 1 C. $= 1$ D. > 1

4. There are 4 blue balls and 6 green balls in a basket. One green ball is picked first and then the second ball is picked from the remaining balls. What is the probability of picking the second ball as blue?

   A. $\frac{3}{10}$ B. $\frac{1}{3}$ C. $\frac{4}{9}$ D. $\frac{4}{10}$

5. What is the probability of taking out a jack from a deck of cards?

   A. $\frac{1}{52}$ B. $\frac{1}{26}$ C. $\frac{1}{13}$ D. $\frac{1}{4}$

KEYWORDS

Event: The collection of some outcomes of an experiment

Random experiment: The experiment in which the outcome is uncertain

Certain event: An event that is sure to happen

Impossible event: An event that cannot happen

Elementary event: An event having only one outcome

Complementary events: Two events are said to be complementary when one event occurs if and only if the other does not

Experimental or empirical probability: The ratio of the number of trials in which an event occurs to the total number of trials the experiment is performed; depends on the result of the actual experiment

Theoretical or classical probability: The ratio of the number of outcomes favourable to an event to the number of all possible outcomes of the experiment; theoretical probability is what we expect to happen

CONCEPT MAP

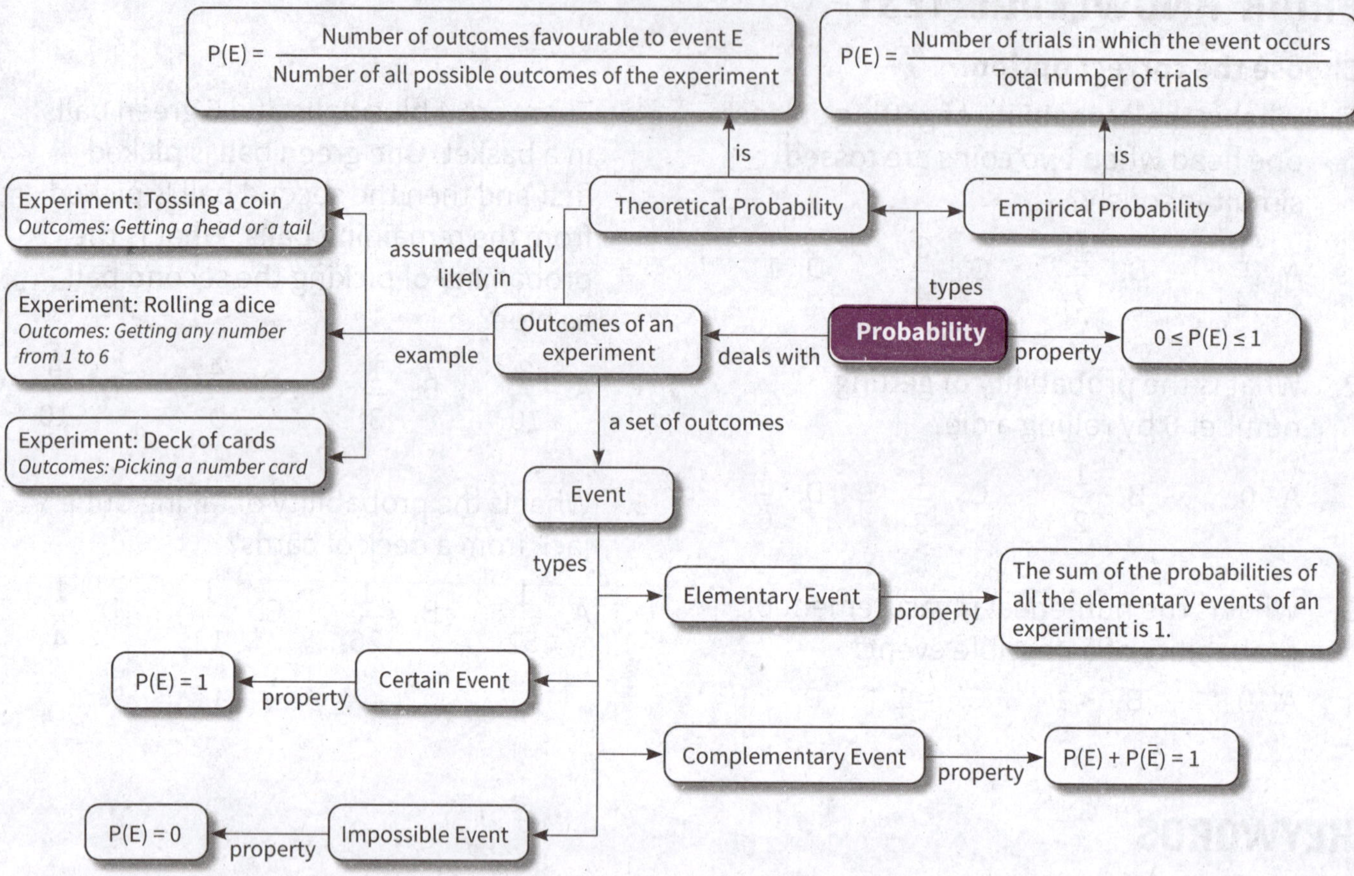
P(E) = Number of outcomes favourable to event E / Number of all possible outcomes of the experiment
P(E) = Number of trials in which the event occurs / Total number of trials
is
is
Theoretical Probability
Empirical Probability
Experiment: Tossing a coin
Outcomes: Getting a head or a tail
assumed equally likely in
types
Experiment: Rolling a dice
Outcomes: Getting any number from 1 to 6
example
Outcomes of an experiment
deals with
Probability
property
0 ≤ P(E) ≤ 1
a set of outcomes
Experiment: Deck of cards
Outcomes: Picking a number card
Event
types
Elementary Event
property
The sum of the probabilities of all the elementary events of an experiment is 1.
P(E) = 1
property
Certain Event
Complementary Event
property
P(E) + P(Ē) = 1
P(E) = 0
property
Impossible Event

PART 1

CHAPTER 15: Probability

SELF-ASSESSMENT 1

Choose the correct option.

1. What is the probability of a certain event?

   A. 0 B. < 1

   C. 1 D. > 1

2. If two coins are tossed simultaneously, what is the probability of not getting a head on any of the coins?

   A. $\frac{1}{4}$ B. $\frac{1}{2}$

   C. $\frac{3}{4}$ D. 1

3. If two dice are rolled at a time, what is the probability of getting the same number on both the dice?

   A. $\frac{1}{6}$ B. $\frac{1}{12}$

   C. $\frac{1}{18}$ D. $\frac{1}{36}$

4. What is the probability of picking a red-coloured ace from a deck of cards?

   A. $\frac{1}{4}$

   B. $\frac{1}{13}$

   C. $\frac{1}{26}$

   D. $\frac{1}{52}$

5. There is an apple, an orange and a guava in a basket. Rishika picked up one fruit from the basket. Identify the correct statement.

   A. The probability of picking an apple is more than that of an orange and a guava.

   B. The probability of picking an orange is more than that of an apple and a guava.

   C. The probability of picking a guava is more than that of an orange and an apple.

   D. The probability of picking an apple is same as that of picking an orange and a guava.

6. If three coins are tossed simultaneously, what is the probability of getting at the most two tails?

   A. $\frac{1}{8}$ B. $\frac{3}{8}$

   C. $\frac{5}{8}$ D. $\frac{7}{8}$

7. What is the probability of getting the sum of numbers greater than 3 by rolling a pair of dice?

   A. $\frac{1}{36}$ B. $\frac{3}{36}$

   C. $\frac{33}{36}$ D. $\frac{35}{36}$

8. One card is drawn from a well-shuffled deck of cards. What is the probability of not getting a black-coloured king?

A. $\frac{3}{4}$ B. $\frac{11}{13}$

C. $\frac{25}{26}$ D. $\frac{51}{52}$

9. Ravi participated in a running race where there were 14 participants. Ravi was the winner and two other participants were declared as foul. What is the probability of other participants to win the runner medal?

A. $\frac{1}{14}$ B. $\frac{2}{14}$

C. $\frac{1}{11}$ D. $\frac{13}{14}$

10. A coin is tossed 100 times and head is obtained 61 times. Now, if a coin is tossed at random, what is the probability of getting a tail?

A. $\frac{61}{100}$ B. $\frac{39}{100}$

C. $\frac{39}{61}$ D. 1

11. One card is drawn from a well-shuffled deck of cards. What is the probability of not getting any red-coloured card?

A. $\frac{3}{4}$ B. $\frac{1}{4}$

C. $\frac{1}{3}$ D. $\frac{1}{2}$

12. What is the probability of getting an extra Sunday in a leap year?

A. $\frac{1}{7}$ B. $\frac{2}{7}$

C. $\frac{4}{7}$ D. $\frac{5}{7}$

13. Ringsuwon and Priya are best friends. Every year, they go to picnic with their families. What is the probability of both best friends going to picnic on the same day in a year?

A. $\frac{1}{365}$ B. $\frac{29}{365}$

C. $\frac{30}{365}$ D. 1

14. What is the probability of getting neither an ace nor a black queen from a well-shuffled deck of 52 cards?

A. $\frac{1}{26}$ B. $\frac{3}{26}$

C. $\frac{1}{13}$ D. $\frac{23}{26}$

15. In a saree showroom, 1500 new designer sarees are kept for sale. If 2% of them are damaged, what is the probability of choosing a non-damaged saree?

A. $\frac{1}{30}$ B. $\frac{1}{1470}$

C. $\frac{30}{1500}$ D. $\frac{1470}{1500}$

16. A pair of dice is rolled together. What is the probability of getting non-square numbers on both the dice?

A. $\frac{4}{9}$

B. $\frac{5}{9}$

C. $\frac{7}{9}$

D. $\frac{8}{9}$

17. Lottery tickets are numbered from 1 to 100. The person who gets either a cube or a square number will get a prize. What is the probability of a person who bought the ticket, not winning a prize?

A. $\frac{1}{25}$

B. $\frac{2}{25}$

C. $\frac{3}{25}$

D. $\frac{22}{25}$

18. The Ace and the Jack of diamonds and the King and the Queen of hearts are removed from a well-shuffled deck of cards. If a card is selected at random from the remaining cards, what is the probability of selecting a heart?

A. $\frac{48}{52}$

B. $\frac{13}{52}$

C. $\frac{11}{48}$

D. $\frac{13}{48}$

19. A television manufacturing company manufactures smart TVs and regular TVs. There are 3% defective pieces among the regular TVs and 8% defective pieces among the smart TVs. What is the probability of selecting a non-defective TV?

A. 0.925

B. 0.975

C. 0.945

D. 0.905

20. A survey was conducted among 100 families related to the number of children in their families. Find the probability of choosing a family having at least 1 girl child?

Type of Family	Number of families
No child	3
Only boy child	41
One boy and one girl child	15
Only girl child	41

A. $\frac{6}{25}$ B. $\frac{11}{25}$

C. $\frac{14}{25}$ D. $\frac{19}{25}$

21. In an ice cream parlour, the following options are available.

Types	Flavour	Toppings
Cup ice cream	Vanilla	Chocolate Sauce
Cone ice cream	*Pista Badam*	Peanut butter
Candy	Chocolate	Sprinkles
	Strawberry	Toasted coconut flakes
		Hot fudge

If a child selects an ice cream, what is the probability that it includes strawberry-flavoured cup ice cream?

A. $\frac{1}{3}$ B. $\frac{2}{3}$

C. $\frac{1}{3}$ D. $\frac{1}{12}$

22. A bag contains two dozen balls of two different colours. There are x red-coloured balls. The probability of picking a red ball will be doubled if 6 more red balls are placed in the bag. What is the value of x?

A. 4

B. 6

C. 8

D. 12

23. A triangle is drawn by joining the centres X, Y and Z of the circles having radii 2 cm each as shown below. If a point is chosen randomly within the triangle, find the probability that the chosen point is in the shaded region?

A. $\frac{4\sqrt{3}-2\pi}{4\sqrt{3}}$

B. $\frac{2\pi}{4\sqrt{3}}$

C. $\frac{4\sqrt{3}}{2\pi}$

D. $\frac{4\sqrt{3}-2\pi}{2\pi}$

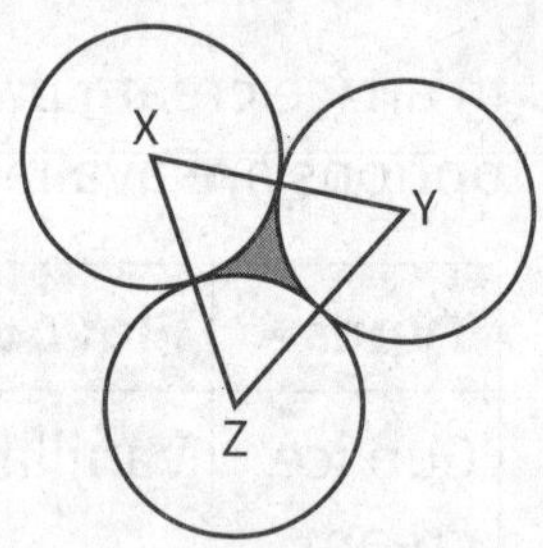

24. The numbered cards of clubs and hearts which are multiples of 3 are removed from a well-shuffled deck of cards. Which of the following statements is true?

A. The probability of getting a club card is half the probability of getting a heart card.

B. The probability of getting a red card is same as the probability of getting a black card.

C. The probability of getting a number card is exactly two times the probability of getting a card other than numbered cards.

D. The probability of getting a numbered card is less than that of getting any red card.

25. Which of the following events is the most likely to occur when two dice are rolled simultaneously?

A. The difference between the numbers that appeared on the dice is 5.

B. Both the numbers that appeared on the dice are multiples of 2.

C. The sum of numbers that appeared on the dice is a factor of 6.

D. The product of the numbers that appeared on the dice is more than 6.

SELF-ASSESSMENT 2

Choose the correct option.

26. Which of the following events will have only one outcome?
    A. Certain event
    B. Elementary event
    C. Impossible event
    D. Complementary event

27. If two coins are tossed simultaneously, what is the probability of getting at least one tail on both the coins?
    A. 1
    B. $\frac{3}{4}$
    C $\frac{1}{2}$
    D $\frac{1}{4}$

28. If two dice are rolled at a time, what is the probability of getting the sum of the numbers on both the dice as even?
    A. $\frac{1}{2}$
    B. $\frac{1}{3}$
    C. $\frac{1}{4}$
    D. $\frac{1}{6}$

29. What is the probability of picking a number card other than a diamond or a spade from the deck of cards?
    A. $\frac{1}{2}$ B. $\frac{1}{18}$
    C. $\frac{1}{26}$ D. $\frac{9}{26}$

30. Which of the following cannot be a probability?
    i. 35% ii. −0.5 iii. 1.25 iv. 0.23
    A. i
    B. ii
    C. iii
    D. Both ii and iii

31. If three coins are tossed simultaneously, what is the probability of getting at least two heads?
    A. $\frac{1}{8}$ B. $\frac{1}{2}$
    C. $\frac{3}{4}$ D. $\frac{5}{8}$

32. What is the probability of getting the first number greater than the second number by rolling a pair of dice?
    A. $\frac{1}{12}$ B. $\frac{5}{12}$
    C. $\frac{7}{12}$ D. $\frac{11}{12}$

33. A shop sells water bottles in many colours. What is the probability of choosing a bottle in the shop, other than yellow and pink in colour?

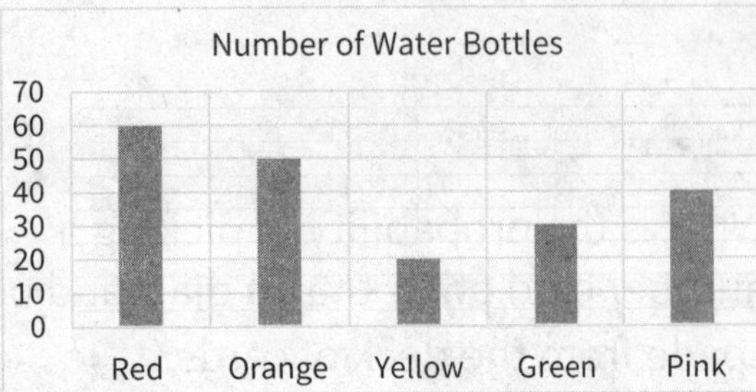

A. $\frac{1}{10}$ B. $\frac{3}{10}$

C. $\frac{7}{10}$ D. $\frac{9}{10}$

34. The spinning wheel has 30 spokes or slots in which 15 are yellow, 10 are brown and 5 are purple in colour. Jasvinder played 3 games and she always bet on the purple slot. What is the probability of Jasvinder winning the game?

A. $\frac{1}{2}$

B. $\frac{1}{6}$

C. $\frac{1}{3}$

D. $\frac{1}{216}$

35. A coin is tossed 150 times and a tail is obtained 58 times. Now, if a coin is tossed at random, what is the probability of getting a head?

A. $\frac{29}{75}$ B. $\frac{46}{75}$

C. $\frac{29}{46}$ D. 1

36. Two apartments A and B are occupied by tenants. Apartment A is occupied 215 days in a year and apartment B is occupied 300 days in a year. What is the probability of choosing apartment A on its vacant number of days?

A. $\frac{13}{73}$

B. $\frac{30}{73}$

C. $\frac{43}{73}$

D. $\frac{60}{73}$

37. What is the probability of getting an extra Sunday in a non-leap year?

A. $\frac{1}{7}$

B. $\frac{2}{7}$

C. $\frac{4}{5}$

D. $\frac{5}{7}$

38. In a nursery, there are 300 saplings of herbs and 100 saplings of climbers for sale. John picks up one sapling at random and keeps it aside. His daughter picks up another sapling at random. Find the probability of John's daughter picking up the sapling of herb if a sapling of climber has already been picked by her father.

A. $\frac{299}{399}$ B. $\frac{33}{133}$

C. $\frac{100}{133}$ D. $\frac{100}{399}$

39. In a class, 25% of girls and 60% of boys travel to school by school bus. The number of girls is twice the number of boys in the class. What is the probability of selecting a student at random who does not travel by school bus, if there are 30 students in the class?

A. $\frac{19}{30}$
B. $\frac{11}{30}$
C. $\frac{3}{4}$
D. $\frac{2}{5}$

40. Joseph needs to attend a video conference in between his busy schedule. 90% of the times, he keeps a reminder call. There is 10% chance of missing the reminder call. Find the probability of Joseph attending the video conference.

A. 90%
B. 81%
C. 19%
D. 10%

41. There are four seats available in a hall and each seat is assigned to a specific person. Though each person is to be seated in the assigned seat, the first person entering the theatre takes a random seat. After that, each person takes the assigned seat if it is unoccupied, otherwise takes a random seat. What is the probability of the last person getting his assigned seat?

A. $\frac{1}{2}$
B. $\frac{1}{4}$
C. $\frac{3}{4}$
D. 1

42. One number is chosen from 1 to 100. What is the probability of picking a number which is neither divisible by 5 nor by 6?

A. $\frac{1}{5}$
B. $\frac{4}{25}$
C. $\frac{33}{100}$
D. $\frac{67}{100}$

43. In a dance academy, there are 60 students. Among them, 50% are learning classical, 30% are learning both classical and western and the remaining students are learning only western. Find the probability of a student learning only western, if four students who were learning both classical and western join western dance form only.

A. $\frac{1}{5}$
B. $\frac{7}{30}$
C. $\frac{4}{15}$
D. $\frac{9}{30}$

44. In class X, 40% students are boys and the remaining are girls. The probability of boys participating in a literary activity is 0.45 and the probability of girls participating in a literary activity is 0.5. One student is selected at random. What is the probability that the selected student is participating in a literary activity?

A. 0.18
B. 0.30
C. 0.48
D. 0.62

45. A survey was conducted among 150 parents about the mode of transport of their child to school. Find the probability of choosing a child who walks or uses a bicycle to reach the school?

Transport	Number of Children
Walking	23
Bicycle	35
School Bus	27
Public Transport	12
Private Transport	29
With Parents	24

A. $\frac{29}{75}$
B. $\frac{34}{75}$
C. $\frac{41}{75}$
D. $\frac{46}{75}$

46. Two five-sided dice are numbered 1, 3, 5, 7, 9 and 2, 4, 6, 8, 10, respectively. Find the probability of getting the sum of the numbers to be a prime number?

A. $\frac{1}{2}$ B. $\frac{1}{18}$

C. $\frac{7}{25}$ D. $\frac{18}{25}$

47. There are 15 pens in a box, out of which y are black pens and the rest are blue pens. If 5 more black pens are put together in the box, then the probability of picking a black pen is two times the previous one. What is the value of y?

A. 3 B. 5

C. 6 D. 15

48. ABCD is a square with each side measuring 8 cm. If a point is selected at random inside the circle, find the probability that the chosen point is outside the square.

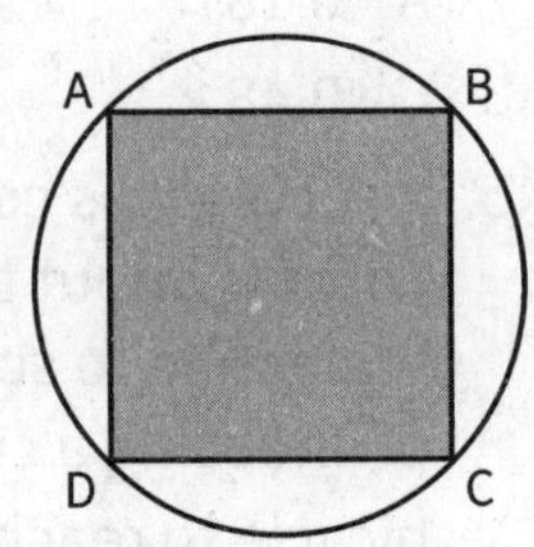

A. $\frac{32\pi-64}{32\pi}$

B. $\frac{64}{32\pi}$

C. $\frac{32\pi}{64}$

D. $\frac{32\pi-64}{32\pi+64}$

49. The graph given below shows the number of students in different sections in a school. What is the probability of choosing a student from the secondary or the senior secondary section?

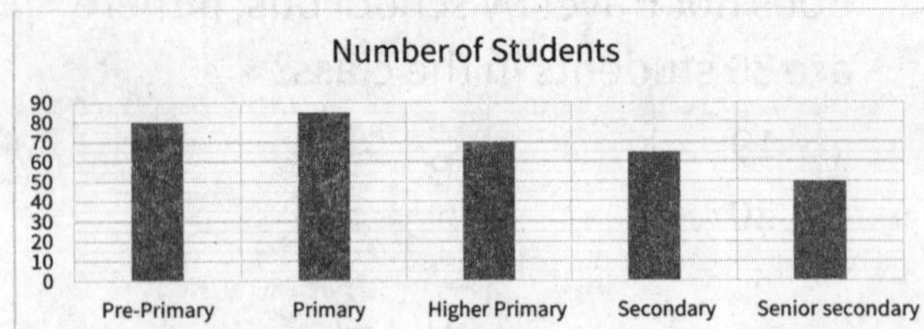

A. $\frac{13}{70}$ B. $\frac{17}{70}$

C. $\frac{23}{70}$ D. $\frac{33}{70}$

50. There are 150 seats left for reservation in an express train. Among the seats, $\frac{1}{3}$ are AC coach tickets, 20 are first class tickets and the leftover are second class tickets. If 5% seats of each are reserved for emergency and other railway employees, what is the probability of getting a second class ticket in the train?

A. $\frac{19}{75}$ B. $\frac{37}{75}$

C. $\frac{38}{75}$ D. $\frac{56}{75}$

PART 2

Subjective type questions

PART 2

CHAPTER 1: Real Numbers

SELF-ASSESSMENT 3

A. Short Answer Type Questions

1. Solve the following.

i. Find the HCF of 1431 and 297 using Euclid's division algorithm.

ii. Find the HCF of 726 and 2532 using Euclid's division algorithm.

iii. Find the HCF of 196 and 2730 using Euclid's division algorithm.

iv. Express 15,246 as the product of prime numbers.

v. Express 36,414 as the product of prime numbers.

2. Answer the following.

i. Find the HCF and LCM of 168, 264 and 840.
   Check whether HCF × LCM = Product of three numbers, or not.

ii. Explain why $(5 \times 7 \times 11 \times 13 + 39)$ is a composite number and is divisible by 13.

iii. Find the value of a, if the HCF of 441 and 1715 is expressed as $441a - 1715$.

iv. Without division, identify whether $\frac{64}{12}$, $\frac{117}{32}$ and $\frac{244}{60}$ have terminating or non-terminating decimal expansion. Find the decimal expansion of the given numbers which has a terminating decimal expansion.

v. Find the decimal expansion of the following.

a. $\frac{75441}{1200}$

b. $\frac{847}{28}$

B. Long Answer Type Questions

1. Answer the following.

i. Using Euclid's division lemma, show that the square of any positive integer is either of the form $4q$ or $4q + 1$ for some integer q.

ii. Using Euclid's division lemma, show that any positive odd integer is of the form $4a + 1$ or $4a + 3$, where a is some integer.

iii. Using Euclid's division lemma, show that the cube of any positive integer is of the form $7x$, $7x + 1$ or $7x + 6$, where x is some integer.

iv. Prove that $5+\sqrt{5}$ is irrational.

v. Prove that $\frac{2}{\sqrt{2}+3}$ is irrational.

2. Solve the following.

i. The traffic lights at three different junctions change every 45 seconds, 80 seconds and 90 seconds. If they change simultaneously at 7:50 a.m., when will they change again simultaneously?

ii. A rectangular courtyard is 31 m 50 cm long and 12 m 60 cm broad. It is to be paved with square tiles of the same size. Find the least possible number of such tiles required.

iii. Find the minimum number of students in a school such that they stand in rows of 12, 42, 36 and form a perfect square.

iv. Mukund is printing blue, green and yellow badges for a school program. He notices that in an A3-sized sheet, only 12 blue badges or 15 green badges or 8 yellow badges can be fitted. If Mukund wants to print exactly the same number of blue, green and yellow badges, what is the minimum number of A3-sized sheets required?

v. What is the greatest number that divides 102, 60 and 46 so as to leave the same remainder in each case?

PART 2

CHAPTER 2: Polynomials

SELF-ASSESSMENT 3

A. Short Answer Type Questions

1. Do as directed.

i. Find the value of the polynomial $4x^3 - 9x^2 - 5x + 12$, if

a. $x = 2$ b. $x = -1$

----

ii. Verify the following.

a. $x = -1$ is a zero of the polynomial $2x^2 - 3x + 1$.

b. $y = \frac{6}{5}$ is a zero of the polynomial $5y^2 - y - 6$.

----

iii. Classify the following polynomials into linear, quadratic and cubic polynomials.

a. $(x+1)(x+2)$ b. $3x^2 - 3x(x+1) + 11$ c. $(x+1)(x^2-1)$

d. $2x^2 + \frac{3}{4}$ e. $7 - 5\sqrt{2x^2}$ f. $\frac{x^4}{x} + 5$

----

iv. Find the zeros and also the polynomial using the graph given below.

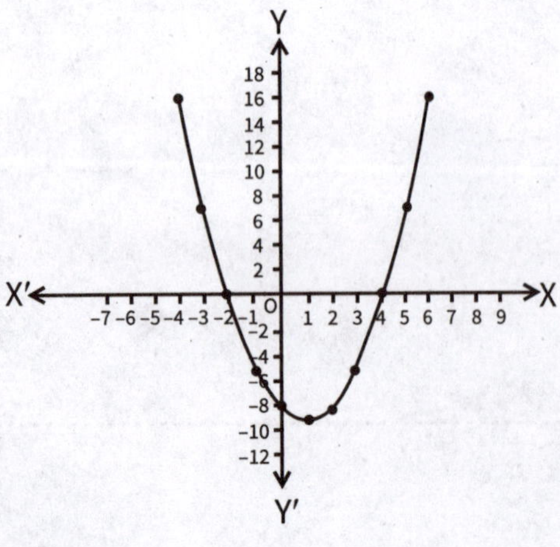

----

v. Write true or false and correct the false statements.

a. If the graph of a polynomial touches *x*-axis at 2 points and *y*-axis at 1 point, then the number of zeros of the polynomial is 3.

b. A polynomial of degree *n* will have more than *n* zeros.

c. The graph of a linear polynomial is a parabola.

d. The degree of the divisor is always less than the degree of the dividend.

---

2. Answer the following.

i. Find the zeros of the following quadratic polynomials.

a. $3x^2 + 7x - 98$ b. $x^2 - x - 56$

---

ii. Find a quadratic polynomial whose sum and product of zeros, respectively, are as given below.

a. $\frac{1}{2}, \frac{-2}{3}$ b. $\sqrt{2}, -5\sqrt{2}$

---

iii. If one zero of the quadratic polynomial $10x^2 - 29x + b$ is the reciprocal of the other, find the value of *b* and the zeros of the polynomial.

---

iv. If α and β are the zeros of the quadratic polynomial $x^2 - 3x - 18$, find the value of the following.

a. $\alpha^2 + \beta^2$ b. $\frac{\alpha}{\beta} + \frac{\beta}{\alpha}$

---

v. If *p* and *q* are the zeros of the polynomial $kx^2 - 9x + 20$ such that $p^2 + q^2 = 41$, find the values of *k*.

B. Long Answer Type Questions

1. Solve the following.

i. Divide $x^3 + 4x^2 - 4x + 7$ by $x + 1$. Write the quotient and the remainder.

ii. Find the zeros of the quadratic polynomial $x^2 - 5x - 24$ and verify the relationship between the zeros and the coefficients.

iii. Find the zeros of the polynomial $x^2 + \frac{13}{6}x + 1$ and verify the relation between the coefficients and the zeros of the polynomial.

iv. Check whether $x^2 - 5$ is a factor of $2x^4 + 5x^3 - 22x^2 - 25x + 60$ or not.

v. If the zeros of the polynomial $x^3 + ax^2 - x - b$ are 1 and 2, find the values of a, b and the value of the third zero.

2. Solve the following.

i. Find the quotient and the remainder when the polynomial $x^3 - 4x^2 + 12x + 16$ is divided by $x + 2$. Verify the division algorithm.

ii. Find all the other zeros of $x^4 + 5x^3 + 4x^2 - 10x - 12$, if two of its zeros are $\sqrt{2}$ and $-\sqrt{2}$.

iii. On dividing the polynomial $x^4 - x^3 + 2x^2 + 5x - 22$ by a polynomial $g(x)$, the quotient and the remainder are $x^2 - x + 6$ and $x + 2$, respectively. Find $g(x)$.

iv. What should be added to $x^4 - 12x^2 + 30$ so that it is exactly divisible by $x+3$?

v. What should be subtracted from $x^4 + x^3 - 5x^2 + x - 2$ so that the resultant polynomial is exactly divisible by $x^2 + 1$?

SELF-ASSESSMENT 3

A. Short Answer Type Questions

1. Solve the following pair of linear equations.

i. $\sqrt{5}y+\sqrt{7}x=0;\ \sqrt{7}y-3\sqrt{5}x=\frac{11}{\sqrt{7}}$

ii. $\frac{2}{5}x+\frac{3}{2}y=6,\ 4x-15y=20$

iii. Solve $6x + 5y = 8$ and $2x + 3y = 12$ and find the value of k for which $x = ky + 2$.

iv. Find out whether the pair of equations $\frac{2}{3}x+\frac{4}{5}y=2$ and $\frac{5}{3}x+2y=5$ is consistent, inconsistent or equivalent by comparing the ratios. If consistent, find the solution.

v. Find out whether the pair of equations $\sqrt{8}x+6y=1$ and $\sqrt{2}x+4y=1$ is consistent or inconsistent by comparing the ratios. If consistent, find the solution.

2. Answer the following.

i. Two lanes of a street are represented by the equations $5x + 15y = 25$ and $2x + 6y = 14$. Represent this situation geometrically. Do the lanes cross each other? If yes, mention the point of intersection.

ii. There are 45 students in a section of class 10 and the number of girls is 15 less than double the number of boys. Find the number of boys and girls in the class geometrically.

iii. Plot the given equations $x + 2y = 3$ and $x + \frac{y}{2} = 3$ on a graph. Also, find the coordinates of the vertices of the triangle formed by these lines and y-axis.

iv. Find the value of t for which the pair of equations $(t - 2)x + 5y = 0$ and $2x + (t + 1)y = 0$ has a unique non-zero solution.

v. Find the value of p for which the pair of equations $(p - 1)x + 16y = 18$ and $4x + (p - 1)y = p$ is inconsistent.

B. **Long Answer Type Questions**

1. **Solve the following pair of linear equations using the method specified.**

i. $4y = 10 + 3x$ and $\frac{5}{7}y = 1 + \frac{x}{7}$ by elimination method

ii. $\frac{15}{x+y} + \frac{28}{x-y} = 7$ and $\frac{20}{x+y} + \frac{63}{x-y} = 13$ by substitution method

iii. $11x + 3y = 333$ and $3x - 5y = 21$ by cross-multiplication method

iv. $\frac{25}{\sqrt{x}}+\frac{15}{\sqrt{y}}=10$ and $\frac{24}{\sqrt{y}}-\frac{15}{\sqrt{x}}=5$ by substitution method

v. $12x+y=5xy$ and $81x-4y=\frac{3}{2}xy$ by substitution method

2. Solve the following word problems.

i. Rishab thinks of a non-zero number which is exactly four times the sum of its digits and three times the product of its digits. Find the number thought by Rishab.

ii. A motorboat can cover 40 km upstream and 90 km downstream in 9 hours and 20 km upstream and 54 km downstream in 5 hours. Find the speed of the boat in still water and the speed of the stream.

iii. Two trains are at two different stations which are 570 km apart. The trains started at the same time at different speeds. They will cross each other in 19 hours when travelling in the same direction and in 3 hours when travelling in the opposite direction. Find the speed of both the trains.

iv. Alkesh travels 320 km to his village partly by bus and partly by cab. He takes 6 hours if he travels 240 km by bus and the remaining by cab. If he travels 120 km by bus and the remaining by cab, he takes 60 minutes longer. Find the speed of the bus and the cab separately.

v. Three women and four girls complete a piece of work in 20 days, whereas 13 women and 24 girls complete the same work in 4 days. Find the number of days required by one woman alone to complete the same work. Also, find the number of days required by one girl alone to complete the same work.

PART 2

CHAPTER 4: Quadratic Equations

SELF-ASSESSMENT 3

A. Short Answer Type Questions

1. Do as directed.

i. Check whether the following are quadratic equations.

a. $(2x+1)(x-1)=5x(x+1)$

b. $x^2-3x=(x-2)^2$

c. $\frac{x}{4}+4=x\left(x-\frac{3}{2}\right)$

d. $(x+1)(x+2)(x+3)=x^3$

ii. Represent the following situations in the form of quadratic equations.

a. The length of a rectangle is 3 cm more than twice its breadth. The area of the rectangle is 119 sq. cm.

b. The product of two consecutive odd numbers is 728.

c. The sum of the ages of Ram and his mother is 45 years. The product of their ages 5 years from now is 546.

d. Two water pipes take $2\frac{2}{5}$ hours to fill a cistern and the larger pipe takes 2 hours less than the smaller one to fill the tank separately.

iii. Find the roots of the following quadratic equations by factorisation.

a. x^2-x-56

b. $2x^2+5x+3$

iv. Find the nature of the roots of the following equations.

a. $x^2-4x+11$

b. $2x^2+3x-\frac{1}{4}$

v. a. Find the value of k for which the equation $kx^2 - 3kx + 9 = 0$ has two equal roots.

b. For what value of k, the equation $x^2 - 16x + k = 0$ has real and distinct roots?

2. Answer the following.

i. Find the roots of the quadratic equation $\frac{1}{x} + \frac{1}{x+2} = \frac{5}{12}$ by factorisation.

ii. Factorise and find the roots of the following equations.

a. $x + \frac{1}{x} = 2$

b. $2\sqrt{2}x^2 - x - 5\sqrt{2} = 0$

iii. Find the roots of the following equations by the method of completing the square.

a. $x^2 + 4x - 15 = 0$

b. $x^2 - 8x + 1 = 0$

iv. Find the roots of the following equations by using the quadratic formula.

a. $2x^2 + 3x - 7 = 0$

b. $x^2 - 5x + 1 = 0$

v. Find the roots of the equation $\frac{1}{x+1} + \frac{1}{x-3} = \frac{1}{8}$ by using the quadratic formula.

B. Long Answer Type Questions

1. Solve the following word problems.

i. The product of two consecutive multiples of 8 is 768. Find these multiples.

ii. Adnan and Nongdren together have 38 marbles. Both of them lost 4 marbles each, and the product of the number of marbles they now have is 224. Find the number of marbles each had in the beginning.

iii. The height of a right-angled triangle is 1 cm less than twice its base. If the hypotenuse is 17 cm, find the other two sides.

iv. Ajay is 8 years older than his brother Anil. Four years ago, the sum of the reciprocals of their ages was $\frac{2}{15}$. Find their present ages.

v. Is it possible to have two square fields in which the length of the larger field is 4 m more than twice that of the smaller field and the difference of their areas is 931 sq. m? If yes, find the length of each field.

2. Answer the following.

i. a. The product of the digits of a two-digit number is 12. When 9 is subtracted from the number, the digits interchange their places. Find the number.

b. A number increased by 8 is equal to 84 times its reciprocal. Find the number.

ii. a. The numerator of a fraction is 3 less than its denominator. If the sum of the fraction and its reciprocal is $2\frac{9}{40}$, find the fraction.

b. A takes 3 days more than B to complete a piece work alone. If they take $3\frac{3}{5}$ days to complete the same work by working together, find the number of days taken by A alone?

iii. a. The speed of a boat in still water is 18 km/h. It can go 40 km upstream and return downstream to the original point in $4\frac{1}{2}$ hours. Find the speed of the stream.

b. If the price of a book is reduced by ₹5, a shopkeeper can buy four more books for ₹600. Find the original price of the book.

iv. a. A plane left 1 hour later than the scheduled time. In order to reach the destination 2500 km away in time, it has to increase its speed by 125 km/h from its usual speed. Find its usual speed.

b. In a bag containing different coloured marbles, $\frac{1}{3}$ of them are red, 4 times the square root of the total number of marbles are green and the remaining 18 are yellow. Find the total number of marbles in the bag.

v. a. Divide 18 in such a way that the product of one-fourth of the larger number and two-thirds of the smaller number is 12. Find the numbers.

b. Is $(x - 0.3)$ a factor of $x^2 - 0.5x + 0.06$? Justify your answer.

PART 2

CHAPTER 5: Arithmetic Progressions

SELF-ASSESSMENT 3

A. Short Answer Type Questions

1. Write the sequence of numbers for the following, and check whether the sequence is an arithmetic progression or not. Justify your answer.

i. Odd numbers between 20 and 30

ii. Prime numbers between 50 and 100

iii. Three-digit numbers which are multiples of both 5 and 7

iv. Factors of 64

v. In a game, the winner gets 30 points and the 1st and 2nd runners-up get consecutively 3 points less than that of winner's points. The 3rd runner-up gets 20 points, and the other players get 18, 15 and 12 points, respectively.

2. Answer the following questions.

i. Find the 15th term and the sum of the first 15 terms, if the first term is -6.8 and the common difference is -3.5.

ii. Find the 20th term and the sum of the first 20 terms, if the first term is $+\frac{1}{5}$ and the common difference is $+\frac{1}{2}$.

----

iii. What is the 6th term from the last term, if an arithmetic progression is multiples of 12 between 50 and 250?

----

iv. What is the 10th term and the sum of the first 10 terms of an arithmetic progression if the terms are of the form $7n - 5$?

----

v. If the 4th term of an arithmetic progression and the 8th term of another arithmetic progression are equal to 2, and their common differences are $\frac{1}{2}$ and $\frac{1}{4}$, find the first terms.

B. Long Answer Type Questions

1. Solve the following.

i. Find the sum of the first 12 terms of an arithmetic progression if the 4th and 9th terms are −15 and −30, respectively.

ii. Find the sum of the first 8 terms, if the sum of the first 16 terms of an arithmetic progression starting at number 1 is 256.

iii. The total height of a staircase is 12 feet. If each step was built at a distance of $\frac{3}{4}$ feet, what is the height of the 6th step from the top?

iv. The given arithmetic progression is $5, 5+\sqrt{6}, 5+2\sqrt{6}, \ldots.$ Find the 18th term and the sum of the first 18 terms.

v. How many terms are there in an arithmetic progression if the first term is 1.25, the common difference is 0.75 and the sum of the terms is 152?

2. Solve the following word problems.

i. Santhosh joined a multinational company for a salary of ₹20,000 per month. He was promised an annual increment of ₹3000 per month.

   a. After how many years will Santhosh get a salary of ₹50,000?

   b. Find the total amount of salary earned by Santhosh in the new company in 5 years.

ii. The monthly fixed rental charges of a telephone connection is ₹500 per month. In this plan, a customer can use 100 minutes of free calls. From the 101st minute, the customer has to pay ₹1.20 per minute.

a. What is the bill amount if a customer uses the phone for 221 minutes in a particular month?

b. If the customer uses 100 minutes in the first month and subsequently increases the talk time by 20 minutes every month, what is the total bill amount paid by the customer for 1 year?

iii. A dance school charges ₹800 in the first month with an increment of ₹50 for the subsequent months.

a. What will be the total amount to be paid in the 9th month?

b. What will be the total fee paid for 2 years?

iv. Akhila started to walk in a park. On the first day, she walked for 20 minutes and gradually increased the walking time by 5 minutes per week.

a. How many weeks does she take to complete an hour's walk?

b. How much time did Akhila dedicate for walking in those many weeks (as obtained in the question above)?

v. A library charges ₹250 as a nominal monthly rent for borrowing books and ₹15 as a penalty for one book per day delay. Kiran paid a total of ₹370 to the library.

a. Find out the number of days delayed by her to return the book.

b. If Kiran pays a penalty of ₹30 in the first month with an increasing penalty of ₹15 in the subsequent months, find the total penalty paid by her for 1 year.

SELF-ASSESSMENT 3

A. Short Answer Type Questions

1. Answer the following.

i. Check if each of the following pairs of triangles are similar or not. If yes, state the similarity criteria.

a.

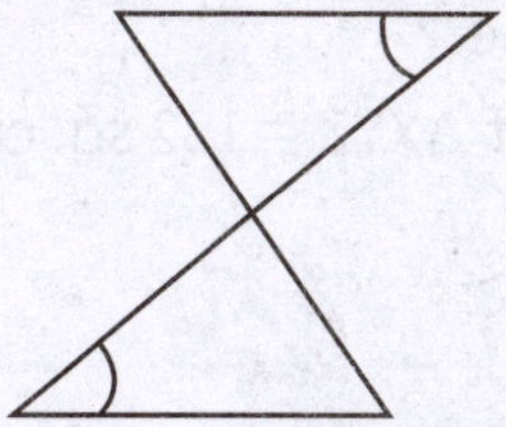

b.

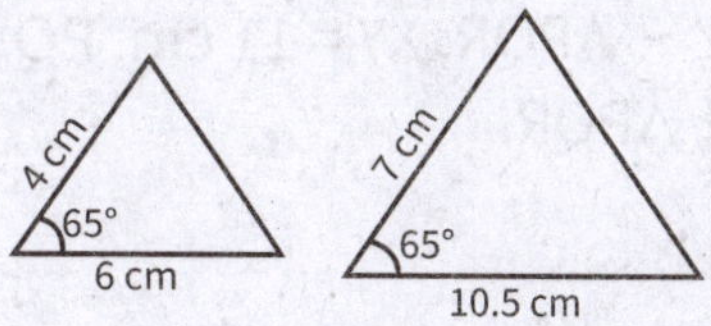

c.

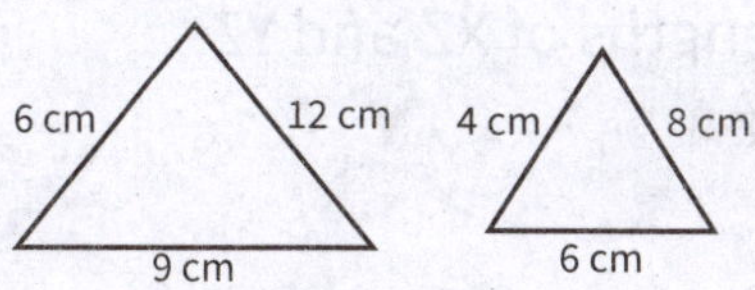

d.

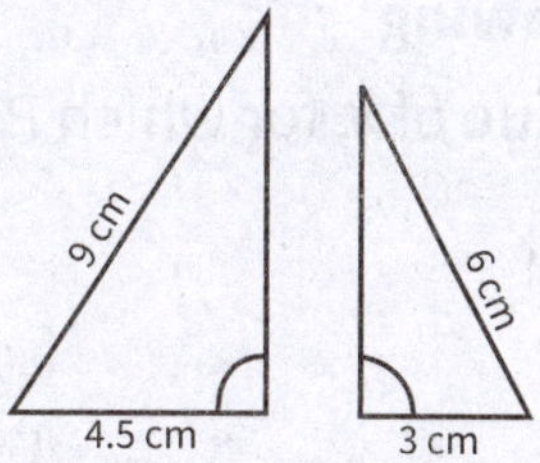

----

ii. a. In triangle ABC, X and Y are the points on AB and AC, respectively, such that XY || BC. If AX = 8.5 cm, BX = 5 cm and YC = 4 cm, find AY.

b. In triangle PQR, S and T are the midpoints of PQ and PR, respectively. If PS = 8 cm, ST = 4.8 cm and PT = 6 cm, find the perimeter of triangle PQR.

----

iii. In triangle XYZ, P and Q are the points on XY and XZ, respectively, such that PQ || YZ. If QX = 4.8 cm, PY = 6.4 cm and 3PQ = YZ, find the lengths of XY and XZ. Is it possible to find the perimeter of triangle PQX? Justify.

----

iv. The lengths of the sides of a few triangles are given below. Determine which of them are right-angled triangles.

a. 5 cm, 12 cm and 13 cm

b. 12 cm, 16 cm and 20 cm

c. 20 cm, 21 cm and 29 cm

d. 8 cm, 15 cm and 19 cm

---

v. a. Areas of two similar triangles are in the ratio 9 : 25. If the altitude of the smaller triangle is 13.5 cm, find the altitude of the bigger triangle.

b. If $\Delta XYZ \sim \Delta PQR$, XY = 11 cm, PQ = 16.5 cm and the area of ΔXYZ = 132 sq. cm, find the area of ΔPQR.

---

2. Solve the following.

i. Find the value of *x*, for which PQ || XY. Also, find the lengths of XZ and YZ.

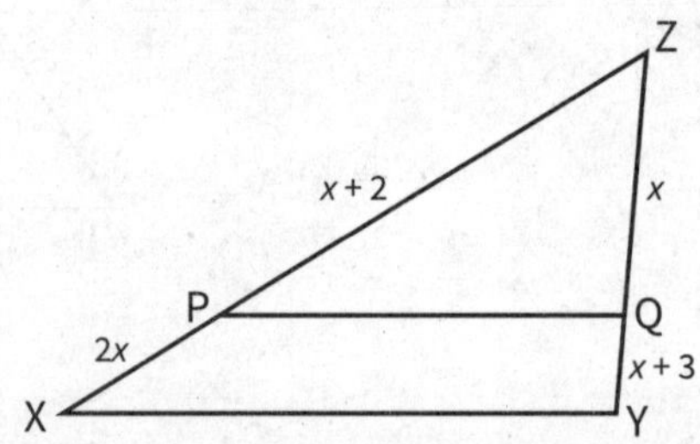

---

ii. Find the measurements of the angles of the ΔAOB.

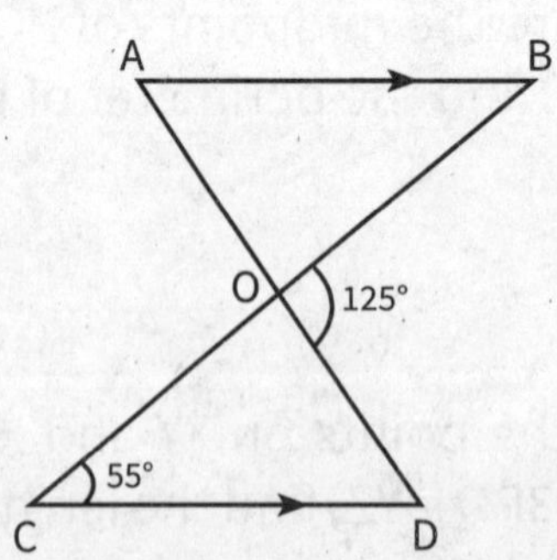

---

iii. Parallel sides are marked in the given figure. Is $\frac{PT}{TU} = \frac{PU}{UQ}$? Justify. If $\angle P = 30°$, $\angle PST = 55°$ and $\angle SUR = 45°$, find the measurements of the other angles of triangle PQR.

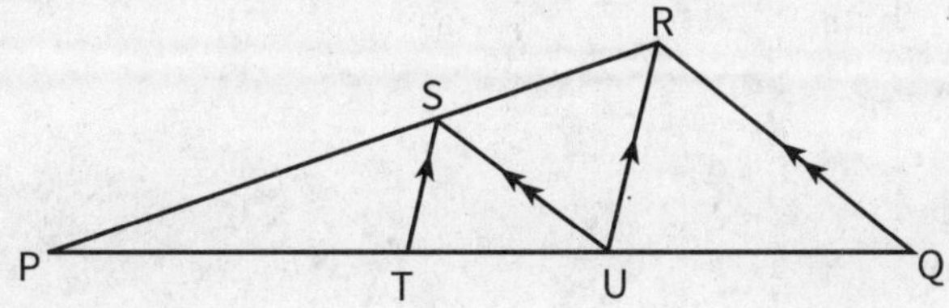

iv. Two vertical poles of height 31 m and 52 m are 20 m apart. Find the distance between their tops.

v. ABC is an isosceles triangle. The unequal base and its corresponding altitude are in the ratio 8 : 3. If the area of the triangle is 300 sq. cm, find the perimeter of the triangle.

B. Long Answer Type Questions

1. Solve the following.

i. A rectangular prism has the width equal to three-fourths its length and has length equal to three-fifths its height. If the internal diagonal of the prism is 75 cm, find its dimension.

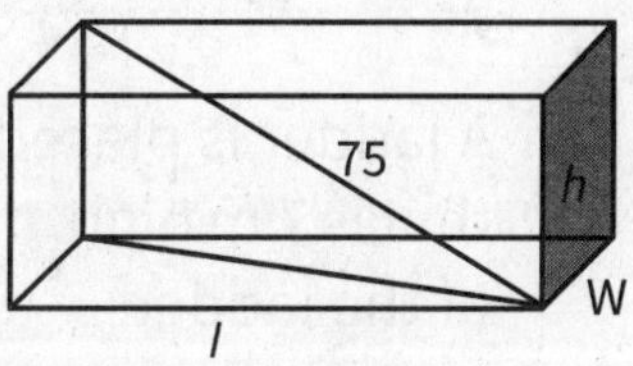

ii. The area of a rhombus is 960 sq. cm. If the diagonals are in the ratio 8 : 15, find the length of the diagonals. Also, find each side of the rhombus.

iii. The diagonal of a square is 32 cm. Find the perimeter and the area of the square. If the length of each side is doubled, what happens to the length of its diagonal? Justify your answer.

iv. A ladder is placed leaning towards a vertical wall such that it reaches the wall at a point that is 7 m high. If the distance of the wall to the foot of the ladder is 24 m, find the length of the ladder.

If the foot of the ladder is moved 4 m towards the wall, then find the distance by which the top of the ladder would slide upwards on the wall.

v. From an airport, two flights A and B leave at the same time towards South and East, respectively. If the speeds of the flights, respectively, are 900 km/h and 1200 km/h, find the distance between them after 3 hours?

After 3 hours, if flight A increases its speed by 200 km/h and flight B by 100 km/h, find the increased distance between them after 3 hours.

2. Prove the following.

i. If a line is drawn parallel to one side of a triangle intersecting the other two sides, then it divides the two sides in the same ratio.

ii. a. ABC is a right-angled triangle, right angled at B. If $BD \perp AC$, prove that $\Delta DAB \sim \Delta DBC$.

b. In the given figure, S and R are the midpoints of OP and OQ, respectively, and SX : XP = 7 : 3.

Prove: A. $\frac{XS}{XP} = \frac{YR}{YQ}$ B. OP : XP = 20 : 3

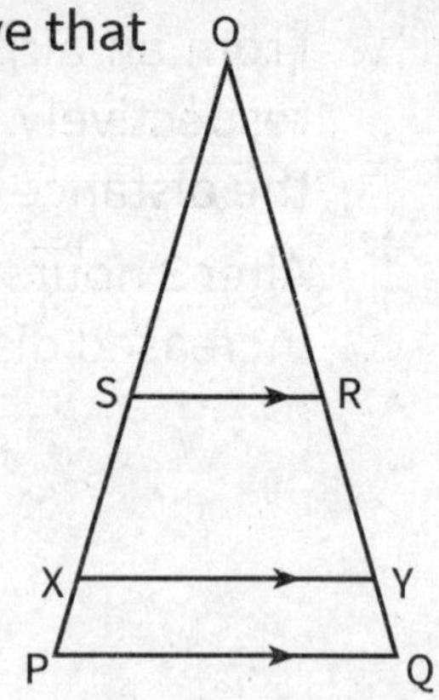

iii. In a right-angled triangle, the square of the hypotenuse is equal to the sum of the squares of the other two sides.

iv. a. In a rectangle PQRS, X is any point on the interior of the rectangle.

Prove that $QX^2 - PX^2 = RX^2 - SX^2$

b. In an equilateral triangle of side a units, prove that its altitude is $\frac{a\sqrt{3}}{2}$ units.

v. ABCD is a trapezium such that AB || CD, and the diagonals AC and BD intersect each other at O.

a. Prove that $\Delta AOB \sim \Delta COD$.

b. If AB = 3CD, prove that $ar(\Delta AOB) : ar(\Delta COD) = 9 : 1$.

c. Is $\Delta AOD \sim \Delta BOC$? Justify your answer.

PART 2

CHAPTER 7: *Coordinate Geometry*

SELF-ASSESSMENT 3

A. Short Answer Type Questions

1. Answer the following.

i. Identify the type of triangle formed by the points X(–3, 6), Y(–6, 10) and Z(2, 18). Find its perimeter.

ii. A circle with centre O(–5, 1) circumscribes a triangle with vertices A(–8, 1), B(x, 4) and C(–2, y). Find the values of x and y.

iii. Find all the possible points on the y–axis which are at a distance of $2\sqrt{34}$ from the point (–6, –3).

iv. Find the ratio in which the point (2, 3) divides the line segment joining the points (–8, –2) and (8, 6).

v. Find the value of x, for which A(–4, 6), B(5, 3) and $C\left(\frac{x+1}{3}, 2\right)$ are collinear.

2. Solve the following.

i. A(6, 1) and B(6, 5) is the diameter of a circle. Find the coordinate of centre of the circle and any two points on it.

ii. Identify the type of quadrilateral formed by joining (–7, –5), (–1, –2), (3, –5) and (–3, –8) in an order. Justify your answer.

iii. Find the value of m such that the midpoint of the line segment joining A(m, 4) and B(7, –12) lies on the line segment $9x - 8y = 14$.

iv. Find the ratio in which the line segment $2x - 5y + 10 = 0$ divides the line segment joining A(–10, –1) and B(8, 5). Also, find the point of intersection.

v. Find the point on x-axis whose distance from (4, –5) and $\left(1, \frac{5}{2}\right)$ is in the ratio 2 : 1.

B. Long Answer Type Questions

1. Answer the following.

i. Find the centroid of the triangle with vertices A(x_1, y_1), B(x_2, y_2) and C(x_3, y_3). Using the above derivation, find the centroid of the triangle PQR with vertices P(2, –6), Q(–7, 5) and R(–4, 4).

ii. Find the coordinates of the points which divide the line segment joining X(–12, –10) and Y(8, 0) into five equal parts.

iii. Find the value of t, for which the points A($2t - 1$, $3t$), B($t + 1$, t) and C($2t$, $t - 3$) are collinear.

iv. Triangle ABC has vertices with coordinates A($x + 5$, y), B(x, $y - 4$) and C($x + 4$, $y + 4$). Show that the area of triangle ABC is constant for any values of x and y.

v. Find the path of the points which are equidistant from the line segment joining the points A(2, −6) and B(10, 2). Also, find the coordinates of the point where the perpendicular bisector of the line segment AB intersects the x-axis and the y-axis.

2. Solve the following.

i. Find the value of n, if the points P(−3, 3), Q(−1, n), R(4, 9) and S(2, 5) form a parallelogram. Also, find the area and the height of the parallelogram, taking PQ as the base.

ii. Find the coordinates of other two vertices of a triangle XYZ with X(−4, 3) and the midpoints of the sides through X being E(−1, 5) and F(2, 4). Also, find the area of triangles XEF and XYZ.

iii. PQRS is a rhombus with vertices P(2, –2), Q(4, 2), R(6, –2) and S(4, –6). E, F, G and H are the midpoints of PQ, QR, RS and SP, respectively. Identify the type of quadrilateral formed by joining E, F, G and H in an order. Justify your answer.

iv. Prove that the triangle formed by joining A (–2, –1), B(–7 , 4) and C(–4, 7) is right angled at B. Also, show that the circle with centre (–3, 3) passes through all the three vertices of triangle ABC.

v. The management team of a stadium decides to install solar light pillars for night practices. They plan to install the lights so that adjacent lights are equidistant. Find the coordinates of all the four lights and the distance between adjacent lights, if the coordinates of the ground are given by A(–8, –2), B (1, 7), C(5, 3) and D(–4, –6).

SELF-ASSESSMENT 3

A. Short Answer Type Questions

1. Evaluate the following.

i. If $\sin A = \frac{5}{13}$, find sec A and cot A.

ii. If $3 \tan A = \sqrt{3} \sec A$, find the value of sin A cos A.

iii. Evaluate: $\frac{\tan 30^\circ}{\operatorname{cosec} 60^\circ + \sec 30^\circ}$

iv. Find the value of $\sin 35^\circ \cos 55^\circ + \sin 55^\circ \cos 35^\circ + \tan 45^\circ \cot 45^\circ$.

v. Find the value of $(1 + \cot^2 \theta)(1 + \cos \theta)(1 - \cos \theta)$.

2. Solve the following.

i. If $\cos A = \frac{20}{29}$, find the values of the other trigonometric ratios.

ii. In a triangle ABC, right angled at B, AB = 24 cm, AC = 25 cm. Find sin A, cos C, tan C and cosec C.

iii. If $\tan A = \frac{1}{2}$, evaluate $\frac{(4+\sin^2 A)}{(4+\cos^2 A)} + \frac{(4-\sin^2 A)}{(4-\cos^2 A)}$.

iv. If $\sin A = \frac{1}{2}$, find the value of $\frac{1}{\cot A} + \frac{1+\cos A}{\sin A} + \frac{2}{\operatorname{cosec} A}$.

v. The measurement of an angle of a rhombus of side 18 cm is 60°. Find the length of the diagonals.

B. Long Answer Type Questions

1. Solve the following.

i. Find the value of x, if

a. $\sin 2x = \sin 60° \sin 30° + \cos 60° \cos 30°$

b. $\tan 3x = \cos 45° \sin 45° + \cos 30° \operatorname{cosec} 30° - \sin 30°$

ii. Find the measurement of A, if

a. $\cos 5A = \sin (A + 18°)$, where 5A is an acute angle.

b. $\cot 5A = \tan 4A$, where 5A and 4A are acute angles.

iii. a. If $\sin \theta + \text{cosec } \theta = 2$, find the value of $\sin^2 \theta + \text{cosec}^2 \theta$.

b. If $\sin \theta + \cos \theta = \sqrt{3}$, find the value of $\sin \theta \cos \theta$.

iv. a. In a right-angled triangle ABC, right angled at B, if $\angle A = 60°$ and AC = 30 cm, find the measurements of the remaining two sides.

b. If a circle is inscribed in an equilateral triangle of side 6 cm, find the radius of the circle.

v. a. Find the value of cot 20 °cot 21° cot 22......cot 68° cot 69° cot 70°.

b. If the angles A, B and C of a right-angled triangle ABC form a decreasing arithmetic progression, find the values of sin A, cos B and tan C.

2. Prove the following.

i. a. $\sqrt{\dfrac{1+\cos A}{1-\cos A}} = \operatorname{cosec} A + \cot A$

b. $\sec^2\theta + \operatorname{cosec}^2\theta = \sec^2\theta \operatorname{cosec}^2\theta$

ii. $\dfrac{2\cos\theta}{1+\cos\theta+\sin\theta} = \dfrac{1-\sin\theta+\cos\theta}{1+\cos\theta}$

iii. a. If $2\operatorname{cosec} A = x$, $\cot A = \frac{1}{2x}$, prove that $x^2 - \frac{1}{x^2} = 4$

b. $\operatorname{cosec} A(1 - \cos A)(\operatorname{cosec} A + \cot A) = 1$

iv. $$\frac{\tan^2 A(\operatorname{cosec} A + 1)}{(1 + \cos A)} - \frac{\operatorname{cosec}^2 A(1 - \cos A)}{(\operatorname{cosec} A - 1)} = 0$$

v. a. $$\frac{\cot\theta - \cos\theta}{\cot\theta + \cos\theta} = \frac{1 - \sin\theta}{1 + \sin\theta}$$

b. $$\frac{\cos^4\theta - \cos^2\theta}{\sin^3\theta - \sin\theta} = \sin\theta$$

SELF-ASSESSMENT 2

A. Short Answer Type Questions

1. Answer the following.

i. The height of a tower is 20 m. What is the length of the shadow of the tower when the sun's altitude is 30°?

ii. The angle of elevation of the top of a building from a point is 60°. What is the angle of elevation from the same point if the height of the building is reduced to its one-third?

iii. A ladder just reaches the top of a vertical wall. The wall is at a distance of 18 m from the foot of the ladder. If the angle of elevation of the ladder with the horizontal is 60°, find the length of the ladder.

iv. Two electric poles of heights 12 m and 8 m, respectively, are connected by an electric wire. If the wire makes an angle of 30° with the horizontal, find the length of the wire.

v. A farmer wants to fence his field which is in the form of a rectangle. If the angle between a diagonal and a side is 30° and the length of the diagonal is 20 m, find the length of the wire required to fence the field.

2. **Solve the following.**

i. The height of a tower is 150 m. The angle of depression of an object from the top of the tower is 60°. Find the distance between the tower and the object. How far should the object be moved so that the angle of depression is changed to 30°?

ii. The angle of depression of an object from the top of a building is 30°. If the height of the building is $60\sqrt{3}$ m, find the distance of the object from the foot of the building. Also, find the angle of depression if the object moves 120 m towards the tower?

iii. Most of the ships use diesel fuel. To reduce diesel consumption, engineers are planning to develop wind power support for ships. Their proposal is to attach kite sails to ships and use the wind's power to help reduce diesel consumption.

In the given diagram, what should be the length of the rope for the kite sail in order to pull the ship at an angle of 60° and be at a vertical height of 240 m?

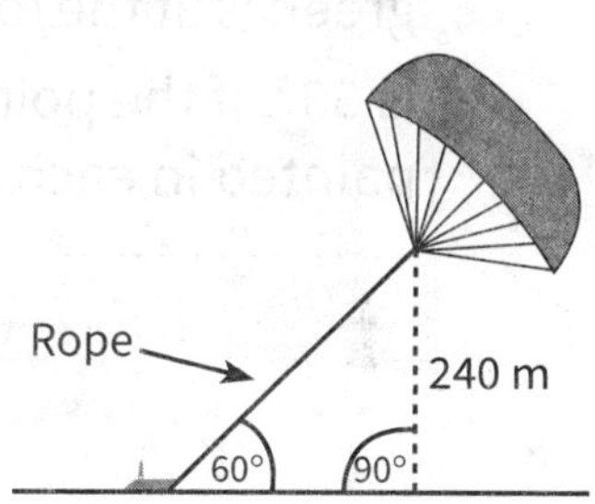

iv. In a circus, a rope is tied from a point on the ground to the top of a vertical pole of height 24 m. If the angle made by the rope with the ground is 30°, find the length of the rope. If the length of the rope available is 40 m, it is tied to a nearer point than the earlier. Find the distance of the point from the pole now.

v. The angles of elevation of the tip of a mountain observed from two consecutive milestones due west are found to be 45° and 60°. Find the height of the mountain. (Take $\sqrt{3} = 1.73$)

B. Long Answer Type Questions

1. Solve the following.

i. From the terrace of a house 12 m high, the angle of elevation and the angle of depression of the top and the bottom of a tower are 30° and 60°, respectively. Find the height of the tower.

ii. A tall vertical pole is painted in two colours, orange and green, in the ratio 1 : 2, where green is at the top. The angle of elevation of the tip of the pole from a point on the ground is 60°. If the point is $21\sqrt{3}$ m away from the pole, find the lengths of the part of the pole painted in each colour.

iii. Two points P and Q are on either side of a 114 m high tower. If the angles of elevation of the tower from the points are 30° and 60°, respectively, find the distance between the points.

iv. Two buildings are 36 m apart. The angle of elevation of the top of the taller building from the top of the shorter building is 30°. If the heights of the buildings are in the ratio 3 : 4, find each of their height.

v. The angle of depression of a car from the top of a vertical tower, which is $120\sqrt{3}$ m high, is 30°. Find the following.

a. The distance between the tower and the car

b. If the car reaches the tower in 24 seconds, find its speed in km/h.

2. Solve the following.

i. The angles of depression of objects A and B from the top of a tower of height h m are complementary. A and B are on the same side of the tower. If the distance from A to the tower is x and the distance from A to B is $3x$, prove that $h = 2x$.

If the height of the tower is 84 m, find the distance of the tower from the objects A and B, respectively.

ii. From the top of a building, the angle of depression of a hen is such that its tangent is $\frac{3}{10}$. The angle of depression of the hen changes in such a way that its tangent is $\frac{4}{5}$ when it moves 175 m towards the building. Find the height of the building. How far is the hen from the building now?

iii. From the top of a $96\sqrt{3}$ m high tower, the angles of depression of the top and the bottom of a building are 30° and 60°, respectively. Find the following.

a. Height of the building

b. Distance between the building and the tower

iv. An aeroplane is flying at a constant height of $4500\sqrt{3}$ m. The angle of elevation of the aeroplane from a point on the ground is 60°. After flying for about 40 seconds, the angle of elevation reduces to 30°. Find the following.

a. Distance travelled in 40 seconds

b. Speed of the aeroplane in km/h

v. The angle of elevation of a cloud from a point *x* m above a lake is 30°, and the angle of depression of the reflection of the cloud in the lake is 60°. If the height of the cloud from the lake is 150 m, find the length of *x* in m.

PART 2

CHAPTER 10: Circles

SELF-ASSESSMENT 3

A. Short Answer Type Questions

1. Find the following.

i. Two concentric circles C_1 and C_2 with centre O have radii 24 cm and 26 cm, respectively. Find the length of the chord of the circle C_2, which is tangent to C_1.

----

ii. In the figure given here, SR and ST are the tangents to the circle with centre O. Find the measure of ∠RTS and ∠RST.

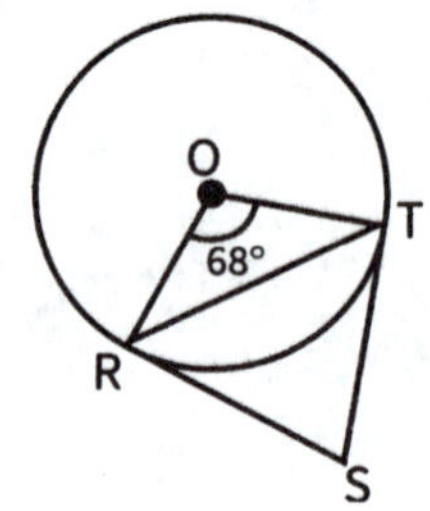

----

iii. In the figure given here, TQ and TR are the tangents to the circle with centre O. Find the measure of ∠QPR.

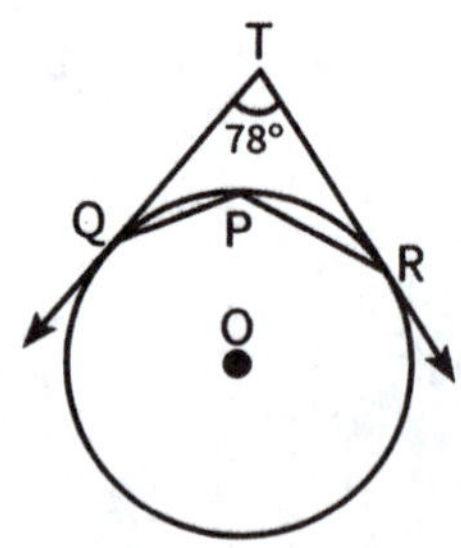

----

iv. In the figure given here, BM and CM are the two chords of the circle with centre O, and AB and CD are the two tangents. Find the value of ∠OBC and ∠BNC if ∠ABM = 17° and ∠DCM = 52°.

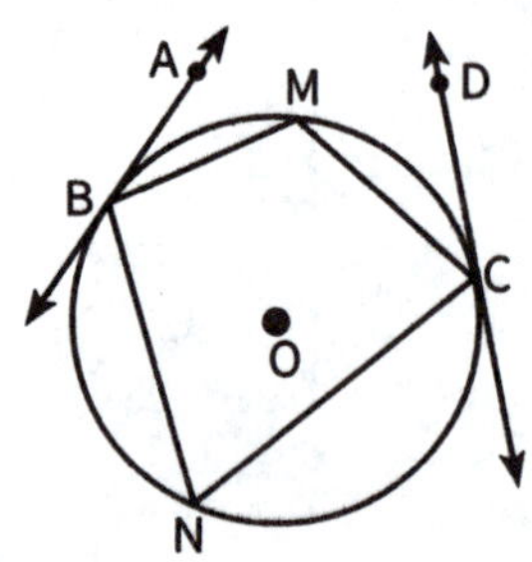

----

v. QP, QR and XY are the tangents to a circle with centre O. Find the length of the tangent QP and the radius of the circle if the perimeter of the triangle QXY is 78 cm and ∠PQR = 60°.

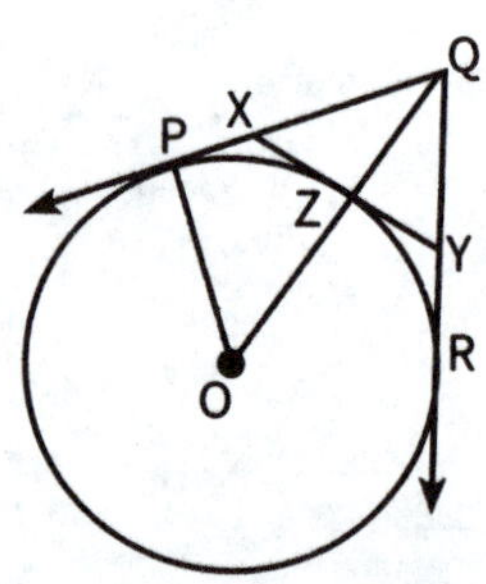

----

2. **Solve the following.**

i. Show that the radius of a circle circumscribed by an isosceles right triangle is given by $a\left(\frac{\sqrt{2}-1}{\sqrt{2}}\right)$, where a is the length of the base of the triangle.

ii. Show that the angle between a chord and a tangent is equal to the angle subtended by the chord in the other segment.

iii. In the figure given here, there are two concentric circles with radii 15 cm and 10 cm. Find the length of XB if the length of XA is 8 cm.

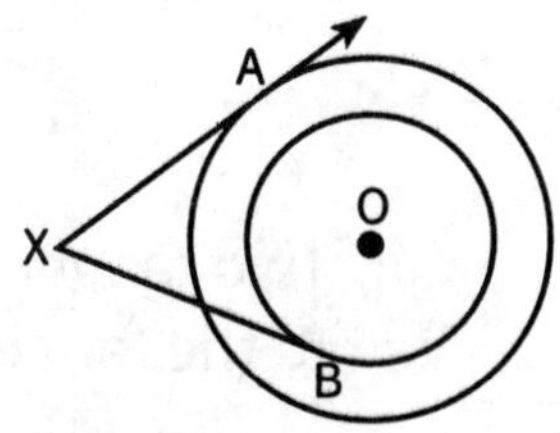

iv. AB and AC are the two tangents to a circle with centre O. Show that ABOC is cyclic.

v. The quadrilateral ABCD is circumscribing a circle with centre O. Show the following.

a. $\angle AOB + \angle COD = \angle BOC + \angle AOD$

b. $\angle AOB$ and $\angle COD$ are supplementary.

B. Long Answer Type Questions

1. **Answer the following.**

i. Given that AX = 6 cm and $\angle AYX = 30°$. Find $\angle XZY$ and the lengths of AY, XZ and the radius of the circle.

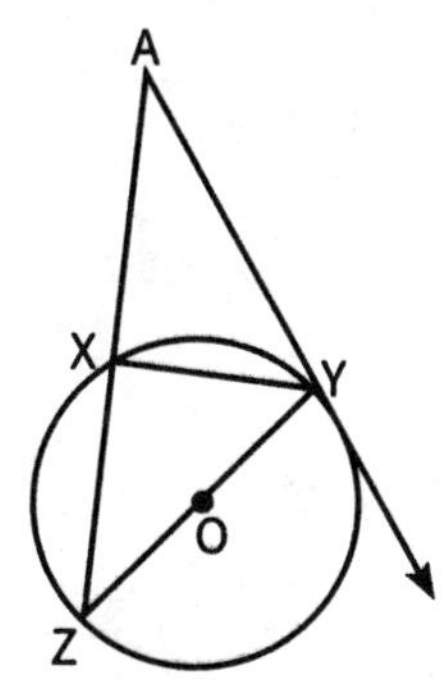

ii. a. MN and MP are the two tangents to a circle with centre O. Show that MNOP is a square if MN ⊥ MP.

b. Prove that a rectangle circumscribing a circle is a square with area $4r^2$, where r is the radius of the circle.

iii. Two tangents AB and AC are drawn to a circle with centre O. A chord CD is drawn parallel to the tangent AB. Show that the triangle CBD is an isosceles triangle and ∠CBD = ∠BAC.

iv. In the figure given here, the centres of the circle are 20 cm apart. Find the length of O′S, OS and PQ.

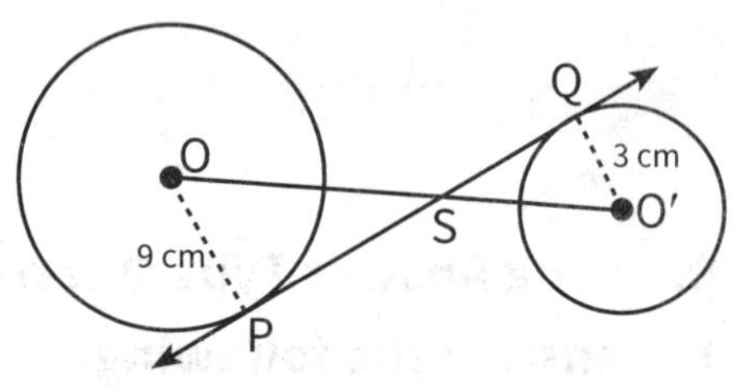

v. In the figure given here, MN is the tangent to the circle with centre O and radius 15 cm. The chord RP when extended meets the point M such that $\angle PMO = 30°$. If the perpendicular distance of the chord from the centre is 9 cm, find the length of PR, MN and MP. (Use $\sqrt{3} = 1.73$)

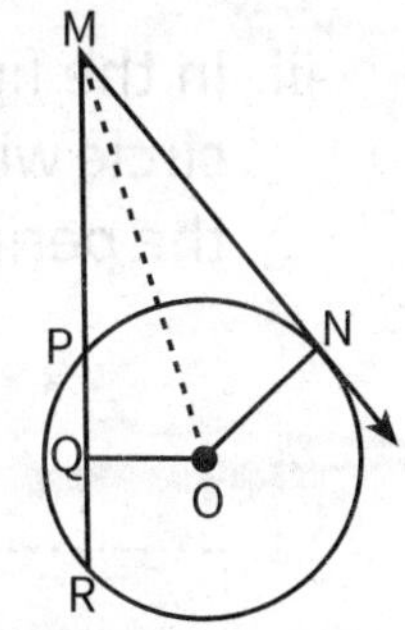

2. Find the following.

i. In the figure given here, XY is the diameter of the circle with centre O. Show that

a. $\angle XOM$ and $\angle NOY$ are complementary.

b. $MN = \sqrt{MX^2 + NY^2 + 2r^2}$, where r is the radius of the circle.

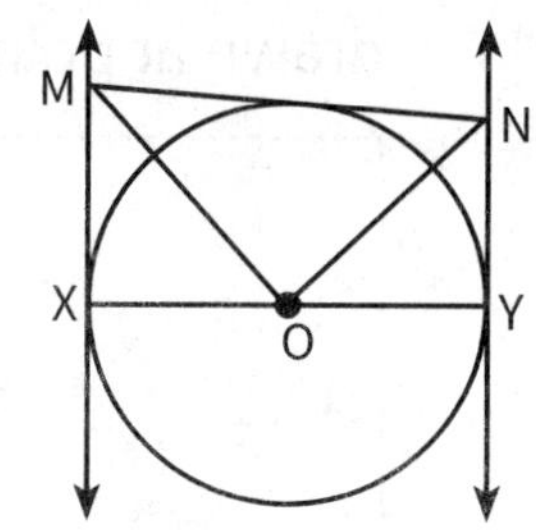

ii. A circle with centre O and radius 2 cm is circumscribed by a triangle XYZ. The perpendicular from the centre intersects the side YZ at a point P such that YP = 4 cm and PZ = 5 cm. Find the area of the triangle XYZ. (*Hint*: Use Heron's formula.)

iii. In the figure given here, two tangents are drawn from a point P to the circle with centre O and radius 6 cm, and the length of OP is 10 cm. Find the perimeter and the area of the triangle PAB.

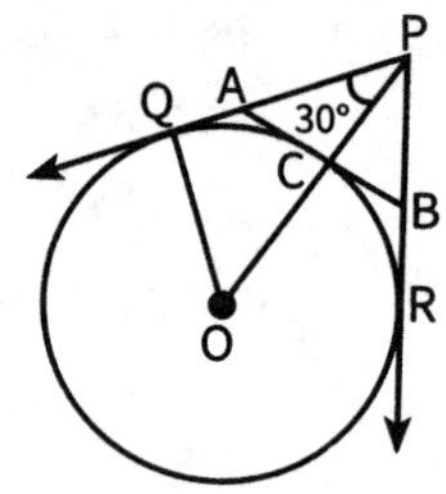

iv. A circle with centre O has a radius of 5 cm and a chord AB of length 6 cm. The tangents drawn at points A and B meet at X. Find the length of OX and AX.

v. XY is the diameter of a circle with centre O. MN is the tangent to the circle from an external point M. XY is extended to meet M. If $\angle NMX = 30°$, show that XN = MN and YN = YM.

SELF-ASSESSMENT 2

A. Short Answer Type Questions

1. Construct the following.

i. Locate the points P and Q which trisect the line segment AB = 5 cm.

ii. Divide the line segment AB = 7 cm in the ratio 4 : 7 internally.

iii. Locate the point M on the line segment XY = 8 cm such that $MY = \frac{3}{11} MX$.

iv. Divide the line segment PQ = 12 cm in the ratio 5 : 9 internally.

v. Locate the point A on the line segment PQ = 8.5 cm such that $PQ = \frac{8}{3} PA$.

2. **Construct the following tangents.**

i. Draw a circle of radius 4.5 cm. From a point 7 cm away from the centre, construct a pair of tangents to the circle. Justify your construction.

ii. Draw a pair of tangents which are inclined at 120° to a circle of diameter 6 cm.

iii. Draw a line segment AB = 9.5 cm. Trisect it such that P and Q are the points of trisection. With Q as centre and the radius equal to PQ, draw a circle. Draw a pair of tangents from the point A.

iv. Draw two concentric circles of radii 4 cm and 7 cm. Draw a pair of tangents from any point on the outer circle to the inner circle.

v. Draw two circles with their centres 10 cm apart and radii as 2 cm and 5 cm. Construct a pair of tangents to each circle from the centre of the other circle.

B. Long Answer Type Questions

1. Do the following constructions.

i. Construct an isosceles right-angled triangle PQR, right angled at Q and PQ = 7 cm. Draw an altitude on PR through Q intersecting it at M. Construct a pair of tangents from P to the circle passing through all the vertices of the triangle QRM.

ii. Construct a ΔXYZ with XY = 8 cm, XZ = 7 cm and $\angle YXZ = 75°$. Then, construct another triangle whose sides are $\frac{2}{5}$ of the corresponding sides of ΔXYZ.

iii. Construct a ΔABC with AB = 4.5 cm, BC = 5 cm and AC = 6.5 cm. Then, construct another triangle $\Delta AB'C'$ similar to ΔABC such that AB′ = 6 cm.

iv. Construct a ΔPQR with $PQ = 7$ cm, $\angle RPQ = 60°$ and $\angle RQP = 45°$. Then, construct another triangle whose sides are $\frac{6}{7}$ of the corresponding sides of ΔPQR.

v. Construct an equilateral triangle ABC whose altitude is 4 cm. Then, construct another triangle whose sides are $\frac{7}{5}$ of the corresponding sides of ΔABC.

2. Construct the following.

i. Construct a ΔABC in which $AB = 2.5$ cm, $\angle A = 30°$ and $AC + AB = 6$ cm. Then, construct another triangle $\Delta AB'C'$ similar to ΔABC such that $AB' = 4.5$ cm.

ii. Construct a square PQRS with the length of each side as 5 cm. Then, draw another square whose sides are $\frac{3}{2}$ of the corresponding sides of the square PQRS.

iii. Construct a ΔXYZ, given that YZ = 4 cm, $\angle XYZ = 45°$ and XY – XZ = 2 cm. Then, construct another triangle whose sides are $\frac{6}{5}$ of the corresponding sides of ΔXYZ.

iv. Construct a rhombus ABCD with the length of its diagonals as 3 cm and 5 cm. Then, construct another rhombus whose sides are $\frac{5}{3}$ of the corresponding sides of the rhombus ABCD.

v. Construct a rectangle MNOP with MN = 7 cm and NO = 4 cm. Draw a circle with MN as the diameter, and then, construct a pair of tangents from the other two vertices to the circle. What can be concluded about the length of both the pair of tangents?

SELF-ASSESSMENT 3

A. Short Answer Type Questions

1. Answer the following.

i. If the circumference of a circle is 220 cm, find its area.

ii. If the sum of the areas of two circular parks of radii 24 m and 32 m is equal to the area of a larger circular park, find the radius of the larger park.

iii. The diameter of each wheel of a car is 16 inches. Find the distance covered (in km), if each wheel makes 980 revolutions.

iv. Find the angle of the sector of a circle of radius 14 cm, if the area of the sector is 123.2 sq. cm.

v. If a pendulum swinging through an angle of 60° sweeps an area of 57.75 sq. cm, find the length of the pendulum.

2. Solve the following.

i. Find the area and arc length of a sector of a circle of radius 21 cm, if the sector angle is 120°.

ii. A chord of length 28 cm is drawn in a circle of radius $14\sqrt{2}$ cm. Find the area of the minor segment to its nearest sq. cm.

iii. If the area of a sector is one-eighth the area of its circle of radius 28 cm, find the angle of the sector and its arc length.

iv. An equilateral triangle of side 42 cm is inscribed in a circle. Find the area of the following.

a. Circle

b. Triangle (Take $\sqrt{3} = 1.73$)

v. A field ABCD is in the form of a square of side 84 m. A semi-circular field with AB as diameter is used to grow onions and the rest is used for growing potatoes. Find the area of the field used for growing the following.

a. Potatoes

b. Onions

B. Long Answer Type Questions

1. Solve the following.

i. A chord of length $14\sqrt{2}$ cm subtends a right angle at the centre. Find the area of the major segment.

ii. A chord of a circle subtends an angle of 2θ at the centre of the circle. If the areas of the minor segment and the major segment cut off by the chord are in the ratio 1 : 5, prove that $\frac{\pi\theta}{60} + \pi = 6 \sin\theta \cos\theta$.

iii. A regular hexagon is inscribed in a circle. If the area of the hexagon is $294\sqrt{3}$ sq. cm, find the radius and area of the circle.

iv. A rectangular field has dimensions 154 m by 98 m. It is surrounded by semicircular grass lawns all around. Find the area of the grass lawns. Find the cost of mowing the lawn at ₹2 per sq. m.

v. A chord of length 10 cm subtends an angle 90° at the centre. Find the areas of the minor and major segments.

2. **Solve the following.**

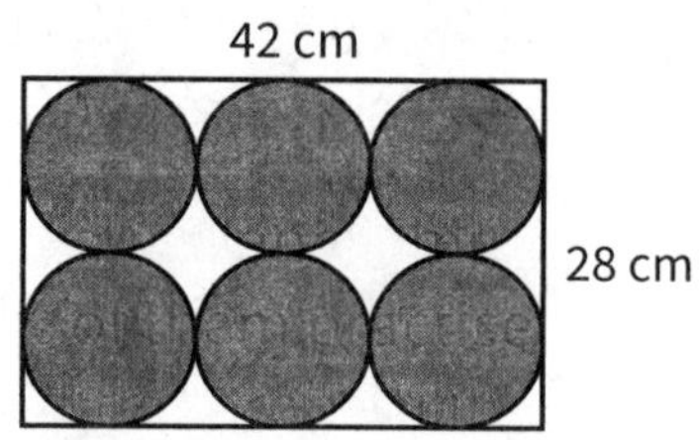

i. Six circles are drawn in a rectangle of dimension 42 cm by 28 cm, as shown in the figure. Find the area of the unshaded figure.

ii. A circle is inscribed in an equilateral triangle of side 24 cm. If a square is inscribed in the circle, as shown in the figure, find the area of the shaded portion.

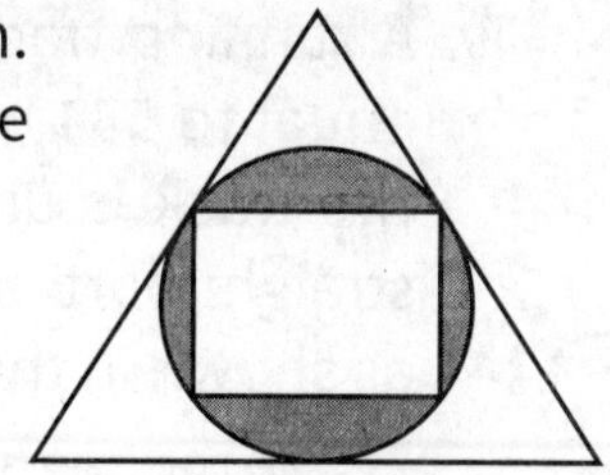

24 cm

iii. A circular dart is divided into three portions of equal areas by drawing concentric circles, as shown in the figure. If the radius of the outer circle is 42 cm, find the radius of the inner circle and the area of each shaded portion.

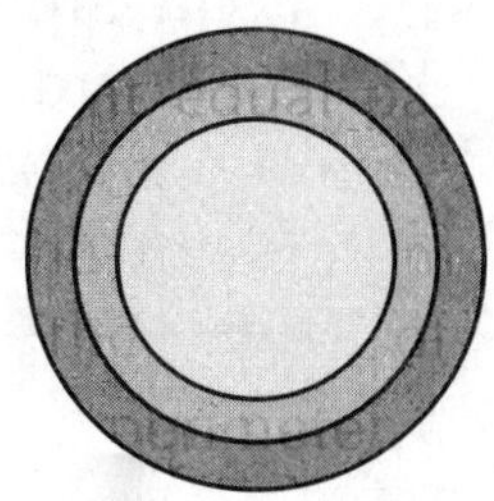

iv. A running track has its outside and inside perimeter equal to 534 m and 446 m, respectively. The width of the track is uniform everywhere. The length of each straight portion is 135 m and the ends are semicircles, as shown in the figure. Find the width of the track.

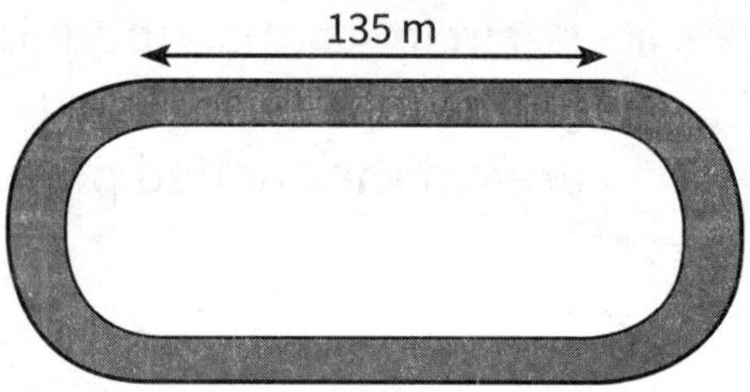

v. From each of the corners of a square-shaped board of side 1 m, a circle of radius 14 cm at the centre and four quadrants of radius 7 cm are shaded. Find the area of the unshaded portion of the board.

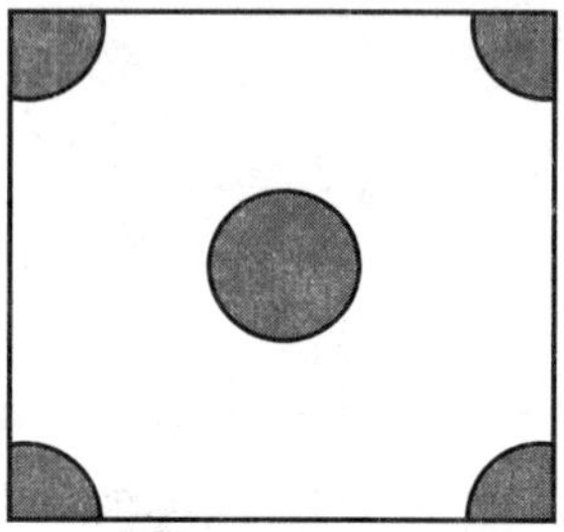

SELF-ASSESSMENT 3

A. Short Answer Type Questions

1. Solve the following.

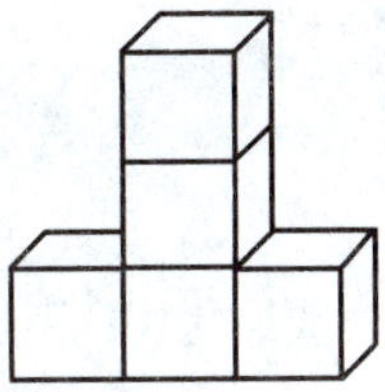

i. Find the total surface area of the given combination of identical cubes with edge measuring 3 cm.

ii. A toy hammer is made by combining two cylinders, as shown here. Find the total surface area of the toy. A cylinder having radius 4 cm and height 10 cm is used as the head, and a cylinder with radius 1 cm and height 18 cm is used as the handle. Find the total surface area of the toy. (Use $\pi = 3.14$)

iii. Find the measurement of cloth required to make a tent, as shown. The height of the cylindrical part, the diameter and the slant height of the conical top measures 3 m, 2 m and 3.5 m, respectively.

iv. Find the total surface area of a hemisphere with diameter 7 cm and the curved surface area of a sphere of the same radius.

v. A cubical wooden block of edge 4 cm has a hemispherical depression of diameter 2 cm at the centre of all the six faces. Find the total surface area of the solid. (Use $\pi = 3.14$)

2. **Answer the following word problems.**

   i. A cylindrical vessel contains a liquid which can be filled into 48 hemispherical bowls with internal diameter 6 cm. Find the height of the cylindrical vessel if its diameter is 12 cm. Also, find the amount of liquid it can hold.

   ii. Find the volume of the sphere in which a cuboid of dimensions 24 cm × 8 cm × 6 cm is inscribed.

   iii. A sphere and cube are melted to form a cone of height *h*. Show that the height of the cone is equal $\left(\frac{3+4\pi}{\pi}\right)r$, if the radius of the sphere and the cone is equal to the edge of the cube.

   iv. Find the curved surface area of a frustum of a cone, if its slant height is 60 cm and the perimeter of its circular ends are 22 cm and 11 cm.

   v. A structure needs to be formed by placing a cone on top of a cubical block of side 8 cm. Find the diameter of the largest possible cone that can be used to make this structure. If the height of the cone is equal to its radius, find the cost of painting the total surface area of the structure at the rate of ₹7 per cm^2.

B. Long Answer Type Questions

1. Solve the following.

i. A solid cone of diameter 14 cm and height 4.5 cm is completely submerged in a cylindrical vessel full of water and having internal radius 8 cm and height 13.3 cm. Find the volume of water displaced out of the cylindrical vessel and the amount of water left in the vessel.

ii. Harinder wants to paint his ladder. The legs of the ladder have the dimensions 2 m × 7 cm × 45 cm. Each step is cylindrical in shape with a diameter 7 cm and length 52 cm. Find the surface area to be painted in a ladder having six steps.

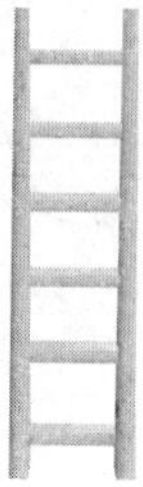

iii. A tank is in the form of a frustum of cone with capacity of 627 litres. Find the height of the tank if the radii of its circular ends are 45 cm and 30 cm.

iv. A right circular cone has the vertex angle of 60° and height 18 cm. A cone of height 9 cm is cut from the top. Find the volume of the cone and the frustum so formed. Also, find the slant height of the frustum.

v. A solid metal cuboid of dimensions 4.2 m × 2.2 m × 1.1 m is melted to form a hollow cylindrical pipe of thickness 7 cm, and the inner diameter of it is 70 cm. Find the length of the pipe.

2. **Answer the following word problems.**

i. Karan has a cylindrical vessel of height 21 cm and radius 6 cm. The vessel is opened at the top and is full of water. He dropped some marbles each of diameter 0.6 cm in the vessel, which makes $\frac{3}{7}$th of the water flow out. How many marbles did Karan put in the vessel?

ii. Mr. Gupta has installed a rain harvesting system in his apartment. The area of the terrace from where the rainwater would be collected is 26,570 m^2. The water would be stored in an underground cuboidal tank with perimeter 280 m. In a week, there was a rainfall of 10 cm. Find the height of the water collected in the tank, if its length and breadth are in the ratio 4 : 3.

iii. A copper candle stand is made by mounting a frustum of cone on another frustum of cone. The height of the top frustum is 9.8 cm and the height of the bottom frustum is 29.4 cm. If the three radii are 9 cm, 3 cm and 6 cm, respectively and the density of copper is 8.96 g per cm^3, find the weight of the candle stand.

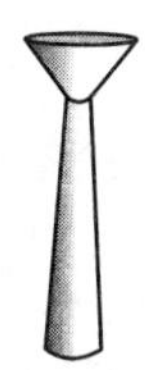

iv. There are two identical cylindrical tanks of height 12 m and radius 4 m. One tank has a circular inlet of radius 1 m, and another tank has a square inlet of side 1 m. Which of the tanks will fill faster if the water flows in at a rate of 320 metre per hour? Also, find the height of water in the second tank after 36 minutes.

v. Nisha is making a terrace garden at her home. She bought 15 pots shaped as the frustum of height 35 cm and radii of two circular ends being 15 cm and 12 cm. The soil bags are available as a 40-kg pack. Find the number of packs required to fill all the pots.
(Use density of soil = 2.6 g per cm^3)

SELF-ASSESSMENT 3

A. Short Answer Type Questions

1. Answer the following.

i. Which are the different methods used to find the arithmetic mean of a grouped data? List the formulae used for each method.

ii. What is the formula used to find the median and the mode of a grouped data? Write the abbreviation used in the formulae.

iii. What is ogive? How is it constructed?

iv. Find the cumulative frequency for the following data.

Class interval	0–5	5–10	10–15	15–20	20–25	25–30
Frequency	3	5	2	7	1	8

v. What is the empirical relationship between the three measures of central tendency?

2. Solve the following.

i. Find the mean for the following data using the assumed mean method and standard deviation method.

Class interval	0–2	2–4	4–6	6–8	8–10	10–12
Frequency	20	35	52	44	38	31

ii. Find the missing value in the given table if the mean for the following data is 15.5.

Class interval	0–5	5–10	10–15	15–20	20–25	25–30	30–35	35–40
Frequency	15	16	x	8	6	8	6	4

iii. Find the median for the following data.

Class interval	400–500	500–600	600–700	700–800	800–900	900–1000
Frequency	10	30	50	25	40	45

iv. Find the value of the missing frequency, if the median of the following data is 23.75 and n is 20.

Class interval	0–10	10–20	20–30	30–40	40–50
Frequency	3	4	p	3	2

v. Find the mode for the following data.

Class interval	0–100	100–200	200–300	300–400	400–500
Frequency	37	85	44	38	11

B. Long Answer Type Questions

1. Answer the following questions.

i. Find the mean, median and mode for the following data.

Class interval	0–10	10–20	20–30	30–40	40–50
Frequency	3	5	9	5	3

ii. Find the missing values and the average in the given table, if the median is 50 and n is 60.

Class interval	25–35	35–45	45–55	55–65	65–75	75–85
Frequency	5	x	20	y	6	2

iii. Find the mean, median and mode for the following data.

Class interval	0–14	14–28	28–42	42–56	56–70
Frequency	7	21	35	11	16

iv. Construct an ogive of the less than type for the following data.

Class interval	45–55	55–65	65–75	75–85	85–95
Frequency	4	11	12	9	4

v. Construct an ogive of the more than type for the following data.

Class interval	10–12	12–14	14–16	16–18
Frequency	8	22	29	5

2. Solve the following word problems.

i. The table given below shows the number of sick leaves taken by different employees in a year. Find the mean, median and mode value for the data.

Sick leaves	0-5	5–10	10–15	15–20	20–25
Number of employees	12	11	10	4	3

ii. The data given below shows the number of correct answers of different number of students in a class. Find the mean, median and mode for the data.

Number of correct answers	0–10	10–20	20–30	30–40	40–50
Number of students	2	8	16	11	3

iii. The table given below shows the number of vehicles sold by different dealers in a month. Find the mean, median and mode for the data.

Dealers	0–20	20–40	40–60	60–80	80–100
Number of vehicles	20	16	24	11	4

iv. The table given below shows the weights of new-born babies. Find the mean, median and mode for the data.

Weights (in kg)	1–2	2–3	3–4	4–5
Number of babies	3	15	6	1

v. The table given below shows the different age group of people infected by a virus during a specific month. Find the median by constructing the ogives.

Age group	0–10	10–20	20–30	30–40	40–50	50–60
Number of people	6	11	21	23	14	5

SELF-ASSESSMENT 3

A. Short Answer Type Questions

1. Write the meaning of each of the following with an example.

i. Certain event

---

ii. Impossible event

---

iii. Elementary event

---

iv. Complementary event

---

v. Experimental and theoretical probability

---

2. Find the probability of each of the following events.

i. Four coins are tossed simultaneously. Find the probability of the following.

a. Getting at least 2 heads

b. Getting only one tail

---

ii. A pair of dice is rolled simultaneously. Find the probability of the following.
   a. Getting a sum of number which is not a multiple of 4
   b. Getting the first number which is half of the second number

iii. A pair of dice with the letters *a*, *b*, *c*, *d*, *e*, *f* and *g*, *h*, *i*, *j*, *k*, *l*, respectively are rolled at a time. Find the probability of the following.
   a. Getting the vowels on both the dice
   b. Getting a vowel on any one die

iv. A card is drawn from a well-shuffled deck of cards. Find the probability of the following.
   a. Not getting a red ace
   b. Getting a spade queen

v. An ace is removed from a well-shuffled deck of cards. If one card is drawn from the remaining number of cards, find the probability of the following.
   a. Getting a card other than ace
   b. Getting a card with a square number

B. **Long Answer Type Questions**

1. **Find the probability for the following events.**

   i. A 2-digit number, at random, is written on a piece of paper. Find the probability of the following.

      a. Writing a number with the same digits

      b. Writing a number that does not have 5 in any place

      c. Writing a number which is divisible by 7

   ii. In a class, 50% students are engaged in sports, 30% are engaged in dance, music and drama, and 10% are artists. Among these talented students, 70% of them practise in the evening, whereas the rest of them practise in the morning. Find the probability of the following.

      a. Choosing a student not engaged in any of the activity

      b. Choosing a student engaged in sports but practices only in the morning

      c. Choosing an artist who spends time for practising in the evening

iii. Dakshayani and Suchitra are best friends who were born in the same year. Find the probability of the following.

   a. They have birthdays in the same month that has less than 30 days.
   b. They have birthdays in the same month that has more than 30 days.
   c. They have birthdays on the same day in a leap year.

iv. Prameela is playing with a spinning wheel, which is divided into eight equal parts numbered from 1 to 8. Find the probability of the following.

   a. An arrow pointing at a composite number
   b. An arrow pointing at the multiple of both 2 and 3
   c. An arrow pointing at a number which is less than the even prime number

v. A coin box contains hundred 5-rupee coins, fifty 10-rupee coins and twenty-five 1-rupee coins. One of the coins falls out when the coin box is turned upside down. Find the probability of the following.

   a. A 1-rupee coin falls out
   b. Other than a 5-rupee coin falls out
   c. Either a 5-rupee coin or a 10-rupee coin falls out

2. Solve the following word problems.

i. There are 54 identical cards in an activity box containing figures of triangles and rectangles of different colours. 34 cards have triangles, out of which nine are red and the remaining are yellow. Out of the cards with rectangles, 11 are yellow-coloured and the rest of the rectangles are red-coloured. Find the probability of the following.

   a. Picking a card with rectangles
   b. Picking a yellow-coloured card
   c. Picking a card with yellow-coloured triangles
   d. Picking a card with red-coloured rectangles

ii. In a paying guest house, the parking space for 30 bikes and 20 cars is reserved for the people staying in the guest house. Apart from this, space for 10 bikes and 5 cars are available for visitors. If required, they can park three bikes instead of one car in the visitors' parking space.

a. If 7 people staying at the guest house have already parked their cars, what is the probability of the next person at the guest house getting the parking space for his car?

b. If 4 bikes and 3 cars are already parked in visitors' place, find the probability of a new visitor getting a place to park his two wheeler.

iii. There are black, blue and brown marbles in a jar. The probability of selecting a black marble is $\frac{1}{2}$ and the probability of selecting a blue marble is $\frac{1}{4}$. Find the total number of marbles, if there are 20 brown marbles in the jar.

iv. Megha draws the circles as given below.

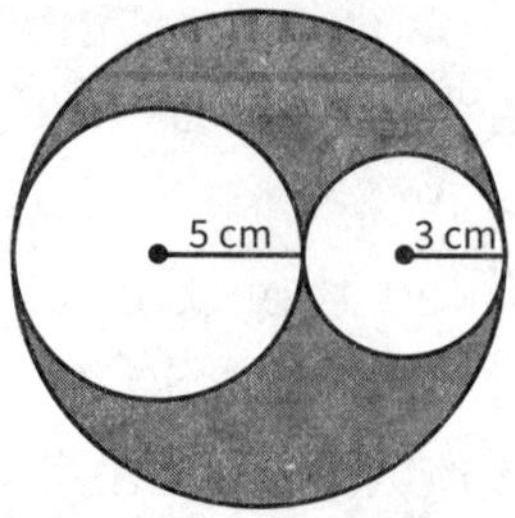

Find the probability of the following.

a. Choosing a point on the shaded part of the circles

b. Choosing a point on the unshaded part of the circles

v. There are pink, maroon and red-coloured thread rolls in a box in the ratio 3 : 5 : 2, respectively. A fresh pack of box contains 50 thread rolls. The shopkeeper has already sold 4 pink, 10 maroon and 7 red thread rolls. If the shopkeeper picks up one thread roll at random, find the probability of the following.

a. A pink-coloured roll is picked

b. A maroon-coloured roll is picked

c. A red-coloured roll is picked

GENERAL TIPS

Use visual aids for quick revision

Graphical representations of concepts stay longer in memory.

Relate to real-life applications

For better understanding of a concept, find its example in real life where it can be applied.

Time-bound study

Daily practice should be time based to keep a check on speed.

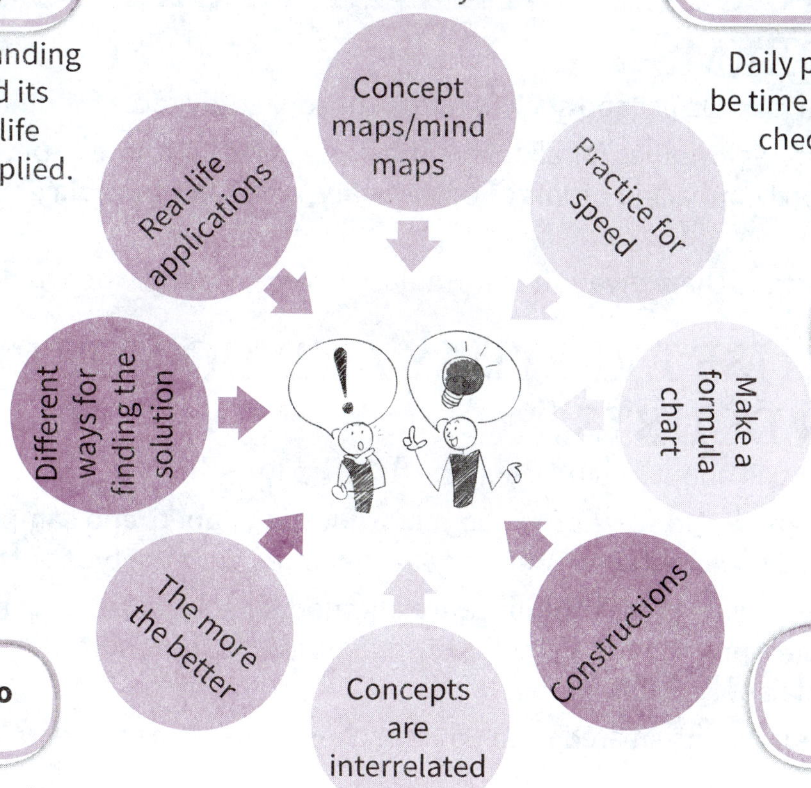

Explore different methodologies

To find the best solution, explore all the methods of solving.

Revise! Recall! Repeat!

Maintain a formula chart or handbook and revise it frequently.

Practice more to excel

Learn from your mistakes and use elaborated question bank for more practice.

Know the logic behind constructions

Justify the constructions.

Study in proper order

New concepts are based on prior knowledge.

QUICK TIPS

1. BE FAMILIAR WITH THE EXAM PATTERN

- Know the weightage for each chapter.
- Know the board exam pattern such as the number of questions of the different types like very short, short and long answer, etc.
- A tip: solve all the simple and easy questions first; number the questions properly and leave space for each question you skip to attempt them later.

2. LIST ALL THE IMPORTANT FORMULAS AND THEOREMS

- Make a formula list and stick it in front of your study table for quick revision.
- Remember formulas for all relevant topics such as arithmetic progression; Euclid's Division Lemma and proofs of irrationality; quadratic formula derivation and its application and so on.
- Understand the derivation of formulas; it comes handy when in doubt.

3. PRACTISE EVERYDAY AND DO NOT CARRY YOUR DOUBTS

- Maths is all about practice. So, practise it daily.
- Set the time and solve previous years' question papers and sample papers published by CBSE for speed check and to get acquainted with the types of questions.
- Be careful with cross-multiplication method for solving a pair of linear equations in two variables; practise the formulas of statistics, as redoing sums takes a lot of time if the formula applied gets wrong.
- Get your doubts cleared from your teachers or peers, try to learn from your mistakes.

4. MAINTAIN SPEED AND ACCURACY

- Be accurate while doing quick calculations. Be careful with the signs and extra careful while copying a question.
- Use some tricks to remember trigonometric ratios and the values of specific angles; memorize the theorems on triangles and related concepts.

5. MENTAL CALCULATION IS A BOOSTER

- Simple calculations can be done mentally but make sure you do not skip any important step while answering.

SOLUTIONS

Prior Knowledge Test

Chapter 1	Chapter 2	Chapter 3	Chapter 4	Chapter 5
1. A	1. B	1. D	1. B	1. C
2. B	2. B	2. B	2. A	2. B
3. C	3. C	3. C	3. C	3. B
4. D	4. D	4. C	4. D	4. A
5. A	5. A	5. D	5. D	5. D

Chapter 6	Chapter 7	Chapter 8	Chapter 9	Chapter 10
1. A	1. A	1. B	1. C	1. B
2. C	2. C	2. B	2. B	2. C
3. B	3. B	3. D	3. D	3. B
4. C	4. C	4. A	4. A	4. D
5. D	5. A	5. C	5. A	5. C

Chapter 11	Chapter 12	Chapter 13	Chapter 14	Chapter 15
1. C	1. C	1. A	1. B	1. C
2. D	2. D	2. C	2. C	2. A
3. B	3. D	3. D	3. C	3. B
4. D	4. A	4. B	4. D	4. C
5. A	5. B	5. B	5. A	5. C

Part 1

Chapter 1		Chapter 2		Chapter 3		Chapter 4	
SA 1	SA 2	SA 1	SA 2	SA 1	SA 2	SA 1	SA 2
1. C	26. B	1. B	26. B	1. C	26. B	1. C	26. D
2. D	27. C	2. C	27. A	2. B	27. B	2. B	27. D
3. B	28. D	3. D	28. D	3. D	28. A	3. C	28. C
4. B	29. B	4. C	29. A	4. B	29. B	4. B	29. B
5. D	30. A	5. C	30. D	5. B	30. D	5. C	30. C
6. C	31. B	6. B	31. D	6. C	31. B	6. C	31. B
7. A	32. B	7. B	32. A	7. B	32. C	7. D	32. B
8. C	33. B	8. B	33. B	8. D	33. D	8. D	33. C
9. A	34. A	9. A	34. D	9. B	34. C	9. D	34. B
10. A	35. A	10. C	35. B	10. B	35. D	10. C	35. A
11. C	36. B	11. D	36. B	11. C	36. B	11. C	36. C
12. C	37. A	12. D	37. C	12. B	37. C	12. D	37. B
13. C	38. C	13. C	38. C	13. A	38. C	13. C	38. C
14. C	39. A	14. B	39. B	14. C	39. B	14. D	39. C
15. B	40. A	15. C	40. C	15. D	40. A	15. D	40. A
16. D	41. C	16. A	41. A	16. D	41. C	16. D	41. C

Chapter 1		Chapter 2		Chapter 3		Chapter 4	
SA 1	**SA 2**	**SA 1**	**SA 2**	**SA 1**	**SA 2**	**SA 1**	**SA 2**
17. D	42. B	17. D	42. C	17. C	42. B	17. B	42. D
18. D	43. B	18. A	43. C	18. C	43. D	18. C	43. C
19. B	44. D	19. A	44. B	19. A	44. C	19. C	44. A
20. A	45. B	20. B	45. A	20. A	45. B	20. C	45. C
21. D	46. B	21. A	46. B	21. A	46. C	21. B	46. D
22. D	47. D	22. C	47. D	22. B	47. B	22. C	47. B
23. C	48. B	23. B	48. C	23. B	48. A	23. D	48. A
24. A	49. A	24. D	49. A	24. D	49. C	24. A	49. B
25. B	50. A	25. A	50. A	25. B	50. D	25. A	50. C

Chapter 5		Chapter 6		Chapter 7		Chapter 8	
SA 1	**SA 2**	**SA 1**	**SA 2**	**SA 1**	**SA 2**	**SA 1**	**SA 2**
1. A	26. C	1. D	26. B	1. C	26. D	1. A	26. A
2. C	27. A	2. D	27. C	2. A	27. B	2. B	27. B
3. B	28. C	3. C	28. B	3. D	28. C	3. B	28. C
4. A	29. B	4. A	29. D	4. C	29. C	4. C	29. B
5. B	30. C	5. C	30. B	5. B	30. B	5. D	30. A
6. A	31. D	6. D	31. D	6. A	31. A	6. D	31. D
7. C	32. B	7. A	32. B	7. C	32. C	7. B	32. C
8. A	33. B	8. A	33. D	8. A	33. A	8. B	33. B
9. C	34. D	9. A	34. D	9. D	34. C	9. B	34. C
10. B	35. D	10. D	35. C	10. A	35. B	10. B	35. D
11. D	36. A	11. C	36. B	11. C	36. D	11. B	36. B
12. D	37. C	12. C	37. D	12. C	37. A	12. B	37. C
13. D	38. D	13. C	38. C	13. D	38. B	13. B	38. D
14. B	39. A	14. D	39. B	14. B	39. B	14. A	39. B
15. C	40. A	15. D	40. C	15. B	40. A	15. D	40. A
16. C	41. A	16. A	41. D	16. A	41. A	16. C	41. A
17. A	42. D	17. C	42. B	17. C	42. A	17. D	42. B
18. D	43. C	18. B	43. B	18. B	43. D	18. D	43. D
19. B	44. B	19. B	44. D	19. A	44. D	19. B	44. A
20. C	45. A	20. D	45. D	20. B	45. B	20. A	45. A
21. D	46. A	21. B	46. C	21. B	46. C	21. B	46. C
22. B	47. C	22. C	47. C	22. C	47. B	22. C	47. C
23. A	48. C	23. C	48. B	23. A	48. A	23. B	48. D
24. C	49. C	24. A	49. D	24. C	49. A	24. A	49. B
25. A	50. C	25. A	50. C	25. A	50. A	25. B	50. D

Chapter 9	Chapter 10		Chapter 11	Chapter 12	
SA 1	**SA 1**	**SA 2**	**SA 1**	**SA 1**	**SA 2**
1. C	1. A	26. C	1. C	1. C	26. A
2. B	2. C	27. A	2. C	2. B	27. A
3. C	3. C	28. C	3. B	3. A	28. B
4. D	4. C	29. B	4. D	4. C	29. B
5. B	5. C	30. A	5. D	5. D	30. C
6. C	6. B	31. C	6. D	6. D	31. A
7. D	7. C	32. B	7. B	7. C	32. D

Chapter 9	Chapter 10		Chapter 11	Chapter 12	
SA 1	SA 1	SA 2	SA 1	SA 1	SA 2
8. B	8. C	33. B	8. C	8. A	33. D
9. C	9. C	34. A	9. C	9. C	34. B
10. A	10. B	35. D	10. B	10. D	35. A
11. C	11. A	36. C	11. D	11. C	36. A
12. B	12. A	37. C	12. C	12. A	37. D
13. A	13. C	38. B	13. D	13. B	38. C
14. C	14. B	39. B	14. A	14. B	39. B
15. C	15. A	40. D	15. D	15. A	40. C
16. C	16. C	41. D	16. C	16. C	41. B
17. B	17. B	42. C	17. A	17. B	42. C
18. C	18. C	43. B	18. C	18. C	43. A
19. B	19. A	44. D	19. B	19. B	44. D
20. B	20. B	45. A	20. A	20. D	45. B
21. A	21. A	46. C	21. A	21. D	46. A
22. B	22. D	47. C	22. B	22. C	47. B
23. C	23. A	48. B	23. C	23. C	48. C
24. B	24. C	49. A	24. D	24. C	49. B
25. C	25. B	50. C	25. B	25. A	50. A

Chapter 13		Chapter 14		Chapter 15	
SA 1	SA 2	SA 1	SA 2	SA 1	SA 2
1. D	26. B	1. C	26. B	1. C	26. B
2. B	27. D	2. C	27. D	2. A	27. B
3. B	28. A	3. A	28. B	3. A	28. A
4. A	29. A	4. C	29. C	4. C	29. D
5. A	30. B	5. D	30. B	5. D	30. D
6. C	31. B	6. B	31. B	6. D	31. B
7. D	32. C	7. D	32. D	7. C	32. B
8. C	33. A	8. D	33. D	8. C	33. C
9. B	34. D	9. B	34. A	9. C	34. D
10. A	35. B	10. B	35. C	10. B	35. B
11. A	36. A	11. C	36. D	11. D	36. B
12. C	37. C	12. C	37. B	12. B	37. A
13. B	38. B	13. A	38. B	13. A	38. C
14. C	39. A	14. C	39. C	14. D	39. A
15. C	40. B	15. B	40. B	15. D	40. B
16. A	41. C	16. B	41. C	16. A	41. A
17. C	42. B	17. B	42. B	17. D	42. D
18. D	43. C	18. D	43. B	18. C	43. C
19. B	44. A	19. B	44. C	19. C	44. C
20. A	45. B	20. D	45. B	20. C	45. A
21. D	46. D	21. A	46. D	21. D	46. D
22. A	47. D	22. C	47. C	22. A	47. A
23. C	48. D	23. B	48. D	23. A	48. A
24. A	49. C	24. D	49. A	24. B	49. C
25. C	50. B	25. A	50. B	25. D	50. C

Part 2

Chapter 1

A. 1. i. 27 ii. 6 iii. 14

iv. $2 \times 3^2 \times 7 \times 11^2$ v. $2 \times 3^2 \times 7 \times 17^2$

2. i. HCF = 24 and LCM = 9240

ii. $5 \times 7 \times 11 \times 13 + 39 = 13\,(5 \times 7 \times 11 + 3) = 13 \times 388$. Since it has more than two factors, it is a composite number. One of the factors is 13; hence, it is divisible by 13.

iii. $a = 4$

iv. $\frac{64}{12}$ and $\frac{244}{60}$ do not have a terminating decimal expansion.

$\frac{117}{32}$ has a terminating decimal expansion, which is

$\frac{117}{32} = 3.65625$.

v. a. 62.8675 b. 30.25

B. 1. i. *Hint*: $a = 4q + r$

ii. *Hint*: $p = 4q + r$

iii. *Hint*: $a = 7q + r$

iv. *Hint*: Prove by contradiction

v. *Hint*: Prove by contradiction

2. i. 8:02 a.m. ii. 10 tiles iii. 1764

iv. 33 sheets v. 14

Chapter 2

A. 1. i. a. –2 b. 4

ii. a. No b. Yes

iii. a. Quadratic b. Quadratic c. Cubic

d. Quadratic e. Linear f. Cubic

iv. –2 and 4; $x^2 - 2x - 8$

v. a. False b. False c. False d. True

2. i. a. $\frac{14}{3}, -7$ b. –7, 8

ii. a. $x^2 - \frac{1}{2}x - \frac{2}{3}$ b. $x^2 - \sqrt{2}\,x - 5\sqrt{2}$

iii. $b = 10$, zeros: $\frac{5}{2}, \frac{2}{5}$

iv. a. 45 b. $\frac{-15}{6}$

v. $1, \frac{-81}{41}$

B. 1. i. Quotient: $x^2 + 3x - 7$; Remainder: 14

ii. –3, 8 iii. $x = \frac{-3}{2}; \frac{-2}{3}$

iv. Yes v. $a = -2$, $b = -2$; third zero is –1

2. i. Quotient: $x^2 - 6x + 24$; Remainder: –32

ii. –2, –3 iii. $x^2 - 4$ iv. –3 v. 4

Chapter 3

A. 1. i. $x = -\frac{\sqrt{5}}{2\sqrt{7}}, y = \frac{1}{2}$

ii. $x = 10, y = \frac{4}{3}$

iii. $x = \frac{-9}{2}, y = 7, k = \frac{-13}{14}$

iv. Equivalent; has infinitely many common solutions

v. Consistent; $x = \frac{-1}{\sqrt{2}}, y = \frac{1}{2}$

2. i. No, the lanes are parallel to each other.

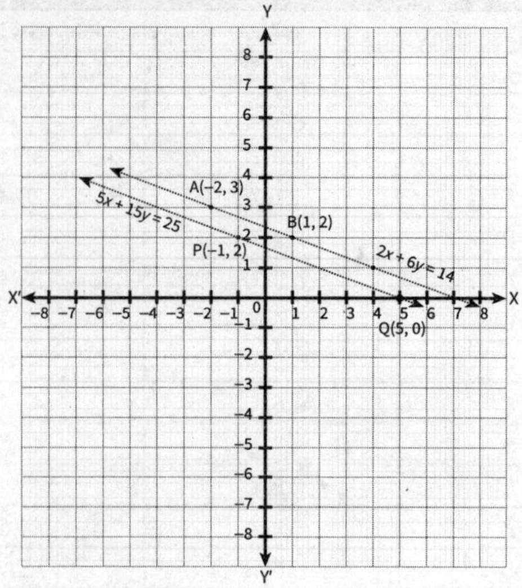

ii. There are 20 boys and 25 girls.

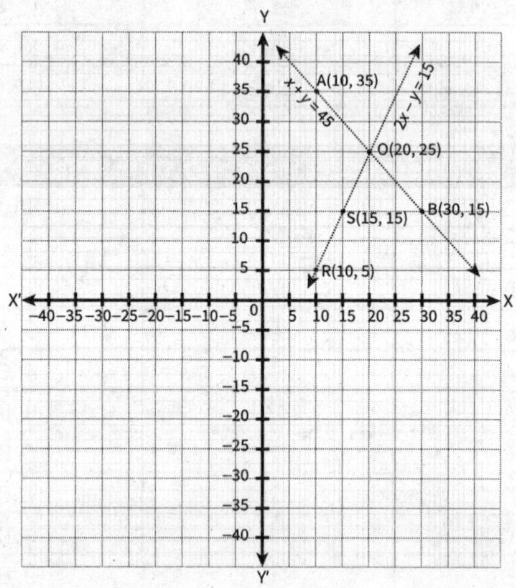

iii.

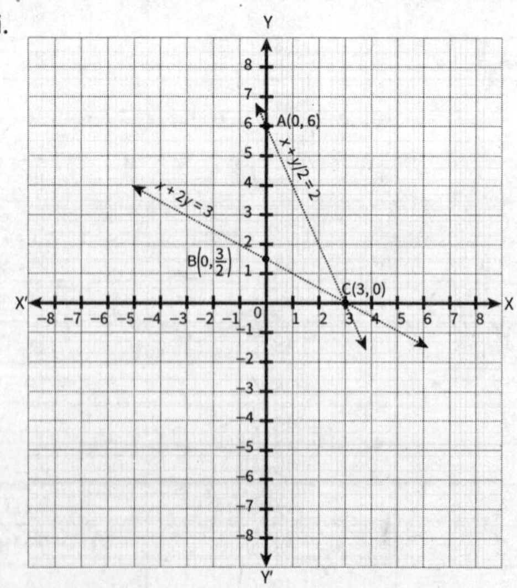

iv. $t = 4$ and $t = -3$ v. $p = -7$

B. 1. i. $x = -2, y = 1$ ii. $x = 6, y = -1$

iii. $x = 27, y = 12$ iv. $x = 25, y = 9$

v. $x = \frac{1}{3}, y = 6$

2. i. 24

ii. Speed of the boat = 14 km/h, speed of the stream = 4 km/h

iii. Speed of the trains = 110 km/h and 80 km/h

iv. Speed of the bus = 60 km/h, speed of the cab = 40 km/h

v. One woman can do the work in 100 days and one girl can do the same work in 200 days.

Chapter 4

A. 1. i. a. Yes; it is a quadratic equation.

b. No; it is not a quadratic equation.

c. Yes; it is a quadratic equation.

d. Yes, it is a quadratic equation.

ii. a. $2x^2 + 3x - 119 = 0$

b. $x^2 + 2x - 728 = 0$

c. $x^2 - 45x + 296 = 0$

d. $5x^2 - 14x - 24 = 0$ or $5x^2 - 34x + 24 = 0$

iii. a. $x = -7$ and 8 b. $x = -\frac{3}{2}$ and -1

iv. a. $D = b^2 - 4ac = [(-4)^2 - 4 \times 1 \times 11] = 16 - 44 = -28 < 0$.

Hence, the given quadratic equation has no real roots.

b. $D = b^2 - 4ac = \left[(3)^2 - 4 \times 2 \times -\frac{1}{4}\right] = 9 + 2 = 11 > 0$.

Hence, the given quadratic equation has real and distinct roots.

v. a. $k = 4$ b. $k < 64$

2. i. $4, \frac{-6}{5}$

ii. a. 1 b. $-\sqrt{2}, \frac{5}{2\sqrt{2}}$

iii. a. $-2 \pm \sqrt{19}$ b. $4 \pm \sqrt{15}$

iv. a. $\frac{-3 \pm \sqrt{65}}{4}$ b. $\frac{5 \pm \sqrt{21}}{2}$

v. $9 \pm 2\sqrt{17}$

B. 1. i. $x = 24$ and 32

ii. $x = 18$ and 20

iii. 8 cm and 15 cm

iv. Anil's age: 16 years, Ajay's age: 24 years

v. Yes; Length of the smaller field = 15 m, Length of the larger field = 34 m

2. i. a. 43 b. $x = 6$

ii. a. $\frac{5}{8}$ b. 9 days

iii. a. 2 km/h b. ₹30

iv. a. 500 km/h b. 81

v. a. 12 and 6 b. Yes

Chapter 5

A. 1. i. The sequence of odd numbers between 20 and 30 is 21, 23, 25, 27, 29.

It is AP as the common difference is 2.

ii. The sequence of numbers is 53, 59, 61, 67, 71, 73, 79, 83, 89, 97.

This is not AP since the difference between any two consecutive terms is not the same.

For example, 59 – 53 = 6 and 61 – 59 = 2

iii. The sequence of numbers is 105, 140, 175, 210, 245, 280, 315, 350, …, 980.

It is AP as the common difference is 35.

iv. The sequence of numbers is 1, 2, 4, 8, 16, 32, 64.

This is not AP since the difference between any two consecutive terms is not the same.

For example, 2 – 1 = 1 and 4 – 2 = 2

v. 30, 27, 24, 20, 18, 15, 12

This is not AP since the difference between any two consecutive terms is not the same.

For example, 27 – 30 = –3 and 20 – 24 = –4

2. i. 15th term = –55.8, S = –469.5

ii. 20th term = 9.7, S = 99

iii. 6th term from the last is 180

iv. $7n - 5$; AP is 2, 9, 16, 23

10th term = 65, S = 335

v. $a_1 = \frac{1}{2}$ and $a_2 = \frac{1}{4}$

B. 1. i. $d = -3$, S = –270

ii. S = 64

iii. $8\frac{1}{4}$ feet

iv. 18th term = $5 + 17\sqrt{6}$; S = $90 + 153\sqrt{6}$

v. 19 terms

2. i. a. 11 years b. ₹15,60,000

ii. a. ₹500 + ₹145.2 = ₹645.2 b. ₹7584

iii. a. ₹1200 b. ₹33,000

iv. a. 9 weeks b. 6 hours

v. a. 8 days b. ₹1350

Chapter 6

A. 1. i. a. Yes, by AA criterion b. Yes, by SAS criterion

c. Yes, by SSS criterion d. No

ii. a. 6.8 cm b. 37.6 cm

iii. 9.6 cm, 14.4 cm; No, PQ or YZ is not given

iv. a. Yes b. Yes c. Yes d. No

v. a. 22.5 cm b. 297 sq. cm

2. i. 6 cm; 20 cm, 15 cm ii. $\angle A = 70°, \angle B = 55°, \angle AOB = 55°$

iii. Yes, $\angle R = 100°, \angle Q = 50°$ iv. 29 m v. 90 cm

B. 1. i. Length = 36 cm, width = 27 cm, height = 60 cm

ii. 32 cm, 60 cm; 34 cm

iii. $64\sqrt{2}$ cm, 512 sq. cm; Length of the diagonal also doubles

iv. 25 m, 8 m v. 4500 km, $15000\sqrt{41}$ km

2. ii. a. *Hint*: Prove ΔABC ~ ΔADB and ΔABC ~ ΔBDC and compare.

b. *Hint*: Use basic proportionality theorem to prove the given ratio.

iv. a. *Hint*: Draw a line AB passing through X, such that AB || PQ || SR.

b. *Hint*: Use Pythagoras theorem to find the altitude in terms of '*a*'.

v. No, two angles are not given equal.

Chapter 7

A. 1. i. Scalene triangle is formed.

Perimeter = $18 + 8\sqrt{2}$ units

ii. $x = -5, y = 1$

iii. $y = -13$ or 7

The possible points are (0, 7) and (0, –13).

iv. Required ratio = $\frac{5}{3} : 1 = 5 : 3$

v. $x = 23$

2. i. Coordinates of centre are (6, 3)

Sample answers: Other points on the circle are (4, 3), (8, 3)

ii. ABCD is a parallelogram as the opposite sides are equal.

iii. $m = -11$

iv. 5 : 1; (5, 4)

v. (2, 0) and (–2, 0)

B. 1. i. Coordinates of centroid of a triangle PQR =

$\left(\frac{x_1 + x_2 + x_3}{3}, \frac{y_1 + y_2 + y_3}{3}\right)$

PQR = (–3, 1)

ii. P(–8, –8), Q(–4, –6), R(0, –4), S(4, –2)

iii. $t = -2$ and $t = \frac{3}{2}$

iv. The lengths of the sides of the triangle ABC are independent of the values of *x* and *y*.

Hence, the area of ΔABC will also be the same.

v. $x + y = 4$

Point of intersection on *x*-axis is (4, 0) and that on *y*-axis is (0, 4).

2. i. $n = 7$; area = 16 square units; height = $\frac{16}{\sqrt{20}}$ units

ii. Y(2, 7) and Z(8, 5); Area of triangle XEF = 4.5 sq. units; Area of triangle XYZ = 18 sq. units

iii. Since the opposite sides are equal, diagonals are equal and bisect each other; hence EFGH is a rectangle.

iv. *Hint*: Find the radii AP, BP and CP and show that they are equal. Hence, the circle with centre P(–3, 3) passes through all the three vertices of triangle ABC.

v. (–6, –4), $\left(\frac{-7}{2}, \frac{5}{2}\right)$, (3, 5), $\left(\frac{1}{2}, \frac{-3}{2}\right)$; $\sqrt{48.5}$ units

Chapter 8

A. 1. i. Sec A = $\frac{13}{12}$, Cot A = $\frac{12}{5}$ ii. $\frac{\sqrt{2}}{3}$ iii. $\frac{1}{4}$ iv. 2 v. 1

2. i. sin A = $\frac{21}{29}$, tan A = $\frac{21}{20}$, cosec A = $\frac{29}{21}$, cot A = $\frac{20}{21}$, sec A = $\frac{29}{20}$

ii. sin A = $\frac{7}{25}$, cos C = $\frac{7}{25}$, tan C = $\frac{24}{7}$, cosec C = $\frac{24}{24}$

iii. $\frac{33}{16}$ iv. $\frac{(4 + 3\sqrt{3})}{\sqrt{3}}$ v. 18 cm, $18\sqrt{3}$ cm

B. 1. i. a. 30° b. 20° ii. a. 12° b. 10°

iii. a. 2 b. 1 iv. a. 15 and $15\sqrt{3}$ b. 3.464

v. a. 1 b. 1, $\frac{1}{2}$ and $\frac{1}{\sqrt{3}}$

2. i. a. *Hint*: Rationalize the expression. Multiply both numerator and denominator by $\sqrt{1 + \cos A}$.

b. *Hint*: Convert sec θ into cos θ and cosec θ into sin θ.

ii. *Hint*: Rationalize the denominator. Multiply both numerator and denominator by (1 + cos θ – sin θ).

iii. a. *Hint*: Use the algebraic identity, $(a + b)(a - b) = a^2 - b^2$.

b. *Hint*: Use the trigonometric identity, $\text{cosec}^2 A - \cot^2 A = 1$

iv. *Hint*: Rationalize the denominator of each term and simplify.

v. a. *Hint*: Use the trigonometric relation for cot θ.

b. *Hint*: Take HCF common in both numerator and denominator.

Chapter 9

A. 1. i. $20\sqrt{3}$ m ii. 30°

iii. 36 m iv. 8 m

v. $20 + 20\sqrt{3}$ m

2. i. $50\sqrt{3}$ m, $100\sqrt{3}$ m ii. 180 m, 60°

iii. $\frac{480}{\sqrt{3}}$ m iv. 48 m, 32 m

v. 2.38 miles

B. 1. i. 16 m ii. 21 m and 42 m

iii. $\frac{456}{\sqrt{3}}$ m iv. $36\sqrt{3}$ m, $48\sqrt{3}$ m

v. a. 360 m b. 15 m/s or 54 km/h

2. i. Use tan θ relation, 42 m, 168 m

ii. 84 m, 105 m iii. $64\sqrt{3}$ m, 96 m

iv. 9000 m, 810 km/h v. 75 m

Chapter 10

A. 1. i. 20 cm

ii. ∠RTS = 34°, ∠RST =112°

iii. ∠QPR = 129°

iv. ∠OBC = 21°, ∠BNC =111°

v. QP = 39 cm, radius = $13\sqrt{3}$ cm

2. i. *Hint*: Area of ΔABC = sum of areas of ΔAOB, ΔBOC, ΔCOA

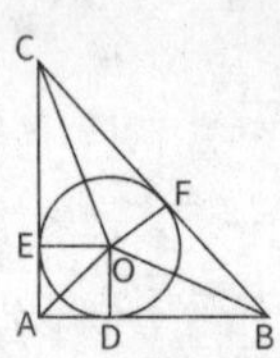

ii. *Hint*: Radius ⊥ tangent

iii. $3\sqrt{21}$ cm

iv. *Hint*: The opposite angles of a cyclic quadrilateral are supplementary.

v. *Hint*: Tangents drawn from an external point of a circle subtend equal angles at the centre.

B. 1. i. ∠XZY = 30°, AY = 12 cm, XZ = 18 cm, Radius = $6\sqrt{3}$ cm

ii. a. *Hint*: Radius ⊥ tangent

b. *Hint*: A rectangle with equal sides is a square.

iii. *Hint*: Use properties of parallel lines and angle sum property.

iv. O'S = 5 cm, OS = 15 cm and PQ = 16 cm

v. PR = 24 cm, MN = $3\sqrt{11}$ cm, MP = 3.57 cm

2. i. *Hint*: Radius ⊥ tangent

ii. 22.5 cm^2

iii. Perimeter = 16 cm, Area = $\frac{16}{\sqrt{3}}$ cm^2

iv. OX = 6.25 cm, AX = 3.75 cm

v. *Hint*: Radius ⊥ tangent

Chapter 11

A. 1. i.

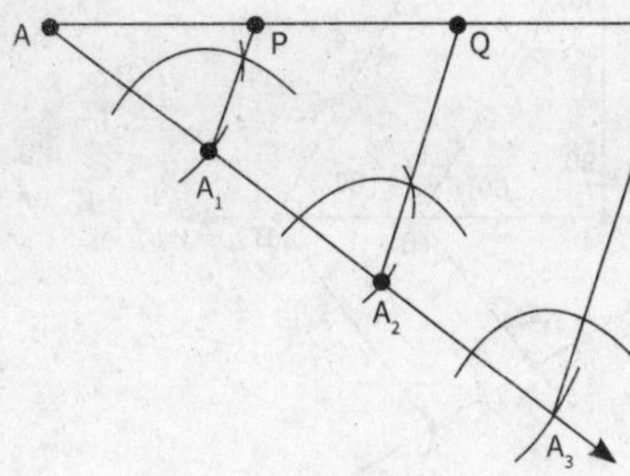

ii.

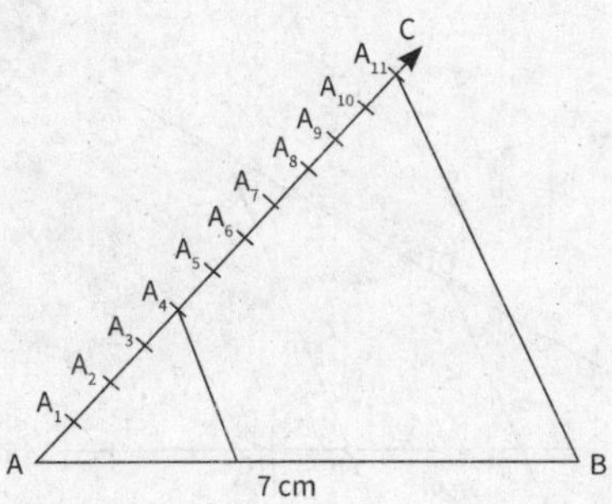

iii.

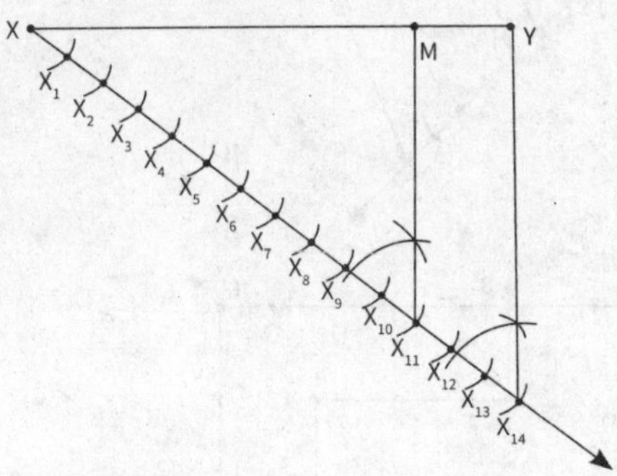

iv.

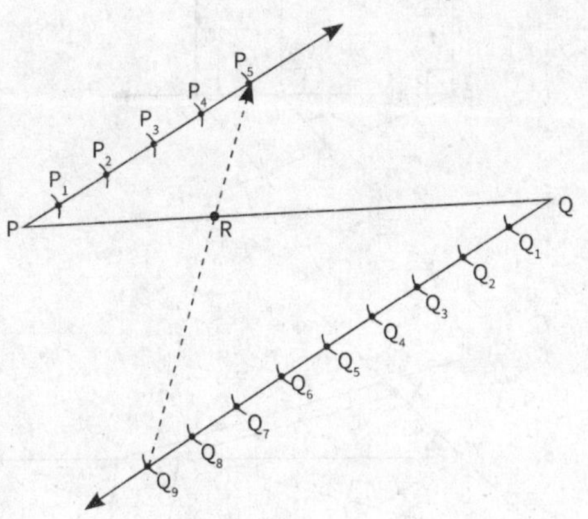

v.

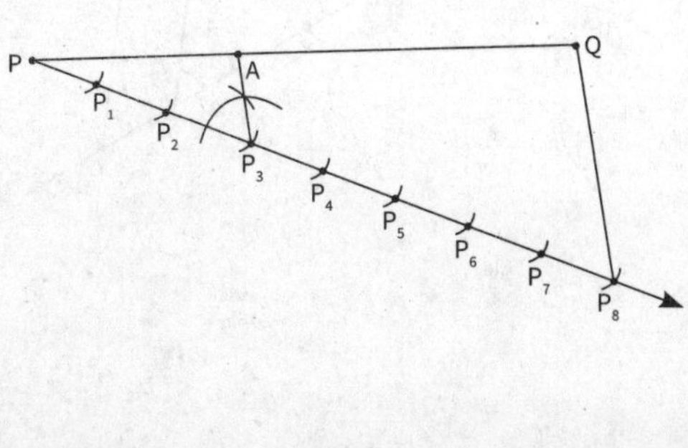

2. i.

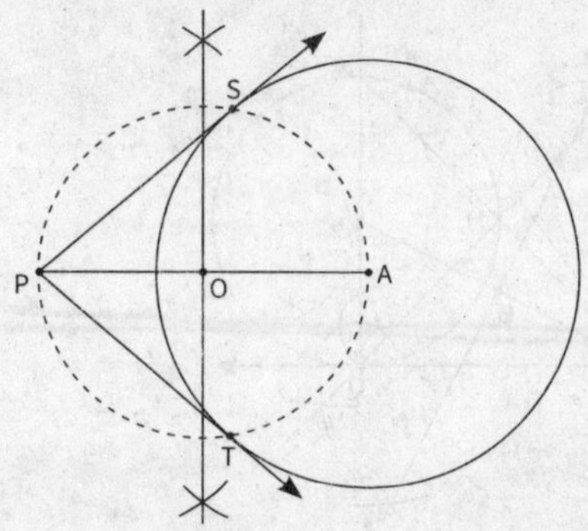

ii.

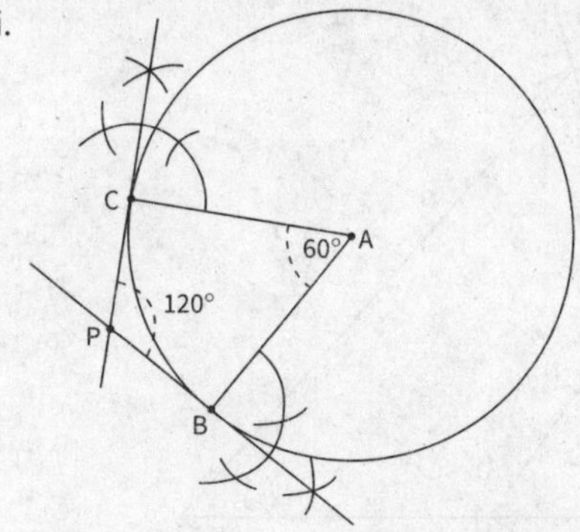

iii.

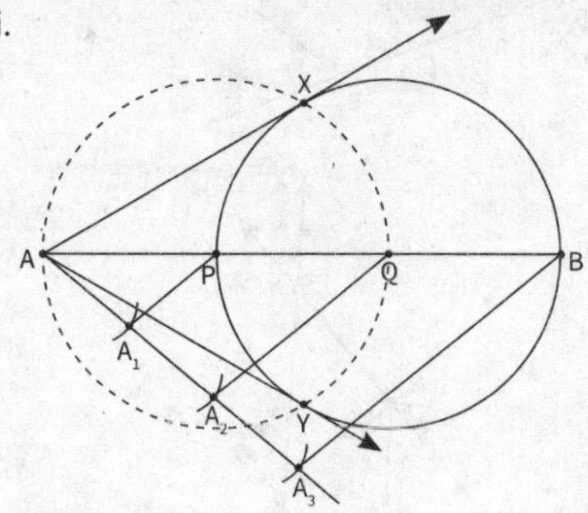

iv.

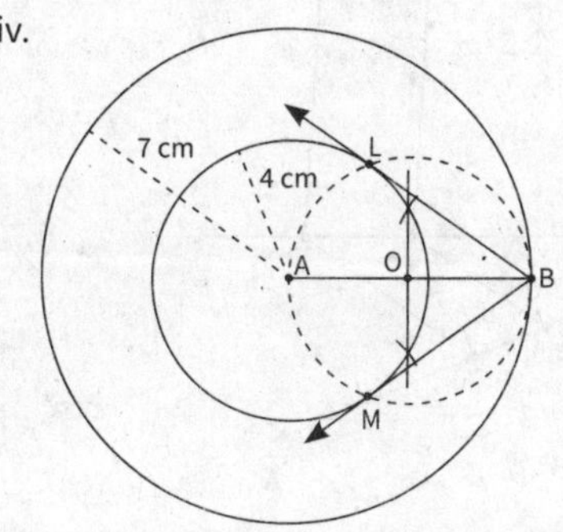

v.

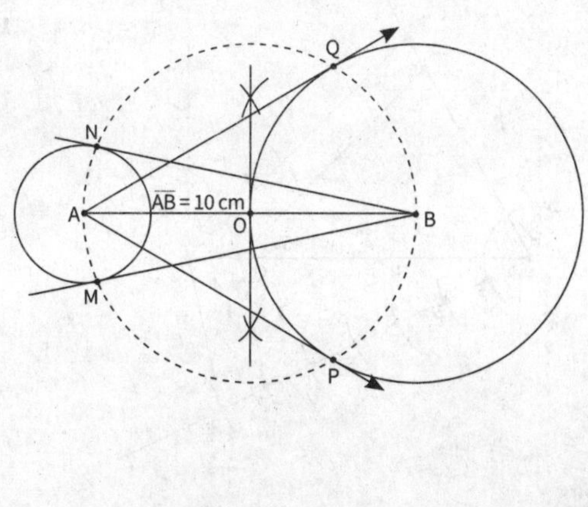

B. 1. i.

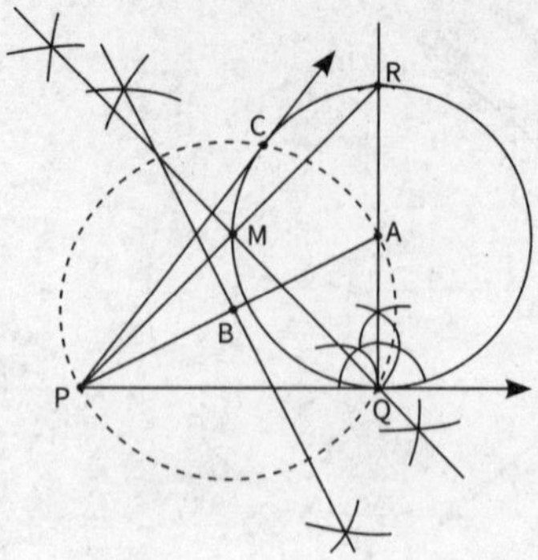

ii.

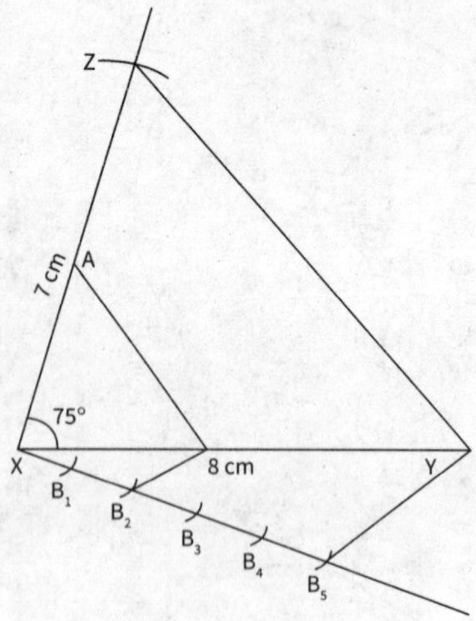

iii.

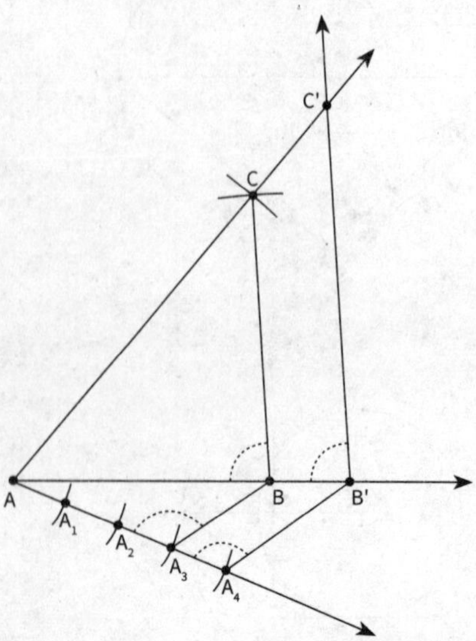

iv.

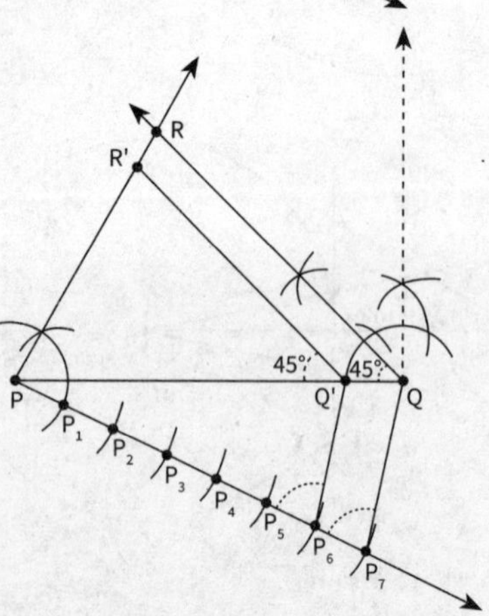

v.

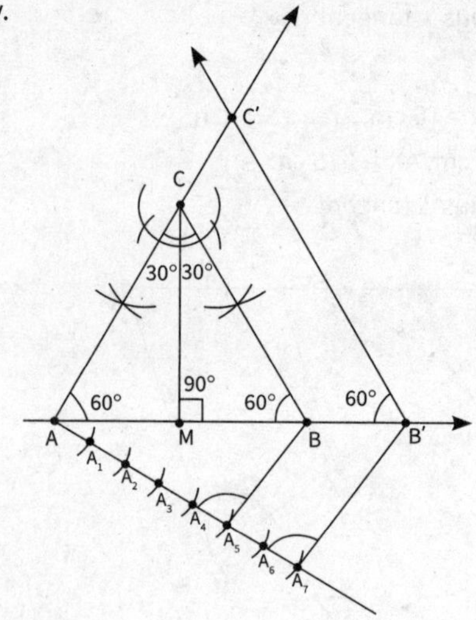

2. i.

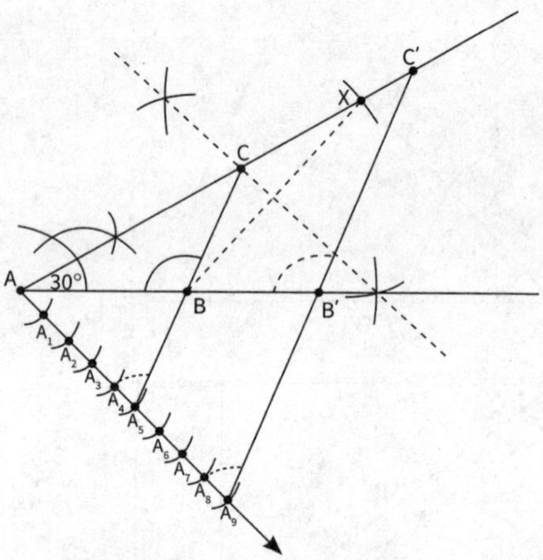

ii.

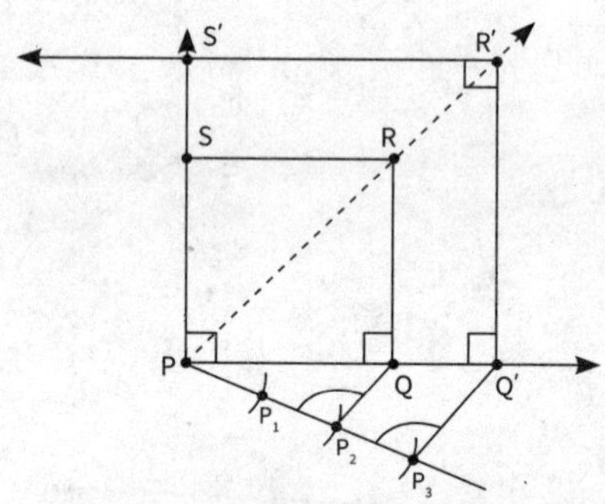

iii.

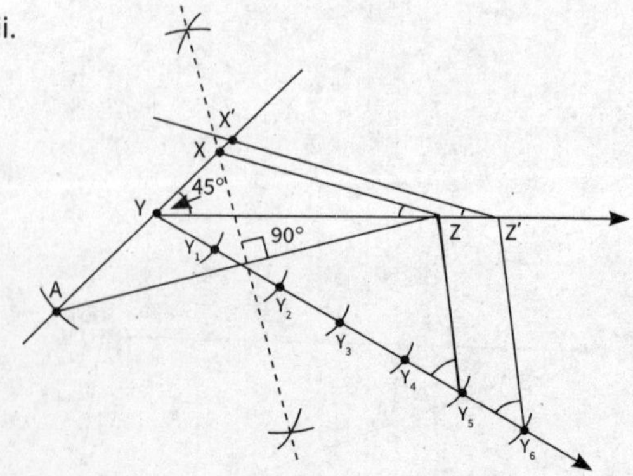

iv.

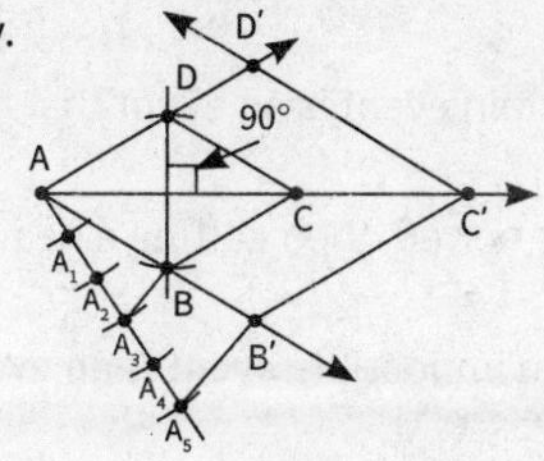

v.

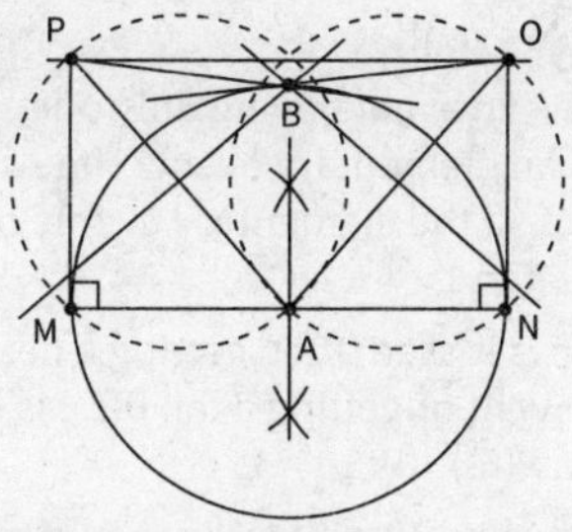

The tangents PM and PB from the vertex P and the tangents ON and OB from the vertex O are equal to the side ON or MP = 4 cm.

Chapter 12

A. 1. i. 3850 cm² ii. 40 m
iii. 1.232 km iv. 72° v. 10.5 cm

2. i. Area = 462 sq. cm and Length = 44 cm ii. 112 sq. cm
iii. $\theta = 45°$, Arc length = 22 cm
iv. a. Area of circle = 1848 cm²;
Area of equilateral triangle = 762.93 cm²
v. a. 4284 sq. m b. 2772 sq. m

B. 1. i. 560 sq. cm
ii. *Hint*: Take ratios the areas of major and minor segments and simplify.
iii. 14 cm, 616 sq. cm iv. 26,180 sq. cm, ₹52,360
v. 14.28 sq. cm, 142.86 sq. cm

2. i. 252 sq. cm ii. 54.86 sq. cm
iii. Radius = $14\sqrt{3}$ cm and area = 1848 sq. cm
iv. 14 m v. 9230 sq. cm

Chapter 13

1. i. 198 cm² ii. 464.8 cm² iii. 29.83 m²
iv. TSA of hemisphere = 115.5 cm²;
CSA of sphere = 154 cm³ v. 114.84 cm²

2. i. Height of cylindrical vessel = 24 cm;
Volume of cylinder = 2712.96 cm³
ii. 9198.1 cm³
iii. *Hint*: The sum of the volumes of cube and sphere is equal to the volume of cone.
iv. 990 cm² v. 8 cm; ₹2833.74

B. 1. i. 231 cm³ and 2444.2 cm³
ii. 49,262 cm² iii. 140 cm
iv. Volume of cone = 253.81 cm³; Volume of frustum = 1782 cm³; Slant height of frustum = $6\sqrt{3}$ cm
v. 60 m

2. i. 9000 marbles ii. 0.55 m iii. 28.148 kg
iv. Tank 1; 3.82 m v. 20 packs

Chapter 14

A. 1. i. The arithmetic mean of a grouped frequency distribution can be found using three different methods. They are,

- Direct method, $\bar{x} = \frac{\Sigma f_i x_i}{\Sigma f_i}$
- Assumed mean method, $\bar{x} = a + \frac{\Sigma f_i d_i}{\Sigma f_i}$
- Step deviation method, $\bar{x} = a + \left(\frac{\Sigma f_i u_i}{\Sigma f_i}\right) \times h$

ii. The formula used to find the median and mode of grouped data are:

- Median = $l + \left(\frac{\frac{n}{2} - cf}{f}\right) \times h$

l = lower limit of the median class
n = number of observations
cf = cumulative frequency of the class preceding the median class
f = frequency of the median class
h = class size (assuming class size to be equal)

- $l + \left(\frac{f_1 - f_0}{2f_1 - f_0 - f_2}\right) \times h$

l = lower limit of the modal class
h = size of the class interval (assuming all class sizes to be equal)
f_1 = frequency of the modal class
f_0 = frequency of the class preceding the modal class
f_2 = frequency of the class succeeding the modal class

iii. Representing a cumulative frequency distribution graphically as a cumulative frequency curve is called an ogive. Ogive can be of less than type or more than type.

iv. The cumulative frequency for the following data is:

Class interval	0–5	5–10	10–15	15–20	20–25	25–30
Frequency	3	5	2	7	1	8
Cumulative Frequency	3	8	10	17	18	26

vi. 3 Median = Mode + 2 Mean

2. i. Assumed mean method: $5 + \frac{276}{220} = 5 + 1.25 = 6.25$

Step deviation method: $5 + \frac{138}{220} \times 2 = 5 + 1.25 = 6.25$

ii. 7 iii. 740 iv. 8 v. 153.93

B. 1. i. Mean = 25, Median = 25, Mode = 25
ii. $x = 15$ and $y = 12$
Average = $\Sigma\frac{f_i x_i}{f_i} = \frac{3050}{60} = 50.833$
iii. Mean = 36.24, Median = 34.8, Mode = 33.16

iv. Less than ogive:

Class interval	45–55	55–65	65–75	75–85	85–95
Frequency	4	11	12	9	4
Cumulative frequency	< 55	< 65	< 75	< 85	< 95
	4	15	27	36	40

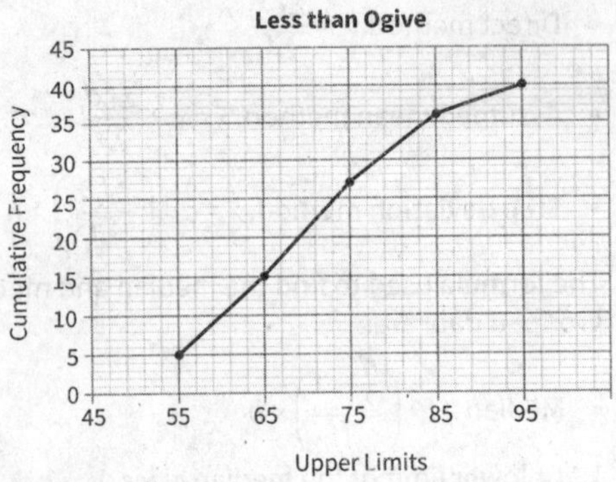

v. More than ogive:

Class interval	10–12	12–14	14–16	16–18
Frequency	8	22	29	5
Cumulative frequency	> 10	> 12	> 14	> 16
	64	56	34	5

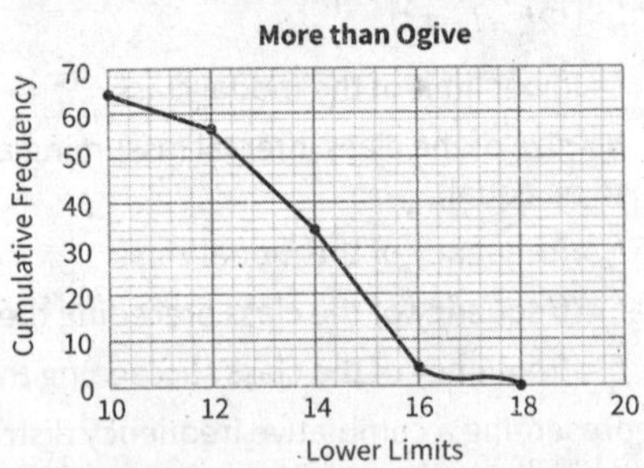

2. i. Mean = 9.375, Median = 8.64, Mode = 4.61

ii. Mean = 26.25, Median = 26.25, Mode = 26.15

iii. Mean = 40.13, Median = 41.25, Mode = 47.62

iv. Mean = 2.7, Median = 2.62, Mode = 2.57

v. Median = 30.86

Class interval	0–10	10–20	20–30	30–40	40–50	50–60
Frequency	6	11	21	23	14	5
Cumulative frequency	6	17	38	61	75	80
	80	74	63	42	19	5

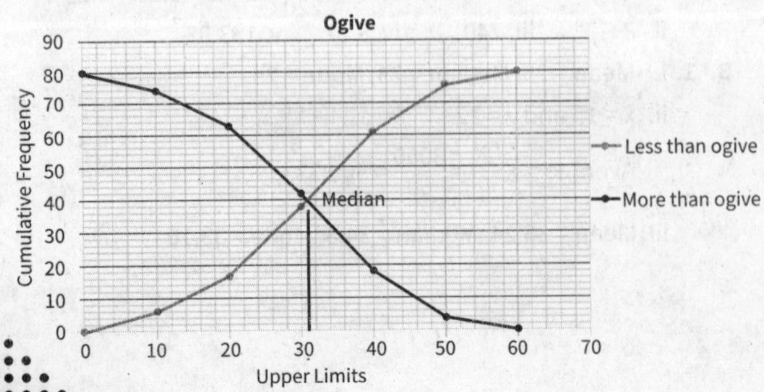

Chapter 15

A. 1. i. Certain event – A certain event is an event that is sure to happen.

Example – If a coin is tossed, then getting a head or a tail is the certain event.

ii. Impossible event - An impossible event is an event that cannot happen.

Example – If a coin is tossed, then getting both head and tail is an impossible event.

iii. Elementary event – An event having only one outcome is called an elementary event. The sum of the probabilities of all the elementary events of an experiment is equal to 1.

Example – If a coin is tossed, then getting a head $P(E_1)$ is an elementary Event or getting a tail $P(E_2)$ is an elementary Event. $P(E_1) + P(E_2) = 1$

iv. Complementary event – Two events are said to be complementary when one event occurs if and only if the other does not.

Example – If a coin is tossed, the head appears when the tail does not appear.

v. Experimental and theoretical probability – Theoretical probability is what we expect to happen, whereas experimental probability is what actually happens when the experiment is carried out.

Example: If a fair die is rolled 10 times and the number 6 occurs 4 times, then the experimental probability of 6 on a given roll of the die is $\frac{4}{10} = \frac{2}{5}$. The theoretical probability of 6 on a given roll is $\frac{1}{6}$.

2. i. a. $\frac{11}{16}$ b. $\frac{1}{4}$ ii. a. $\frac{3}{4}$ b. $\frac{1}{12}$

iii. a. $\frac{1}{18}$ b. $\frac{7}{18}$ iv. a. $\frac{25}{26}$ b. $\frac{1}{52}$

v. a. $\frac{48}{51}$ b. $\frac{8}{51}$

B. 1. i. a. $\frac{1}{10}$ b. $\frac{4}{5}$ c. $\frac{13}{90}$

ii. a. $\frac{1}{10}$ or 10% b. $\frac{3}{20}$ c. $\frac{7}{100}$

iii. a. $\frac{1}{12}$ b. $\frac{7}{12}$ c. $\frac{1}{366}$

iv. a. $\frac{3}{8}$ b. $\frac{1}{8}$ c. $\frac{1}{8}$

v. a. $\frac{1}{7}$ b. $\frac{3}{7}$ c. $\frac{6}{7}$

2. i. a. $\frac{10}{27}$ b. $\frac{2}{3}$ c. $\frac{25}{54}$ d. $\frac{1}{6}$

ii. a. $\frac{13}{20}$ b. $\frac{12}{25}$ iii. 80

iv. a. $\frac{30\pi}{64\pi} = \frac{15}{32}$ b. $\frac{34\pi}{64\pi} = \frac{17}{32}$

v. a. $\frac{11}{29}$ b. $\frac{15}{29}$ c. $\frac{3}{29}$

Hints for Difficult Questions

Chapter 1

Self-Assessment 1

3. Write the number as the product of prime numbers.
11. LCM of the time taken by each person to complete a round will give the time when they will meet.
16. Find the HCF of the numbers and then find the sum of the total number of pieces in each ribbon.
18. Factorise both the terms to find the factors.
22. Simplify the question and compare with each option.

Self-Assessment 2

26. Use Euclid's division algorithm.
33. Find the LCM and then find the multiple of LCM to get the smallest 5-digit number.
34. Divide the total number of pots by HCF to find the total number of rows.
49. Check the decimal expansion and compare.
50. Write the denominator in the form of 2^n5^m.

Chapter 2

Self-Assessment 1

20. Substitute $(x - 2)$ in the given polynomial and solve two simultaneous linear equations.
22. Check if each of the options leaves a remainder zero on dividing the given polynomial using long division method.
23. Use division algorithm to find $g(x)$.
24. $(x+\sqrt{3})$ and $(x-\sqrt{3})) = x^2 - 3$. Divide the given polynomial by $(x^2 - 3)$ and split the quotient to find the other two zeros.
25. Divide each of the options by $x^2 + 3$ and check if the remainder is zero.

Self-Assessment 2

45. Substitute $x = 1$ and $x = 8$ in the given polynomial and solve two simultaneous linear equations.
47. Check if each of the options leaves a remainder zero on dividing the given polynomial using long division method.
48. Use division algorithm to find $g(x)$.
49. $\left(x-\frac{3}{2}\right)$ and $\left(x-\frac{5}{2}\right) = 4x^2 - 16x + 15$. Divide the given polynomial by $4x^2 - 16x + 15$ and split the quotient to find the other two zeros.
50. Divide the given polynomial by $(x - 3)$ and subtract the remainder.

Chapter 3

Self-Assessment 1

13. Let the present age of Harish be x and his sister's be y. Then, a year ago, $x - 1 = 2(y - 1)$; and 4 years from now, $x + 4 = \left(\frac{y+4}{2}\right) + 10$.
17. Use the substitution method to solve.
18. Let the cost price of the bags be $4x$ and $5x$. The selling price of the bags be $5y$ and $6y$.
20. Let one girl can do the work in x days and one boy can do the work in y days. So, $\frac{3}{x}+\frac{4}{y}=\frac{1}{3}$ and $\frac{5}{x}+\frac{3}{y}=\frac{1}{2}$.
25. Let the speed of the boat be x km/h and stream be y km/h. The speed of the boat downstream = $(x + y)$ km/h and the speed of the boat upstream = $(x - y)$ km/h.

Self-Assessment 2

39. Let the present age of Ram be x and his son's be y. Then, 5 years ago, $x - 5 = 7(y - 5)$; and 5 years from now, $x + 5 = 3(y + 5)$.
43. Let the relative speed of the train when moving in the same direction be $(x - y)$ km/h and the relative speed of the train when moving in the opposite direction be $(x + y)$ km/h, where x and y are the speeds of the trains.
48. Let the length of the rectangle be x and width be y.
49. Let one woman can do the work in x days and one man can do the work in y days. So, $\frac{2}{x}+\frac{5}{y}=\frac{1}{4}$ and $\frac{4}{x}+\frac{2}{y}=\frac{1}{3}$.
50. Use the angle sum property of a triangle.

Chapter 4

Self-Assessment 1

8. Replace 1 by $\left(\frac{a+b}{a-b}\times\frac{a-b}{a+b}\right)$ and split the middle term.
17. $\frac{540}{x}-\frac{540}{x+9}=2$; solve for x to find the roots.
19. $\frac{1}{x+2}+\frac{1}{x}=\frac{7}{24}$; solve for x to find the roots.
20. Let the CP be ₹x; Gain = $\frac{x}{100}\times x=\frac{x^2}{100}$; $x+\frac{x^2}{100}=39$. Simplify to form a quadratic equation and solve.
21. Let the original fraction be $\frac{x}{x+3}$.

Self-Assessment 2

33. $\frac{288}{x}-\frac{288}{x+16}=\frac{3}{2}$; solve for x to find the roots.
36. Let the larger part be x, and the smaller part is $14 - x$. Then, $2x^2 - 3(14 - x)^2 = 20$.
39. A two-digit number is of the form $10x + y$.

44. $\frac{480}{x} - \frac{480}{x+3} = 8$; solve for x to find the roots.

48. $b^2 - 4ac = 0$, if the roots are equal.

Chapter 5

Self-Assessment 1

16. Two-digit numbers that are divisible by 6 are 12, 18, 24, ..., 96. Here $a = 12$ and $d = 6$. Use the formula $a_n = a + (n - 1)d$. Substitute the values of a_n, a, d and find the value of n.
18. The fare for the first 4 km is ₹50. Fare for the remaining distance travelled = ₹140 – ₹50 = ₹90.

    The cost after 4 km is 6, 12, 18, ...Here $a = 6$, $n = 6$. Using the formula for a_n, we get, $90 = 6 + (n - 1)6$. Find n and add 4 to the answer.
22. Use the formula, $S = \frac{n}{2}[2a + (n - 1)d]$. Substitute the values of S, n, d and find the value of a. The value of maximum amount is the value of the last term, i.e., find the value of a_5.
24. List the multiples of 9. Use the formula $S = \frac{n}{2}[2a + (n - 1)d]$ to find out the value of S.
    (1 minute = 60 seconds)
25. Use the formula $a_n = a + (n - 1)d$. Substitute the values of a_n, d, n and find out the value of a.

Self-Assessment 2

33. Find the difference between any two consecutive terms.
42. Given AP is 500, 1000, 1500, . . . Find a_9 using the formula, $a_9 = a + (9 - 1)d$. Add 15,000 which is the initial deposit to a_9.
46. Use the formula $S = \frac{n}{2}[2a + (n - 1)d]$. Substitute the values of S, n, d and find the value of a.
47. Write the arithmetic progression by substituting $n = 1, 2, 3, \ldots$ in the given formula. Use the formula $S = \frac{n}{2}[2a + (n - 1)d]$. Substitute the values of a, d, n and find the value of S.
50. Find the cost for 30 pages by substituting the value $a_n = a + (n - 1)d$. Add the fixed cost to it.

Chapter 6

Self-Assessment 1

10. If two triangles are similar, then their corresponding sides are proportional.
14. ar(PQYX) = ar(PQR) – ar(RXY)
15. A diagonal of a parallelogram divides it into two congruent triangles. Congruent triangles have equal areas.
22. Find each side of the square and divide it in the ratio 3 : 5 and 1 : 4. Use Pythagoras theorem to find the length of XY.
24. Let the height at which the tree broke be x m, then the other part is $(36 - x)$ m.

Self-Assessment 2

37. Area of trapezium ADEC = area of triangle ABC – area of triangle BDE
38. A diagonal of a parallelogram divides it into two congruent triangles. Congruent triangles have equal areas.
43. Use Pythagoras theorem to find the unknown.
46. Diagonals divide a rhombus into four right-angled triangles.
50. Let each equal side of the triangle be x cm, then its base is $(2x - 2)$ cm.

Chapter 7

Self-Assessment 1

9. Diagonal of a quadrilateral divides it into two triangles.
12. AP = BP; equate the distance using distance formula to find the relation between x and y.
17. The diagonals of a parallelogram bisect each other. Find the midpoint of BD and equate it to the midpoint of AC to find the value of a.
24. All the points on a perpendicular bisector are equidistant from both the ends of the line segment. The ordinate of the point on the x-axis is always zero.
25. Centroid of a triangle divides the median in the ratio 2 : 1.

Self-Assessment 2

28. Find the length of each side using distance formula.
32. Diagonal of a quadrilateral divides it into two triangles.
42. Let the line divide the line segment AB in the ratio k : 1.
44. Find the midpoint and substitute in the equation to find the variable.
50. Centroid of a triangle divides the median in the ratio 2 : 1.

Chapter 8

Self-Assessment 1

12. Solve the quadratic equation to find the value of tan θ.
13. Draw an altitude for the triangle and use trigonometric ratio for 30° to find the unknown.
23. $1 - \cos^4\theta = (1 + \cos^2\theta)(1 - \cos^2\theta)$
24. Divide the given equation by $\sin^2\theta$. Solve the quadratic equation $2\cot^2\theta - 3\cot\theta + 1 = 0$ to find the values of cot θ.
25. Take cos A as common and substitute $\cos^2 A = 1 - \sin^2 A$.

Self-Assessment 2

34. Divide the numerator and denominator by sin A.
36. Solve the quadratic equation to find the value of sin θ, and hence the value of cos θ.
37. Draw an altitude for the triangle and use trigonometric ratio for 30° to find the unknown.
43. $(\sin^6 A + \cos^6 A) = (\sin^2 A + \cos^2 A)(\sin^4 A - \sin^2 A\cos^2 A + \cos^4 A)$; use the identity $(a^3 + b^3) = (a + b)(a^2 - ab + b^2)$
44. Recall all the trigonometric identities and use the algebraic identity $x^2 - y^2 = (x + y)(x - y)$.

Chapter 9

Self-Assessment 1

16.

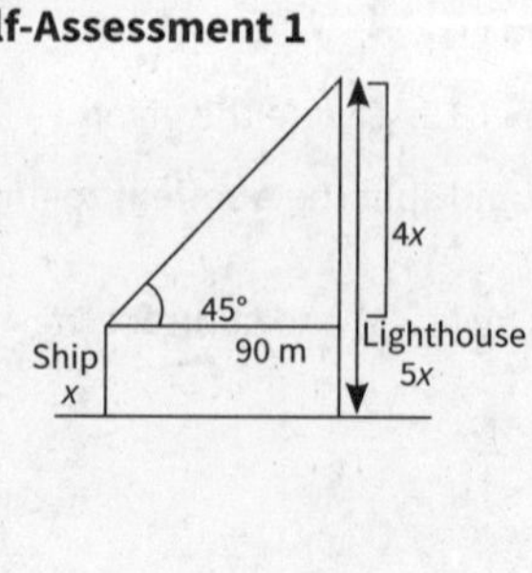

18.

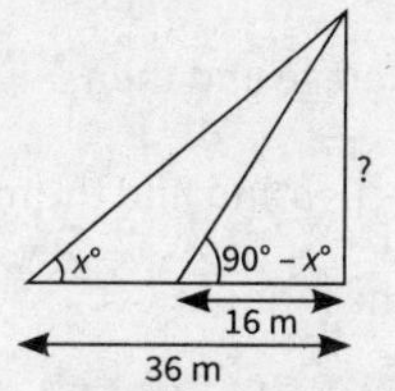

21. Find the distance travelled in 4 seconds, and hence, compute the speed of the car in km/h.

23.

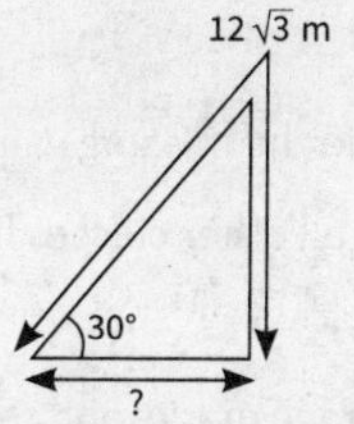

25. The distance between two milestones is 1 mile. Use tan *x* and tan *y* to find the height of the aeroplane.

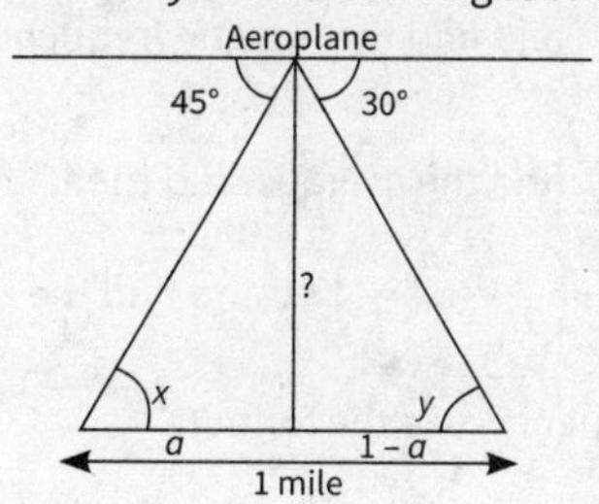

Chapter 10

Self-Assessment 1

8. ΔAXO and ΔAYO are congruent.

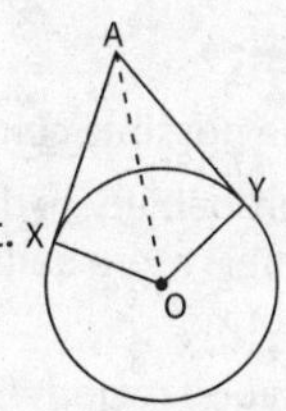

11. Find the length of the tangent using trigonometric ratios.
22. The sides opposite to equal angles are equal.
23. PC = PD; QC = QB; RA = RB; SA = SD ⇒ PQ + SR = PS + QR

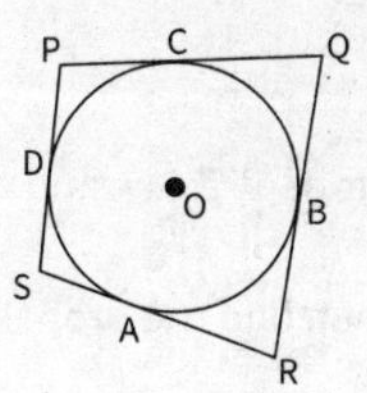

25. OR is parallel to SX.

Self-Assessment 2

33. ΔPXO and ΔPYO are congruent.
34. The angles subtended by a chord in the same segment are equal.

39. ΔPQR is an isosceles triangle.

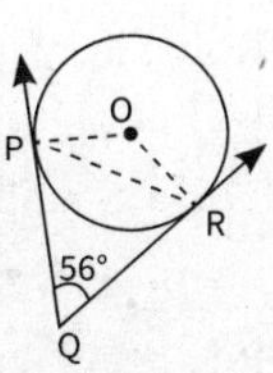

46. ∠OAM = 90°

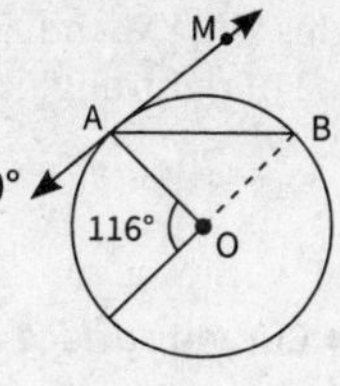

47. ∠OBA = 90° and ∠ODE = 90°

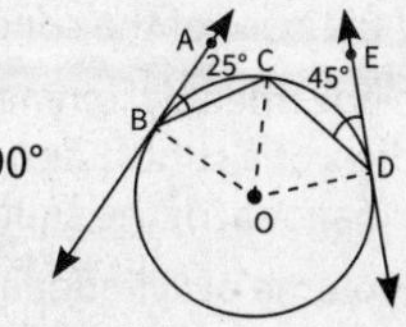

Chapter 11

Self-Assessment 1

4. Perpendicular bisectors of the chord pass through the centre of the circle.

11.

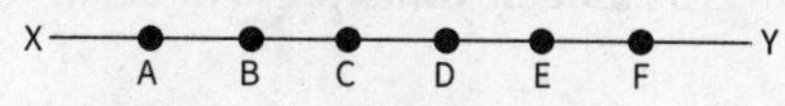

12. Simplify the given ratio.
13. Simplify each ratio.
21. Use trigonometric ratios to find the missing measurements.

Chapter 12

Self-Assessment 1

14. Find the length of the wire and hence, compute the area of a semicircle.

21.

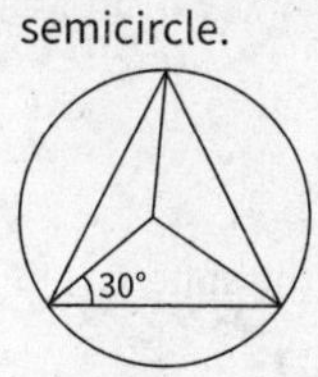

22. Find the area of the quadrants and hence, find the difference of the area of square and area of 4 quadrants.
24. Divide the difference of the areas of square and circle by 2. Find the area of the sector with angle 150°.
25. Find four times the difference in the area of the bigger sector and the smaller sector.

Self-Assessment 2

37. Use sin 45° to find the unknown.
39. $\pi \times 7^2 = \pi(r^2 - 7^2) = \pi(R^2 - r^2)$. Find R.

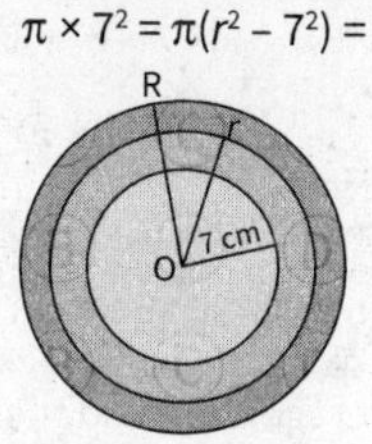

45. Find the difference in the areas of the minor segment and the semi-circle.
46. Find the radius of the circle using tan 30°.

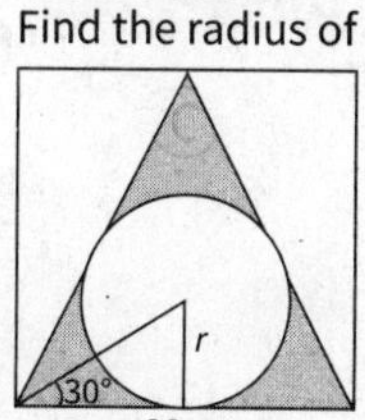

48. Find the areas of the triangles ZYI, YXI and XZI in terms of r and compare it with the area of right-angled triangle XYZ.

Chapter 13

Self-Assessment 1

7. Total surface area of cube + Curved surface area of cone – Area of the base of the cone

11. A square is formed by joining the midpoint of the edges of a cube. Edge of the cube is equal to diagonal of the square painted.

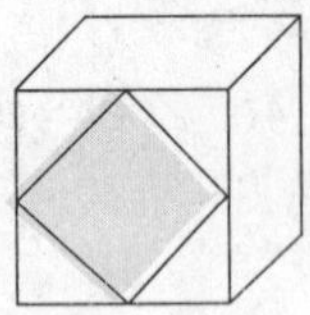

13. Add the volume of cylinder and volume of hemisphere.

17. 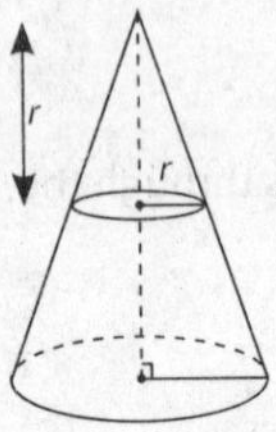

Two cones are similar; hence, the height and radius of both the cones are in the same ratio.

25. Number of glasses that can be filled = $\frac{\text{Volume of can} \times \text{Number of cans}}{\text{Volume of a glass}}$

Self-Assessment 2

32. 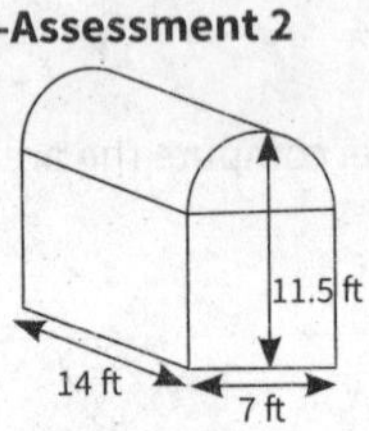

33. Diagonal of the cube is the diameter of the sphere.

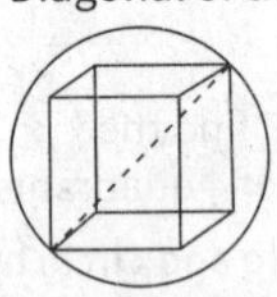

38. Find the volume of hemisphere using $\frac{2}{3}\pi r^3$; weight = volume × density.

43. Add the pasting margin to the lateral surface area.

44. The height of the frustum is equal to edge of the cube; radii are 3 cm and 1.5 cm.

Chapter 14

Self-Assessment 1

21. Use the formula $l + \left(\frac{\frac{n}{2} - cf}{f}\right) \times h$ and find the missing value.

22. Use the formula $\bar{x} = \frac{\Sigma f_i x_i}{\Sigma f_i}$; find the average time and then compare.

23. Use the formula $\bar{x} = \frac{\Sigma f_i x_i}{\Sigma f_i}$; find the missing frequency

24. Use the formula $\bar{x} = \frac{\Sigma f_i x_i}{\Sigma f_i}$, find the average and then substitute the formula $l + \left(\frac{f_1 - f_0}{2f_1 - f_0 - f_2}\right) \times h$ and find the mode.

25. List the cumulative frequency, use the formula $l + \left(\frac{f_1 - f_0}{2f_1 - f_0 - f_2}\right) \times h$ and find the mode.

Self-Assessment 2

46. Use the formula $l + \left(\frac{\frac{n}{2} - cf}{f}\right) \times h$ and find the missing value x.
Subtract the cumulative frequency of all other classes from the total number of people.

47. Use the formula $\bar{x} = \frac{\Sigma f_i x_i}{\Sigma f_i}$, find the average marks and then compare.

48. Use the formula $\bar{x} = \frac{\Sigma f_i x_i}{\Sigma f_i}$, and find the missing frequency.

49. Use the formula $\bar{x} = \frac{\Sigma f_i x_i}{\Sigma f_i}$, find the average and then substitute the formula $l + \left(\frac{f_1 - f_0}{2f_1 - f_0 - f_2}\right) \times h$ and find the mode.

50. List the cumulative frequency, use the formula $l + \left(\frac{f_1 - f_0}{2f_1 - f_0 - f_2}\right) \times h$ and find the mode.

Chapter 15

Self-Assessment 1

21. Find all the possible combinations of ice creams.

22. Find the probability of drawing red-coloured ball before and after adding 6 more balls, and then compare both to find the value of x.

23. Area of shaded region = Area of equilateral triangle – Area of 3 sectors of the circle.

24. Analyse each statement given and find the correct one.

25. Find out the probability of each event; choose the event with the highest probability.

Self-Assessment 2

41. Take the persons as a, b, c, d and seats as 1, 2, 3, 4 and write all the possibilities.

46. List all the possible outcomes, and then find the probability of getting the sum as a prime number.

47. Find the probability of drawing a black-coloured pen before and after adding 5 more pens, and then compare both to find the value of y.

48. Subtract the area of square from the area of circle.

50. Find the number of available seats in the second class tickets.

Collins Perfect Maths Assessments 10

CHAPTER 1

SAMPLE OMR ANSWER SHEET

IMPORTANT: *PLEASE FILL IN NAME, SCHOOL CODE, CLASS, SECTION & ROLL NO. CORRECTLY*

PERSONAL DETAILS

1. STUDENT NAME (IN ENGLISH CAPITAL LETTERS ONLY)

2. SCHOOL CODE

Ⓐ Ⓑ Ⓒ Ⓓ Ⓔ Ⓕ Ⓖ Ⓗ Ⓘ Ⓙ Ⓚ Ⓛ Ⓜ Ⓝ Ⓞ Ⓟ Ⓠ Ⓡ Ⓢ Ⓣ Ⓤ Ⓥ Ⓦ Ⓧ Ⓨ Ⓩ (two letter columns)

⓪ ① ② ③ ④ ⑤ ⑥ ⑦ ⑧ ⑨ (four digit columns)

3. CLASS

⓪ ①

⓪ ① ② ③ ④ ⑤ ⑥ ⑦ ⑧ ⑨

4. SECTION

Ⓐ Ⓑ Ⓒ Ⓓ Ⓔ Ⓕ Ⓖ Ⓗ Ⓘ Ⓙ Ⓚ Ⓛ Ⓜ Ⓝ Ⓞ Ⓟ Ⓠ Ⓡ Ⓢ Ⓣ Ⓤ Ⓥ Ⓦ Ⓧ Ⓨ Ⓩ

5. ROLL NO.

⓪ ① ② ③ ④ ⑤ ⑥ ⑦ ⑧ ⑨ (five digit columns)

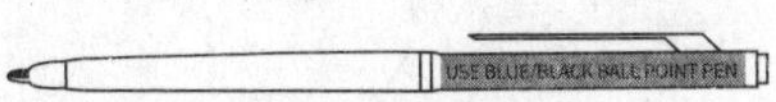

MARK YOUR ANSWERS

1.	Ⓐ	Ⓑ	Ⓒ	Ⓓ	**26.**	Ⓐ	Ⓑ	Ⓒ	Ⓓ
2.	Ⓐ	Ⓑ	Ⓒ	Ⓓ	**27.**	Ⓐ	Ⓑ	Ⓒ	Ⓓ
3.	Ⓐ	Ⓑ	Ⓒ	Ⓓ	**28.**	Ⓐ	Ⓑ	Ⓒ	Ⓓ
4.	Ⓐ	Ⓑ	Ⓒ	Ⓓ	**29.**	Ⓐ	Ⓑ	Ⓒ	Ⓓ
5.	Ⓐ	Ⓑ	Ⓒ	Ⓓ	**30.**	Ⓐ	Ⓑ	Ⓒ	Ⓓ
6.	Ⓐ	Ⓑ	Ⓒ	Ⓓ	**31.**	Ⓐ	Ⓑ	Ⓒ	Ⓓ
7.	Ⓐ	Ⓑ	Ⓒ	Ⓓ	**32.**	Ⓐ	Ⓑ	Ⓒ	Ⓓ
8.	Ⓐ	Ⓑ	Ⓒ	Ⓓ	**33.**	Ⓐ	Ⓑ	Ⓒ	Ⓓ
9.	Ⓐ	Ⓑ	Ⓒ	Ⓓ	**34.**	Ⓐ	Ⓑ	Ⓒ	Ⓓ
10.	Ⓐ	Ⓑ	Ⓒ	Ⓓ	**35.**	Ⓐ	Ⓑ	Ⓒ	Ⓓ
11.	Ⓐ	Ⓑ	Ⓒ	Ⓓ	**36.**	Ⓐ	Ⓑ	Ⓒ	Ⓓ
12.	Ⓐ	Ⓑ	Ⓒ	Ⓓ	**37.**	Ⓐ	Ⓑ	Ⓒ	Ⓓ
13.	Ⓐ	Ⓑ	Ⓒ	Ⓓ	**38.**	Ⓐ	Ⓑ	Ⓒ	Ⓓ
14.	Ⓐ	Ⓑ	Ⓒ	Ⓓ	**39.**	Ⓐ	Ⓑ	Ⓒ	Ⓓ
15.	Ⓐ	Ⓑ	Ⓒ	Ⓓ	**40.**	Ⓐ	Ⓑ	Ⓒ	Ⓓ
16.	Ⓐ	Ⓑ	Ⓒ	Ⓓ	**41.**	Ⓐ	Ⓑ	Ⓒ	Ⓓ
17.	Ⓐ	Ⓑ	Ⓒ	Ⓓ	**42.**	Ⓐ	Ⓑ	Ⓒ	Ⓓ
18.	Ⓐ	Ⓑ	Ⓒ	Ⓓ	**43.**	Ⓐ	Ⓑ	Ⓒ	Ⓓ
19.	Ⓐ	Ⓑ	Ⓒ	Ⓓ	**44.**	Ⓐ	Ⓑ	Ⓒ	Ⓓ
20.	Ⓐ	Ⓑ	Ⓒ	Ⓓ	**45.**	Ⓐ	Ⓑ	Ⓒ	Ⓓ
21.	Ⓐ	Ⓑ	Ⓒ	Ⓓ	**46.**	Ⓐ	Ⓑ	Ⓒ	Ⓓ
22.	Ⓐ	Ⓑ	Ⓒ	Ⓓ	**47.**	Ⓐ	Ⓑ	Ⓒ	Ⓓ
23.	Ⓐ	Ⓑ	Ⓒ	Ⓓ	**48.**	Ⓐ	Ⓑ	Ⓒ	Ⓓ
24.	Ⓐ	Ⓑ	Ⓒ	Ⓓ	**49.**	Ⓐ	Ⓑ	Ⓒ	Ⓓ
25.	Ⓐ	Ⓑ	Ⓒ	Ⓓ	**50.**	Ⓐ	Ⓑ	Ⓒ	Ⓓ

CHAPTER 2

SAMPLE OMR ANSWER SHEET

IMPORTANT: *PLEASE FILL IN NAME, SCHOOL CODE, CLASS, SECTION & ROLL NO. CORRECTLY*

PERSONAL DETAILS

1. STUDENT NAME (IN ENGLISH CAPITAL LETTERS ONLY)

2. SCHOOL CODE

A–Z	A–Z	0–9	0–9	0–9	0–9

3. CLASS

0–1	0–9

4. SECTION

A B C D E F G H I J K L M N O P Q R S T U V W X Y Z

5. ROLL NO.

0–9	0–9	0–9	0–9	0–9

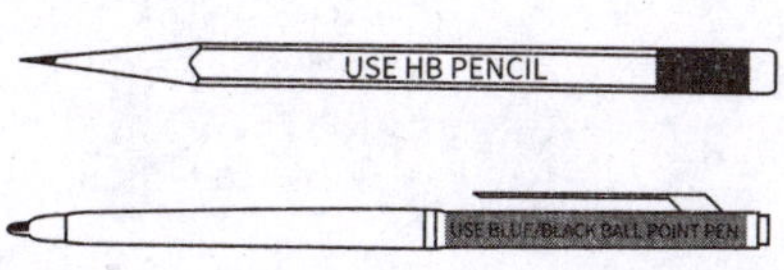

MARK YOUR ANSWERS

1.	A	B	C	D	**26.**	A	B	C	D
2.	A	B	C	D	**27.**	A	B	C	D
3.	A	B	C	D	**28.**	A	B	C	D
4.	A	B	C	D	**29.**	A	B	C	D
5.	A	B	C	D	**30.**	A	B	C	D
6.	A	B	C	D	**31.**	A	B	C	D
7.	A	B	C	D	**32.**	A	B	C	D
8.	A	B	C	D	**33.**	A	B	C	D
9.	A	B	C	D	**34.**	A	B	C	D
10.	A	B	C	D	**35.**	A	B	C	D
11.	A	B	C	D	**36.**	A	B	C	D
12.	A	B	C	D	**37.**	A	B	C	D
13.	A	B	C	D	**38.**	A	B	C	D
14.	A	B	C	D	**39.**	A	B	C	D
15.	A	B	C	D	**40.**	A	B	C	D
16.	A	B	C	D	**41.**	A	B	C	D
17.	A	B	C	D	**42.**	A	B	C	D
18.	A	B	C	D	**43.**	A	B	C	D
19.	A	B	C	D	**44.**	A	B	C	D
20.	A	B	C	D	**45.**	A	B	C	D
21.	A	B	C	D	**46.**	A	B	C	D
22.	A	B	C	D	**47.**	A	B	C	D
23.	A	B	C	D	**48.**	A	B	C	D
24.	A	B	C	D	**49.**	A	B	C	D
25.	A	B	C	D	**50.**	A	B	C	D

CHAPTER 3

SAMPLE OMR ANSWER SHEET

IMPORTANT: *PLEASE FILL IN NAME, SCHOOL CODE, CLASS, SECTION & ROLL NO. CORRECTLY*

PERSONAL DETAILS

1. STUDENT NAME (IN ENGLISH CAPITAL LETTERS ONLY)

2. SCHOOL CODE

Ⓐ Ⓑ Ⓒ Ⓓ Ⓔ Ⓕ Ⓖ Ⓗ Ⓘ Ⓙ Ⓚ Ⓛ Ⓜ Ⓝ Ⓞ Ⓟ Ⓠ Ⓡ Ⓢ Ⓣ Ⓤ Ⓥ Ⓦ Ⓧ Ⓨ Ⓩ

Ⓐ Ⓑ Ⓒ Ⓓ Ⓔ Ⓕ Ⓖ Ⓗ Ⓘ Ⓙ Ⓚ Ⓛ Ⓜ Ⓝ Ⓞ Ⓟ Ⓠ Ⓡ Ⓢ Ⓣ Ⓤ Ⓥ Ⓦ Ⓧ Ⓨ Ⓩ

⓪ ① ② ③ ④ ⑤ ⑥ ⑦ ⑧ ⑨

⓪ ① ② ③ ④ ⑤ ⑥ ⑦ ⑧ ⑨

⓪ ① ② ③ ④ ⑤ ⑥ ⑦ ⑧ ⑨

⓪ ① ② ③ ④ ⑤ ⑥ ⑦ ⑧ ⑨

3. CLASS

⓪ ①

⓪ ① ② ③ ④ ⑤ ⑥ ⑦ ⑧ ⑨

4. SECTION

Ⓐ Ⓑ Ⓒ Ⓓ Ⓔ Ⓕ Ⓖ Ⓗ Ⓘ Ⓙ Ⓚ Ⓛ Ⓜ Ⓝ Ⓞ Ⓟ Ⓠ Ⓡ Ⓢ Ⓣ Ⓤ Ⓥ Ⓦ Ⓧ Ⓨ Ⓩ

5. ROLL NO.

⓪ ① ② ③ ④ ⑤ ⑥ ⑦ ⑧ ⑨

⓪ ① ② ③ ④ ⑤ ⑥ ⑦ ⑧ ⑨

⓪ ① ② ③ ④ ⑤ ⑥ ⑦ ⑧ ⑨

⓪ ① ② ③ ④ ⑤ ⑥ ⑦ ⑧ ⑨

⓪ ① ② ③ ④ ⑤ ⑥ ⑦ ⑧ ⑨

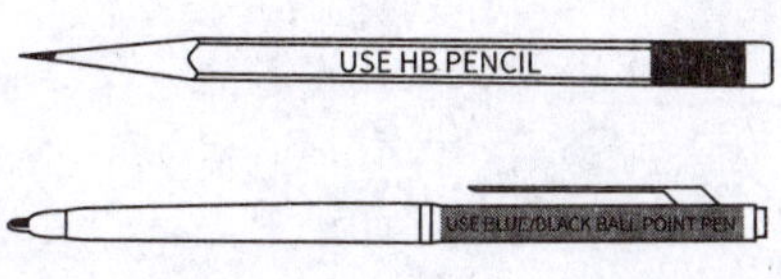

MARK YOUR ANSWERS

1.	Ⓐ	Ⓑ	Ⓒ	Ⓓ	**26.**	Ⓐ	Ⓑ	Ⓒ	Ⓓ
2.	Ⓐ	Ⓑ	Ⓒ	Ⓓ	**27.**	Ⓐ	Ⓑ	Ⓒ	Ⓓ
3.	Ⓐ	Ⓑ	Ⓒ	Ⓓ	**28.**	Ⓐ	Ⓑ	Ⓒ	Ⓓ
4.	Ⓐ	Ⓑ	Ⓒ	Ⓓ	**29.**	Ⓐ	Ⓑ	Ⓒ	Ⓓ
5.	Ⓐ	Ⓑ	Ⓒ	Ⓓ	**30.**	Ⓐ	Ⓑ	Ⓒ	Ⓓ
6.	Ⓐ	Ⓑ	Ⓒ	Ⓓ	**31.**	Ⓐ	Ⓑ	Ⓒ	Ⓓ
7.	Ⓐ	Ⓑ	Ⓒ	Ⓓ	**32.**	Ⓐ	Ⓑ	Ⓒ	Ⓓ
8.	Ⓐ	Ⓑ	Ⓒ	Ⓓ	**33.**	Ⓐ	Ⓑ	Ⓒ	Ⓓ
9.	Ⓐ	Ⓑ	Ⓒ	Ⓓ	**34.**	Ⓐ	Ⓑ	Ⓒ	Ⓓ
10.	Ⓐ	Ⓑ	Ⓒ	Ⓓ	**35.**	Ⓐ	Ⓑ	Ⓒ	Ⓓ
11.	Ⓐ	Ⓑ	Ⓒ	Ⓓ	**36.**	Ⓐ	Ⓑ	Ⓒ	Ⓓ
12.	Ⓐ	Ⓑ	Ⓒ	Ⓓ	**37.**	Ⓐ	Ⓑ	Ⓒ	Ⓓ
13.	Ⓐ	Ⓑ	Ⓒ	Ⓓ	**38.**	Ⓐ	Ⓑ	Ⓒ	Ⓓ
14.	Ⓐ	Ⓑ	Ⓒ	Ⓓ	**39.**	Ⓐ	Ⓑ	Ⓒ	Ⓓ
15.	Ⓐ	Ⓑ	Ⓒ	Ⓓ	**40.**	Ⓐ	Ⓑ	Ⓒ	Ⓓ
16.	Ⓐ	Ⓑ	Ⓒ	Ⓓ	**41.**	Ⓐ	Ⓑ	Ⓒ	Ⓓ
17.	Ⓐ	Ⓑ	Ⓒ	Ⓓ	**42.**	Ⓐ	Ⓑ	Ⓒ	Ⓓ
18.	Ⓐ	Ⓑ	Ⓒ	Ⓓ	**43.**	Ⓐ	Ⓑ	Ⓒ	Ⓓ
19.	Ⓐ	Ⓑ	Ⓒ	Ⓓ	**44.**	Ⓐ	Ⓑ	Ⓒ	Ⓓ
20.	Ⓐ	Ⓑ	Ⓒ	Ⓓ	**45.**	Ⓐ	Ⓑ	Ⓒ	Ⓓ
21.	Ⓐ	Ⓑ	Ⓒ	Ⓓ	**46.**	Ⓐ	Ⓑ	Ⓒ	Ⓓ
22.	Ⓐ	Ⓑ	Ⓒ	Ⓓ	**47.**	Ⓐ	Ⓑ	Ⓒ	Ⓓ
23.	Ⓐ	Ⓑ	Ⓒ	Ⓓ	**48.**	Ⓐ	Ⓑ	Ⓒ	Ⓓ
24.	Ⓐ	Ⓑ	Ⓒ	Ⓓ	**49.**	Ⓐ	Ⓑ	Ⓒ	Ⓓ
25.	Ⓐ	Ⓑ	Ⓒ	Ⓓ	**50.**	Ⓐ	Ⓑ	Ⓒ	Ⓓ

CHAPTER 4

SAMPLE OMR ANSWER SHEET

IMPORTANT: *PLEASE FILL IN NAME, SCHOOL CODE, CLASS, SECTION & ROLL NO. CORRECTLY*

PERSONAL DETAILS

1. STUDENT NAME (IN ENGLISH CAPITAL LETTERS ONLY)

2. SCHOOL CODE

Ⓐ–Ⓩ	Ⓐ–Ⓩ	⓪–⑨	⓪–⑨	⓪–⑨	⓪–⑨

3. CLASS

⓪ ①	⓪–⑨

4. SECTION

Ⓐ Ⓑ Ⓒ Ⓓ Ⓔ Ⓕ Ⓖ Ⓗ Ⓘ	Ⓙ Ⓚ Ⓛ Ⓜ Ⓝ Ⓞ Ⓟ Ⓠ Ⓡ	Ⓢ Ⓣ Ⓤ Ⓥ Ⓦ Ⓧ Ⓨ Ⓩ

5. ROLL NO.

⓪–⑨	⓪–⑨	⓪–⑨	⓪–⑨	⓪–⑨

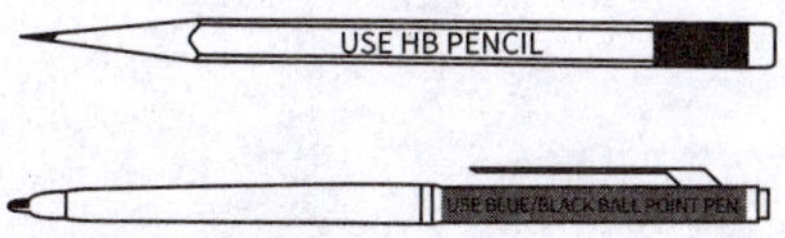

MARK YOUR ANSWERS

No.					No.				
1.	Ⓐ	Ⓑ	Ⓒ	Ⓓ	26.	Ⓐ	Ⓑ	Ⓒ	Ⓓ
2.	Ⓐ	Ⓑ	Ⓒ	Ⓓ	27.	Ⓐ	Ⓑ	Ⓒ	Ⓓ
3.	Ⓐ	Ⓑ	Ⓒ	Ⓓ	28.	Ⓐ	Ⓑ	Ⓒ	Ⓓ
4.	Ⓐ	Ⓑ	Ⓒ	Ⓓ	29.	Ⓐ	Ⓑ	Ⓒ	Ⓓ
5.	Ⓐ	Ⓑ	Ⓒ	Ⓓ	30.	Ⓐ	Ⓑ	Ⓒ	Ⓓ
6.	Ⓐ	Ⓑ	Ⓒ	Ⓓ	31.	Ⓐ	Ⓑ	Ⓒ	Ⓓ
7.	Ⓐ	Ⓑ	Ⓒ	Ⓓ	32.	Ⓐ	Ⓑ	Ⓒ	Ⓓ
8.	Ⓐ	Ⓑ	Ⓒ	Ⓓ	33.	Ⓐ	Ⓑ	Ⓒ	Ⓓ
9.	Ⓐ	Ⓑ	Ⓒ	Ⓓ	34.	Ⓐ	Ⓑ	Ⓒ	Ⓓ
10.	Ⓐ	Ⓑ	Ⓒ	Ⓓ	35.	Ⓐ	Ⓑ	Ⓒ	Ⓓ
11.	Ⓐ	Ⓑ	Ⓒ	Ⓓ	36.	Ⓐ	Ⓑ	Ⓒ	Ⓓ
12.	Ⓐ	Ⓑ	Ⓒ	Ⓓ	37.	Ⓐ	Ⓑ	Ⓒ	Ⓓ
13.	Ⓐ	Ⓑ	Ⓒ	Ⓓ	38.	Ⓐ	Ⓑ	Ⓒ	Ⓓ
14.	Ⓐ	Ⓑ	Ⓒ	Ⓓ	39.	Ⓐ	Ⓑ	Ⓒ	Ⓓ
15.	Ⓐ	Ⓑ	Ⓒ	Ⓓ	40.	Ⓐ	Ⓑ	Ⓒ	Ⓓ
16.	Ⓐ	Ⓑ	Ⓒ	Ⓓ	41.	Ⓐ	Ⓑ	Ⓒ	Ⓓ
17.	Ⓐ	Ⓑ	Ⓒ	Ⓓ	42.	Ⓐ	Ⓑ	Ⓒ	Ⓓ
18.	Ⓐ	Ⓑ	Ⓒ	Ⓓ	43.	Ⓐ	Ⓑ	Ⓒ	Ⓓ
19.	Ⓐ	Ⓑ	Ⓒ	Ⓓ	44.	Ⓐ	Ⓑ	Ⓒ	Ⓓ
20.	Ⓐ	Ⓑ	Ⓒ	Ⓓ	45.	Ⓐ	Ⓑ	Ⓒ	Ⓓ
21.	Ⓐ	Ⓑ	Ⓒ	Ⓓ	46.	Ⓐ	Ⓑ	Ⓒ	Ⓓ
22.	Ⓐ	Ⓑ	Ⓒ	Ⓓ	47.	Ⓐ	Ⓑ	Ⓒ	Ⓓ
23.	Ⓐ	Ⓑ	Ⓒ	Ⓓ	48.	Ⓐ	Ⓑ	Ⓒ	Ⓓ
24.	Ⓐ	Ⓑ	Ⓒ	Ⓓ	49.	Ⓐ	Ⓑ	Ⓒ	Ⓓ
25.	Ⓐ	Ⓑ	Ⓒ	Ⓓ	50.	Ⓐ	Ⓑ	Ⓒ	Ⓓ

CHAPTER 5

SAMPLE OMR ANSWER SHEET

IMPORTANT: *PLEASE FILL IN NAME, SCHOOL CODE, CLASS, SECTION & ROLL NO. CORRECTLY*

PERSONAL DETAILS

1. STUDENT NAME (IN ENGLISH CAPITAL LETTERS ONLY)

2. SCHOOL CODE

Columns 1–2: Ⓐ Ⓑ Ⓒ Ⓓ Ⓔ Ⓕ Ⓖ Ⓗ Ⓘ Ⓙ Ⓚ Ⓛ Ⓜ Ⓝ Ⓞ Ⓟ Ⓠ Ⓡ Ⓢ Ⓣ Ⓤ Ⓥ Ⓦ Ⓧ Ⓨ Ⓩ

Columns 3–6: ⓪ ① ② ③ ④ ⑤ ⑥ ⑦ ⑧ ⑨

3. CLASS

Column 1: ⓪ ①

Column 2: ⓪ ① ② ③ ④ ⑤ ⑥ ⑦ ⑧ ⑨

4. SECTION

Ⓐ Ⓑ Ⓒ Ⓓ Ⓔ Ⓕ Ⓖ Ⓗ Ⓘ Ⓙ Ⓚ Ⓛ Ⓜ Ⓝ Ⓞ Ⓟ Ⓠ Ⓡ Ⓢ Ⓣ Ⓤ Ⓥ Ⓦ Ⓧ Ⓨ Ⓩ

5. ROLL NO.

Columns 1–5: ⓪ ① ② ③ ④ ⑤ ⑥ ⑦ ⑧ ⑨

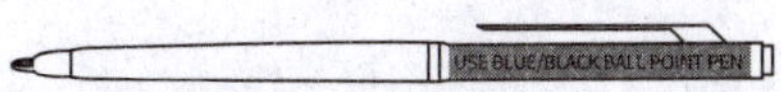

MARK YOUR ANSWERS

No.					No.				
1.	Ⓐ	Ⓑ	Ⓒ	Ⓓ	26.	Ⓐ	Ⓑ	Ⓒ	Ⓓ
2.	Ⓐ	Ⓑ	Ⓒ	Ⓓ	27.	Ⓐ	Ⓑ	Ⓒ	Ⓓ
3.	Ⓐ	Ⓑ	Ⓒ	Ⓓ	28.	Ⓐ	Ⓑ	Ⓒ	Ⓓ
4.	Ⓐ	Ⓑ	Ⓒ	Ⓓ	29.	Ⓐ	Ⓑ	Ⓒ	Ⓓ
5.	Ⓐ	Ⓑ	Ⓒ	Ⓓ	30.	Ⓐ	Ⓑ	Ⓒ	Ⓓ
6.	Ⓐ	Ⓑ	Ⓒ	Ⓓ	31.	Ⓐ	Ⓑ	Ⓒ	Ⓓ
7.	Ⓐ	Ⓑ	Ⓒ	Ⓓ	32.	Ⓐ	Ⓑ	Ⓒ	Ⓓ
8.	Ⓐ	Ⓑ	Ⓒ	Ⓓ	33.	Ⓐ	Ⓑ	Ⓒ	Ⓓ
9.	Ⓐ	Ⓑ	Ⓒ	Ⓓ	34.	Ⓐ	Ⓑ	Ⓒ	Ⓓ
10.	Ⓐ	Ⓑ	Ⓒ	Ⓓ	35.	Ⓐ	Ⓑ	Ⓒ	Ⓓ
11.	Ⓐ	Ⓑ	Ⓒ	Ⓓ	36.	Ⓐ	Ⓑ	Ⓒ	Ⓓ
12.	Ⓐ	Ⓑ	Ⓒ	Ⓓ	37.	Ⓐ	Ⓑ	Ⓒ	Ⓓ
13.	Ⓐ	Ⓑ	Ⓒ	Ⓓ	38.	Ⓐ	Ⓑ	Ⓒ	Ⓓ
14.	Ⓐ	Ⓑ	Ⓒ	Ⓓ	39.	Ⓐ	Ⓑ	Ⓒ	Ⓓ
15.	Ⓐ	Ⓑ	Ⓒ	Ⓓ	40.	Ⓐ	Ⓑ	Ⓒ	Ⓓ
16.	Ⓐ	Ⓑ	Ⓒ	Ⓓ	41.	Ⓐ	Ⓑ	Ⓒ	Ⓓ
17.	Ⓐ	Ⓑ	Ⓒ	Ⓓ	42.	Ⓐ	Ⓑ	Ⓒ	Ⓓ
18.	Ⓐ	Ⓑ	Ⓒ	Ⓓ	43.	Ⓐ	Ⓑ	Ⓒ	Ⓓ
19.	Ⓐ	Ⓑ	Ⓒ	Ⓓ	44.	Ⓐ	Ⓑ	Ⓒ	Ⓓ
20.	Ⓐ	Ⓑ	Ⓒ	Ⓓ	45.	Ⓐ	Ⓑ	Ⓒ	Ⓓ
21.	Ⓐ	Ⓑ	Ⓒ	Ⓓ	46.	Ⓐ	Ⓑ	Ⓒ	Ⓓ
22.	Ⓐ	Ⓑ	Ⓒ	Ⓓ	47.	Ⓐ	Ⓑ	Ⓒ	Ⓓ
23.	Ⓐ	Ⓑ	Ⓒ	Ⓓ	48.	Ⓐ	Ⓑ	Ⓒ	Ⓓ
24.	Ⓐ	Ⓑ	Ⓒ	Ⓓ	49.	Ⓐ	Ⓑ	Ⓒ	Ⓓ
25.	Ⓐ	Ⓑ	Ⓒ	Ⓓ	50.	Ⓐ	Ⓑ	Ⓒ	Ⓓ

CHAPTER 6

SAMPLE OMR ANSWER SHEET

IMPORTANT: *PLEASE FILL IN NAME, SCHOOL CODE, CLASS, SECTION & ROLL NO. CORRECTLY*

PERSONAL DETAILS

1. STUDENT NAME (IN ENGLISH CAPITAL LETTERS ONLY)

2. SCHOOL CODE

Ⓐ–Ⓩ	Ⓐ–Ⓩ	⓪–⑨	⓪–⑨	⓪–⑨	⓪–⑨

3. CLASS

⓪–①	⓪–⑨

4. SECTION

Ⓐ–Ⓩ

5. ROLL NO.

⓪–⑨	⓪–⑨	⓪–⑨	⓪–⑨	⓪–⑨

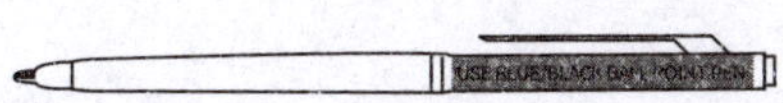

MARK YOUR ANSWERS

1.	Ⓐ	Ⓑ	Ⓒ	Ⓓ	**26.**	Ⓐ	Ⓑ	Ⓒ	Ⓓ
2.	Ⓐ	Ⓑ	Ⓒ	Ⓓ	**27.**	Ⓐ	Ⓑ	Ⓒ	Ⓓ
3.	Ⓐ	Ⓑ	Ⓒ	Ⓓ	**28.**	Ⓐ	Ⓑ	Ⓒ	Ⓓ
4.	Ⓐ	Ⓑ	Ⓒ	Ⓓ	**29.**	Ⓐ	Ⓑ	Ⓒ	Ⓓ
5.	Ⓐ	Ⓑ	Ⓒ	Ⓓ	**30.**	Ⓐ	Ⓑ	Ⓒ	Ⓓ
6.	Ⓐ	Ⓑ	Ⓒ	Ⓓ	**31.**	Ⓐ	Ⓑ	Ⓒ	Ⓓ
7.	Ⓐ	Ⓑ	Ⓒ	Ⓓ	**32.**	Ⓐ	Ⓑ	Ⓒ	Ⓓ
8.	Ⓐ	Ⓑ	Ⓒ	Ⓓ	**33.**	Ⓐ	Ⓑ	Ⓒ	Ⓓ
9.	Ⓐ	Ⓑ	Ⓒ	Ⓓ	**34.**	Ⓐ	Ⓑ	Ⓒ	Ⓓ
10.	Ⓐ	Ⓑ	Ⓒ	Ⓓ	**35.**	Ⓐ	Ⓑ	Ⓒ	Ⓓ
11.	Ⓐ	Ⓑ	Ⓒ	Ⓓ	**36.**	Ⓐ	Ⓑ	Ⓒ	Ⓓ
12.	Ⓐ	Ⓑ	Ⓒ	Ⓓ	**37.**	Ⓐ	Ⓑ	Ⓒ	Ⓓ
13.	Ⓐ	Ⓑ	Ⓒ	Ⓓ	**38.**	Ⓐ	Ⓑ	Ⓒ	Ⓓ
14.	Ⓐ	Ⓑ	Ⓒ	Ⓓ	**39.**	Ⓐ	Ⓑ	Ⓒ	Ⓓ
15.	Ⓐ	Ⓑ	Ⓒ	Ⓓ	**40.**	Ⓐ	Ⓑ	Ⓒ	Ⓓ
16.	Ⓐ	Ⓑ	Ⓒ	Ⓓ	**41.**	Ⓐ	Ⓑ	Ⓒ	Ⓓ
17.	Ⓐ	Ⓑ	Ⓒ	Ⓓ	**42.**	Ⓐ	Ⓑ	Ⓒ	Ⓓ
18.	Ⓐ	Ⓑ	Ⓒ	Ⓓ	**43.**	Ⓐ	Ⓑ	Ⓒ	Ⓓ
19.	Ⓐ	Ⓑ	Ⓒ	Ⓓ	**44.**	Ⓐ	Ⓑ	Ⓒ	Ⓓ
20.	Ⓐ	Ⓑ	Ⓒ	Ⓓ	**45.**	Ⓐ	Ⓑ	Ⓒ	Ⓓ
21.	Ⓐ	Ⓑ	Ⓒ	Ⓓ	**46.**	Ⓐ	Ⓑ	Ⓒ	Ⓓ
22.	Ⓐ	Ⓑ	Ⓒ	Ⓓ	**47.**	Ⓐ	Ⓑ	Ⓒ	Ⓓ
23.	Ⓐ	Ⓑ	Ⓒ	Ⓓ	**48.**	Ⓐ	Ⓑ	Ⓒ	Ⓓ
24.	Ⓐ	Ⓑ	Ⓒ	Ⓓ	**49.**	Ⓐ	Ⓑ	Ⓒ	Ⓓ
25.	Ⓐ	Ⓑ	Ⓒ	Ⓓ	**50.**	Ⓐ	Ⓑ	Ⓒ	Ⓓ

CHAPTER 7

SAMPLE OMR ANSWER SHEET

IMPORTANT: *PLEASE FILL IN NAME, SCHOOL CODE, CLASS, SECTION & ROLL NO. CORRECTLY*

PERSONAL DETAILS

1. STUDENT NAME (IN ENGLISH CAPITAL LETTERS ONLY)

2. SCHOOL CODE

Ⓐ–Ⓩ (two columns); 0 1 2 3 4 5 6 7 8 9 (four columns)

3. CLASS

0 1 (first column); 0 1 2 3 4 5 6 7 8 9 (second column)

4. SECTION

A B C D E F G H I J K L M N O P Q R S T U V W X Y Z

5. ROLL NO.

0 1 2 3 4 5 6 7 8 9 (five columns)

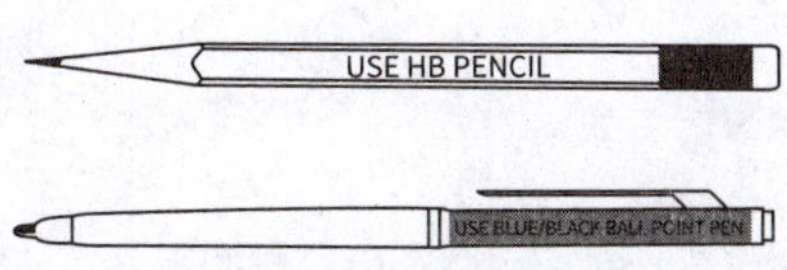

MARK YOUR ANSWERS

Q.					Q.				
1.	A	B	C	D	26.	A	B	C	D
2.	A	B	C	D	27.	A	B	C	D
3.	A	B	C	D	28.	A	B	C	D
4.	A	B	C	D	29.	A	B	C	D
5.	A	B	C	D	30.	A	B	C	D
6.	A	B	C	D	31.	A	B	C	D
7.	A	B	C	D	32.	A	B	C	D
8.	A	B	C	D	33.	A	B	C	D
9.	A	B	C	D	34.	A	B	C	D
10.	A	B	C	D	35.	A	B	C	D
11.	A	B	C	D	36.	A	B	C	D
12.	A	B	C	D	37.	A	B	C	D
13.	A	B	C	D	38.	A	B	C	D
14.	A	B	C	D	39.	A	B	C	D
15.	A	B	C	D	40.	A	B	C	D
16.	A	B	C	D	41.	A	B	C	D
17.	A	B	C	D	42.	A	B	C	D
18.	A	B	C	D	43.	A	B	C	D
19.	A	B	C	D	44.	A	B	C	D
20.	A	B	C	D	45.	A	B	C	D
21.	A	B	C	D	46.	A	B	C	D
22.	A	B	C	D	47.	A	B	C	D
23.	A	B	C	D	48.	A	B	C	D
24.	A	B	C	D	49.	A	B	C	D
25.	A	B	C	D	50.	A	B	C	D

CHAPTER 8

SAMPLE OMR ANSWER SHEET

IMPORTANT: *PLEASE FILL IN NAME, SCHOOL CODE, CLASS, SECTION & ROLL NO. CORRECTLY*

PERSONAL DETAILS

1. STUDENT NAME (IN ENGLISH CAPITAL LETTERS ONLY)

2. SCHOOL CODE

Ⓐ–Ⓩ	Ⓐ–Ⓩ	⓪–⑨	⓪–⑨	⓪–⑨	⓪–⑨

3. CLASS

⓪ ①	⓪–⑨

4. SECTION

Ⓐ–Ⓩ

5. ROLL NO.

⓪–⑨	⓪–⑨	⓪–⑨	⓪–⑨	⓪–⑨

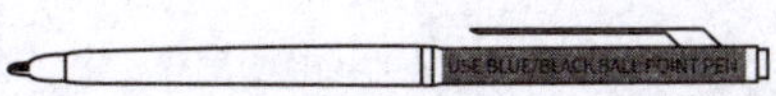

MARK YOUR ANSWERS

1.	Ⓐ Ⓑ Ⓒ Ⓓ	26.	Ⓐ Ⓑ Ⓒ Ⓓ
2.	Ⓐ Ⓑ Ⓒ Ⓓ	27.	Ⓐ Ⓑ Ⓒ Ⓓ
3.	Ⓐ Ⓑ Ⓒ Ⓓ	28.	Ⓐ Ⓑ Ⓒ Ⓓ
4.	Ⓐ Ⓑ Ⓒ Ⓓ	29.	Ⓐ Ⓑ Ⓒ Ⓓ
5.	Ⓐ Ⓑ Ⓒ Ⓓ	30.	Ⓐ Ⓑ Ⓒ Ⓓ
6.	Ⓐ Ⓑ Ⓒ Ⓓ	31.	Ⓐ Ⓑ Ⓒ Ⓓ
7.	Ⓐ Ⓑ Ⓒ Ⓓ	32.	Ⓐ Ⓑ Ⓒ Ⓓ
8.	Ⓐ Ⓑ Ⓒ Ⓓ	33.	Ⓐ Ⓑ Ⓒ Ⓓ
9.	Ⓐ Ⓑ Ⓒ Ⓓ	34.	Ⓐ Ⓑ Ⓒ Ⓓ
10.	Ⓐ Ⓑ Ⓒ Ⓓ	35.	Ⓐ Ⓑ Ⓒ Ⓓ
11.	Ⓐ Ⓑ Ⓒ Ⓓ	36.	Ⓐ Ⓑ Ⓒ Ⓓ
12.	Ⓐ Ⓑ Ⓒ Ⓓ	37.	Ⓐ Ⓑ Ⓒ Ⓓ
13.	Ⓐ Ⓑ Ⓒ Ⓓ	38.	Ⓐ Ⓑ Ⓒ Ⓓ
14.	Ⓐ Ⓑ Ⓒ Ⓓ	39.	Ⓐ Ⓑ Ⓒ Ⓓ
15.	Ⓐ Ⓑ Ⓒ Ⓓ	40.	Ⓐ Ⓑ Ⓒ Ⓓ
16.	Ⓐ Ⓑ Ⓒ Ⓓ	41.	Ⓐ Ⓑ Ⓒ Ⓓ
17.	Ⓐ Ⓑ Ⓒ Ⓓ	42.	Ⓐ Ⓑ Ⓒ Ⓓ
18.	Ⓐ Ⓑ Ⓒ Ⓓ	43.	Ⓐ Ⓑ Ⓒ Ⓓ
19.	Ⓐ Ⓑ Ⓒ Ⓓ	44.	Ⓐ Ⓑ Ⓒ Ⓓ
20.	Ⓐ Ⓑ Ⓒ Ⓓ	45.	Ⓐ Ⓑ Ⓒ Ⓓ
21.	Ⓐ Ⓑ Ⓒ Ⓓ	46.	Ⓐ Ⓑ Ⓒ Ⓓ
22.	Ⓐ Ⓑ Ⓒ Ⓓ	47.	Ⓐ Ⓑ Ⓒ Ⓓ
23.	Ⓐ Ⓑ Ⓒ Ⓓ	48.	Ⓐ Ⓑ Ⓒ Ⓓ
24.	Ⓐ Ⓑ Ⓒ Ⓓ	49.	Ⓐ Ⓑ Ⓒ Ⓓ
25.	Ⓐ Ⓑ Ⓒ Ⓓ	50.	Ⓐ Ⓑ Ⓒ Ⓓ

CHAPTER 9

SAMPLE OMR ANSWER SHEET

IMPORTANT: *PLEASE FILL IN NAME, SCHOOL CODE, CLASS, SECTION & ROLL NO. CORRECTLY*

PERSONAL DETAILS

1. STUDENT NAME (IN ENGLISH CAPITAL LETTERS ONLY)

2. SCHOOL CODE

Ⓐ–Ⓩ	Ⓐ–Ⓩ	⓪–⑨	⓪–⑨	⓪–⑨	⓪–⑨

3. CLASS

⓪ ①	⓪–⑨

4. SECTION

Ⓐ Ⓑ Ⓒ Ⓓ Ⓔ Ⓕ Ⓖ Ⓗ Ⓘ Ⓙ Ⓚ Ⓛ Ⓜ Ⓝ Ⓞ Ⓟ Ⓠ Ⓡ Ⓢ Ⓣ Ⓤ Ⓥ Ⓦ Ⓧ Ⓨ Ⓩ

5. ROLL NO.

⓪–⑨	⓪–⑨	⓪–⑨	⓪–⑨	⓪–⑨

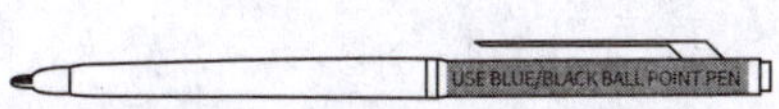

MARK YOUR ANSWERS

1.	Ⓐ	Ⓑ	Ⓒ	Ⓓ
2.	Ⓐ	Ⓑ	Ⓒ	Ⓓ
3.	Ⓐ	Ⓑ	Ⓒ	Ⓓ
4.	Ⓐ	Ⓑ	Ⓒ	Ⓓ
5.	Ⓐ	Ⓑ	Ⓒ	Ⓓ
6.	Ⓐ	Ⓑ	Ⓒ	Ⓓ
7.	Ⓐ	Ⓑ	Ⓒ	Ⓓ
8.	Ⓐ	Ⓑ	Ⓒ	Ⓓ
9.	Ⓐ	Ⓑ	Ⓒ	Ⓓ
10.	Ⓐ	Ⓑ	Ⓒ	Ⓓ
11.	Ⓐ	Ⓑ	Ⓒ	Ⓓ
12.	Ⓐ	Ⓑ	Ⓒ	Ⓓ
13.	Ⓐ	Ⓑ	Ⓒ	Ⓓ
14.	Ⓐ	Ⓑ	Ⓒ	Ⓓ
15.	Ⓐ	Ⓑ	Ⓒ	Ⓓ
16.	Ⓐ	Ⓑ	Ⓒ	Ⓓ
17.	Ⓐ	Ⓑ	Ⓒ	Ⓓ
18.	Ⓐ	Ⓑ	Ⓒ	Ⓓ
19.	Ⓐ	Ⓑ	Ⓒ	Ⓓ
20.	Ⓐ	Ⓑ	Ⓒ	Ⓓ
21.	Ⓐ	Ⓑ	Ⓒ	Ⓓ
22.	Ⓐ	Ⓑ	Ⓒ	Ⓓ
23.	Ⓐ	Ⓑ	Ⓒ	Ⓓ
24.	Ⓐ	Ⓑ	Ⓒ	Ⓓ
25.	Ⓐ	Ⓑ	Ⓒ	Ⓓ

CHAPTER 10

SAMPLE OMR ANSWER SHEET

IMPORTANT: *PLEASE FILL IN NAME, SCHOOL CODE, CLASS, SECTION & ROLL NO. CORRECTLY*

PERSONAL DETAILS

1. STUDENT NAME (IN ENGLISH CAPITAL LETTERS ONLY)

2. SCHOOL CODE

Ⓐ–Ⓩ | Ⓐ–Ⓩ | ⓪–⑨ | ⓪–⑨ | ⓪–⑨ | ⓪–⑨

3. CLASS

⓪–① | ⓪–⑨

4. SECTION

Ⓐ–Ⓩ

5. ROLL NO.

⓪–⑨ | ⓪–⑨ | ⓪–⑨ | ⓪–⑨ | ⓪–⑨

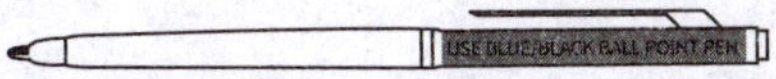

MARK YOUR ANSWERS

No.					No.				
1.	Ⓐ	Ⓑ	Ⓒ	Ⓓ	26.	Ⓐ	Ⓑ	Ⓒ	Ⓓ
2.	Ⓐ	Ⓑ	Ⓒ	Ⓓ	27.	Ⓐ	Ⓑ	Ⓒ	Ⓓ
3.	Ⓐ	Ⓑ	Ⓒ	Ⓓ	28.	Ⓐ	Ⓑ	Ⓒ	Ⓓ
4.	Ⓐ	Ⓑ	Ⓒ	Ⓓ	29.	Ⓐ	Ⓑ	Ⓒ	Ⓓ
5.	Ⓐ	Ⓑ	Ⓒ	Ⓓ	30.	Ⓐ	Ⓑ	Ⓒ	Ⓓ
6.	Ⓐ	Ⓑ	Ⓒ	Ⓓ	31.	Ⓐ	Ⓑ	Ⓒ	Ⓓ
7.	Ⓐ	Ⓑ	Ⓒ	Ⓓ	32.	Ⓐ	Ⓑ	Ⓒ	Ⓓ
8.	Ⓐ	Ⓑ	Ⓒ	Ⓓ	33.	Ⓐ	Ⓑ	Ⓒ	Ⓓ
9.	Ⓐ	Ⓑ	Ⓒ	Ⓓ	34.	Ⓐ	Ⓑ	Ⓒ	Ⓓ
10.	Ⓐ	Ⓑ	Ⓒ	Ⓓ	35.	Ⓐ	Ⓑ	Ⓒ	Ⓓ
11.	Ⓐ	Ⓑ	Ⓒ	Ⓓ	36.	Ⓐ	Ⓑ	Ⓒ	Ⓓ
12.	Ⓐ	Ⓑ	Ⓒ	Ⓓ	37.	Ⓐ	Ⓑ	Ⓒ	Ⓓ
13.	Ⓐ	Ⓑ	Ⓒ	Ⓓ	38.	Ⓐ	Ⓑ	Ⓒ	Ⓓ
14.	Ⓐ	Ⓑ	Ⓒ	Ⓓ	39.	Ⓐ	Ⓑ	Ⓒ	Ⓓ
15.	Ⓐ	Ⓑ	Ⓒ	Ⓓ	40.	Ⓐ	Ⓑ	Ⓒ	Ⓓ
16.	Ⓐ	Ⓑ	Ⓒ	Ⓓ	41.	Ⓐ	Ⓑ	Ⓒ	Ⓓ
17.	Ⓐ	Ⓑ	Ⓒ	Ⓓ	42.	Ⓐ	Ⓑ	Ⓒ	Ⓓ
18.	Ⓐ	Ⓑ	Ⓒ	Ⓓ	43.	Ⓐ	Ⓑ	Ⓒ	Ⓓ
19.	Ⓐ	Ⓑ	Ⓒ	Ⓓ	44.	Ⓐ	Ⓑ	Ⓒ	Ⓓ
20.	Ⓐ	Ⓑ	Ⓒ	Ⓓ	45.	Ⓐ	Ⓑ	Ⓒ	Ⓓ
21.	Ⓐ	Ⓑ	Ⓒ	Ⓓ	46.	Ⓐ	Ⓑ	Ⓒ	Ⓓ
22.	Ⓐ	Ⓑ	Ⓒ	Ⓓ	47.	Ⓐ	Ⓑ	Ⓒ	Ⓓ
23.	Ⓐ	Ⓑ	Ⓒ	Ⓓ	48.	Ⓐ	Ⓑ	Ⓒ	Ⓓ
24.	Ⓐ	Ⓑ	Ⓒ	Ⓓ	49.	Ⓐ	Ⓑ	Ⓒ	Ⓓ
25.	Ⓐ	Ⓑ	Ⓒ	Ⓓ	50.	Ⓐ	Ⓑ	Ⓒ	Ⓓ

CHAPTER 11

SAMPLE OMR ANSWER SHEET

IMPORTANT: *PLEASE FILL IN NAME, SCHOOL CODE, CLASS, SECTION & ROLL NO. CORRECTLY*

PERSONAL DETAILS

1. STUDENT NAME (IN ENGLISH CAPITAL LETTERS ONLY)

2. SCHOOL CODE

A B C D E F G H I J K L M N O P Q R S T U V W X Y Z

A B C D E F G H I J K L M N O P Q R S T U V W X Y Z

0 1 2 3 4 5 6 7 8 9

0 1 2 3 4 5 6 7 8 9

0 1 2 3 4 5 6 7 8 9

0 1 2 3 4 5 6 7 8 9

3. CLASS

0 1

0 1 2 3 4 5 6 7 8 9

4. SECTION

A B C D E F G H I

J K L M N O P Q R

S T U V W X Y Z

5. ROLL NO.

0 1 2 3 4 5 6 7 8 9

0 1 2 3 4 5 6 7 8 9

0 1 2 3 4 5 6 7 8 9

0 1 2 3 4 5 6 7 8 9

0 1 2 3 4 5 6 7 8 9

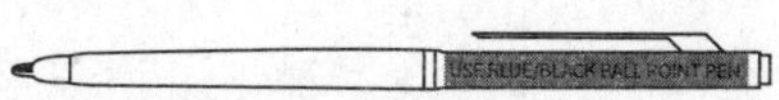

MARK YOUR ANSWERS

1.	A	B	C	D
2.	A	B	C	D
3.	A	B	C	D
4.	A	B	C	D
5.	A	B	C	D
6.	A	B	C	D
7.	A	B	C	D
8.	A	B	C	D
9.	A	B	C	D
10.	A	B	C	D
11.	A	B	C	D
12.	A	B	C	D
13.	A	B	C	D
14.	A	B	C	D
15.	A	B	C	D
16.	A	B	C	D
17.	A	B	C	D
18.	A	B	C	D
19.	A	B	C	D
20.	A	B	C	D
21.	A	B	C	D
22.	A	B	C	D
23.	A	B	C	D
24.	A	B	C	D
25.	A	B	C	D

CHAPTER 12

SAMPLE OMR ANSWER SHEET

IMPORTANT: *PLEASE FILL IN NAME, SCHOOL CODE, CLASS, SECTION & ROLL NO. CORRECTLY*

PERSONAL DETAILS

1. STUDENT NAME (IN ENGLISH CAPITAL LETTERS ONLY)

2. SCHOOL CODE

Ⓐ Ⓑ Ⓒ Ⓓ Ⓔ Ⓕ Ⓖ Ⓗ Ⓘ Ⓙ Ⓚ Ⓛ Ⓜ Ⓝ Ⓞ Ⓟ Ⓠ Ⓡ Ⓢ Ⓣ Ⓤ Ⓥ Ⓦ Ⓧ Ⓨ Ⓩ

Ⓐ Ⓑ Ⓒ Ⓓ Ⓔ Ⓕ Ⓖ Ⓗ Ⓘ Ⓙ Ⓚ Ⓛ Ⓜ Ⓝ Ⓞ Ⓟ Ⓠ Ⓡ Ⓢ Ⓣ Ⓤ Ⓥ Ⓦ Ⓧ Ⓨ Ⓩ

⓪ ① ② ③ ④ ⑤ ⑥ ⑦ ⑧ ⑨

⓪ ① ② ③ ④ ⑤ ⑥ ⑦ ⑧ ⑨

⓪ ① ② ③ ④ ⑤ ⑥ ⑦ ⑧ ⑨

⓪ ① ② ③ ④ ⑤ ⑥ ⑦ ⑧ ⑨

3. CLASS

⓪ ①

⓪ ① ② ③ ④ ⑤ ⑥ ⑦ ⑧ ⑨

4. SECTION

Ⓐ Ⓑ Ⓒ Ⓓ Ⓔ Ⓕ Ⓖ Ⓗ Ⓘ

Ⓙ Ⓚ Ⓛ Ⓜ Ⓝ Ⓞ Ⓟ Ⓠ Ⓡ

Ⓢ Ⓣ Ⓤ Ⓥ Ⓦ Ⓧ Ⓨ Ⓩ

5. ROLL NO.

⓪ ① ② ③ ④ ⑤ ⑥ ⑦ ⑧ ⑨

⓪ ① ② ③ ④ ⑤ ⑥ ⑦ ⑧ ⑨

⓪ ① ② ③ ④ ⑤ ⑥ ⑦ ⑧ ⑨

⓪ ① ② ③ ④ ⑤ ⑥ ⑦ ⑧ ⑨

⓪ ① ② ③ ④ ⑤ ⑥ ⑦ ⑧ ⑨

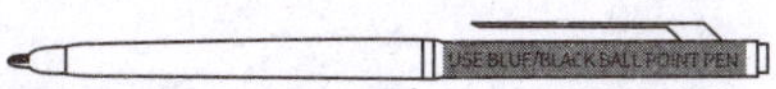

MARK YOUR ANSWERS

1.	Ⓐ	Ⓑ	Ⓒ	Ⓓ	26.	Ⓐ	Ⓑ	Ⓒ	Ⓓ
2.	Ⓐ	Ⓑ	Ⓒ	Ⓓ	27.	Ⓐ	Ⓑ	Ⓒ	Ⓓ
3.	Ⓐ	Ⓑ	Ⓒ	Ⓓ	28.	Ⓐ	Ⓑ	Ⓒ	Ⓓ
4.	Ⓐ	Ⓑ	Ⓒ	Ⓓ	29.	Ⓐ	Ⓑ	Ⓒ	Ⓓ
5.	Ⓐ	Ⓑ	Ⓒ	Ⓓ	30.	Ⓐ	Ⓑ	Ⓒ	Ⓓ
6.	Ⓐ	Ⓑ	Ⓒ	Ⓓ	31.	Ⓐ	Ⓑ	Ⓒ	Ⓓ
7.	Ⓐ	Ⓑ	Ⓒ	Ⓓ	32.	Ⓐ	Ⓑ	Ⓒ	Ⓓ
8.	Ⓐ	Ⓑ	Ⓒ	Ⓓ	33.	Ⓐ	Ⓑ	Ⓒ	Ⓓ
9.	Ⓐ	Ⓑ	Ⓒ	Ⓓ	34.	Ⓐ	Ⓑ	Ⓒ	Ⓓ
10.	Ⓐ	Ⓑ	Ⓒ	Ⓓ	35.	Ⓐ	Ⓑ	Ⓒ	Ⓓ
11.	Ⓐ	Ⓑ	Ⓒ	Ⓓ	36.	Ⓐ	Ⓑ	Ⓒ	Ⓓ
12.	Ⓐ	Ⓑ	Ⓒ	Ⓓ	37.	Ⓐ	Ⓑ	Ⓒ	Ⓓ
13.	Ⓐ	Ⓑ	Ⓒ	Ⓓ	38.	Ⓐ	Ⓑ	Ⓒ	Ⓓ
14.	Ⓐ	Ⓑ	Ⓒ	Ⓓ	39.	Ⓐ	Ⓑ	Ⓒ	Ⓓ
15.	Ⓐ	Ⓑ	Ⓒ	Ⓓ	40.	Ⓐ	Ⓑ	Ⓒ	Ⓓ
16.	Ⓐ	Ⓑ	Ⓒ	Ⓓ	41.	Ⓐ	Ⓑ	Ⓒ	Ⓓ
17.	Ⓐ	Ⓑ	Ⓒ	Ⓓ	42.	Ⓐ	Ⓑ	Ⓒ	Ⓓ
18.	Ⓐ	Ⓑ	Ⓒ	Ⓓ	43.	Ⓐ	Ⓑ	Ⓒ	Ⓓ
19.	Ⓐ	Ⓑ	Ⓒ	Ⓓ	44.	Ⓐ	Ⓑ	Ⓒ	Ⓓ
20.	Ⓐ	Ⓑ	Ⓒ	Ⓓ	45.	Ⓐ	Ⓑ	Ⓒ	Ⓓ
21.	Ⓐ	Ⓑ	Ⓒ	Ⓓ	46.	Ⓐ	Ⓑ	Ⓒ	Ⓓ
22.	Ⓐ	Ⓑ	Ⓒ	Ⓓ	47.	Ⓐ	Ⓑ	Ⓒ	Ⓓ
23.	Ⓐ	Ⓑ	Ⓒ	Ⓓ	48.	Ⓐ	Ⓑ	Ⓒ	Ⓓ
24.	Ⓐ	Ⓑ	Ⓒ	Ⓓ	49.	Ⓐ	Ⓑ	Ⓒ	Ⓓ
25.	Ⓐ	Ⓑ	Ⓒ	Ⓓ	50.	Ⓐ	Ⓑ	Ⓒ	Ⓓ

CHAPTER 13

SAMPLE OMR ANSWER SHEET

IMPORTANT: *PLEASE FILL IN NAME, SCHOOL CODE, CLASS, SECTION & ROLL NO. CORRECTLY*

PERSONAL DETAILS

1. STUDENT NAME (IN ENGLISH CAPITAL LETTERS ONLY)

2. SCHOOL CODE

Ⓐ–Ⓩ	Ⓐ–Ⓩ	⓪–⑨	⓪–⑨	⓪–⑨	⓪–⑨

3. CLASS

⓪–①	⓪–⑨

4. SECTION

Ⓐ–Ⓩ

5. ROLL NO.

⓪–⑨	⓪–⑨	⓪–⑨	⓪–⑨	⓪–⑨

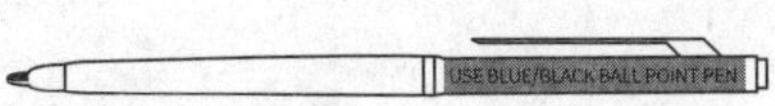

MARK YOUR ANSWERS

1.	Ⓐ	Ⓑ	Ⓒ	Ⓓ	**26.**	Ⓐ	Ⓑ	Ⓒ	Ⓓ
2.	Ⓐ	Ⓑ	Ⓒ	Ⓓ	**27.**	Ⓐ	Ⓑ	Ⓒ	Ⓓ
3.	Ⓐ	Ⓑ	Ⓒ	Ⓓ	**28.**	Ⓐ	Ⓑ	Ⓒ	Ⓓ
4.	Ⓐ	Ⓑ	Ⓒ	Ⓓ	**29.**	Ⓐ	Ⓑ	Ⓒ	Ⓓ
5.	Ⓐ	Ⓑ	Ⓒ	Ⓓ	**30.**	Ⓐ	Ⓑ	Ⓒ	Ⓓ
6.	Ⓐ	Ⓑ	Ⓒ	Ⓓ	**31.**	Ⓐ	Ⓑ	Ⓒ	Ⓓ
7.	Ⓐ	Ⓑ	Ⓒ	Ⓓ	**32.**	Ⓐ	Ⓑ	Ⓒ	Ⓓ
8.	Ⓐ	Ⓑ	Ⓒ	Ⓓ	**33.**	Ⓐ	Ⓑ	Ⓒ	Ⓓ
9.	Ⓐ	Ⓑ	Ⓒ	Ⓓ	**34.**	Ⓐ	Ⓑ	Ⓒ	Ⓓ
10.	Ⓐ	Ⓑ	Ⓒ	Ⓓ	**35.**	Ⓐ	Ⓑ	Ⓒ	Ⓓ
11.	Ⓐ	Ⓑ	Ⓒ	Ⓓ	**36.**	Ⓐ	Ⓑ	Ⓒ	Ⓓ
12.	Ⓐ	Ⓑ	Ⓒ	Ⓓ	**37.**	Ⓐ	Ⓑ	Ⓒ	Ⓓ
13.	Ⓐ	Ⓑ	Ⓒ	Ⓓ	**38.**	Ⓐ	Ⓑ	Ⓒ	Ⓓ
14.	Ⓐ	Ⓑ	Ⓒ	Ⓓ	**39.**	Ⓐ	Ⓑ	Ⓒ	Ⓓ
15.	Ⓐ	Ⓑ	Ⓒ	Ⓓ	**40.**	Ⓐ	Ⓑ	Ⓒ	Ⓓ
16.	Ⓐ	Ⓑ	Ⓒ	Ⓓ	**41.**	Ⓐ	Ⓑ	Ⓒ	Ⓓ
17.	Ⓐ	Ⓑ	Ⓒ	Ⓓ	**42.**	Ⓐ	Ⓑ	Ⓒ	Ⓓ
18.	Ⓐ	Ⓑ	Ⓒ	Ⓓ	**43.**	Ⓐ	Ⓑ	Ⓒ	Ⓓ
19.	Ⓐ	Ⓑ	Ⓒ	Ⓓ	**44.**	Ⓐ	Ⓑ	Ⓒ	Ⓓ
20.	Ⓐ	Ⓑ	Ⓒ	Ⓓ	**45.**	Ⓐ	Ⓑ	Ⓒ	Ⓓ
21.	Ⓐ	Ⓑ	Ⓒ	Ⓓ	**46.**	Ⓐ	Ⓑ	Ⓒ	Ⓓ
22.	Ⓐ	Ⓑ	Ⓒ	Ⓓ	**47.**	Ⓐ	Ⓑ	Ⓒ	Ⓓ
23.	Ⓐ	Ⓑ	Ⓒ	Ⓓ	**48.**	Ⓐ	Ⓑ	Ⓒ	Ⓓ
24.	Ⓐ	Ⓑ	Ⓒ	Ⓓ	**49.**	Ⓐ	Ⓑ	Ⓒ	Ⓓ
25.	Ⓐ	Ⓑ	Ⓒ	Ⓓ	**50.**	Ⓐ	Ⓑ	Ⓒ	Ⓓ

CHAPTER 14

SAMPLE OMR ANSWER SHEET

IMPORTANT: *PLEASE FILL IN NAME, SCHOOL CODE, CLASS, SECTION & ROLL NO. CORRECTLY*

PERSONAL DETAILS

1. STUDENT NAME (IN ENGLISH CAPITAL LETTERS ONLY)

2. SCHOOL CODE

Columns 1–2: Ⓐ–Ⓩ (A B C D E F G H I J K L M N O P Q R S T U V W X Y Z)

Columns 3–6: 0 1 2 3 4 5 6 7 8 9

3. CLASS

Column 1: 0 1

Column 2: 0 1 2 3 4 5 6 7 8 9

4. SECTION

A B C D E F G H I J K L M N O P Q R S T U V W X Y Z

5. ROLL NO.

Columns 1–5: 0 1 2 3 4 5 6 7 8 9

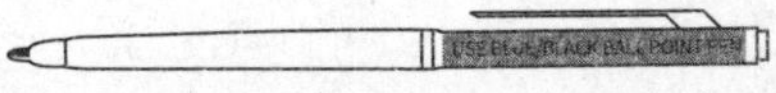

MARK YOUR ANSWERS

1.	A	B	C	D	**26.**	A	B	C	D
2.	A	B	C	D	**27.**	A	B	C	D
3.	A	B	C	D	**28.**	A	B	C	D
4.	A	B	C	D	**29.**	A	B	C	D
5.	A	B	C	D	**30.**	A	B	C	D
6.	A	B	C	D	**31.**	A	B	C	D
7.	A	B	C	D	**32.**	A	B	C	D
8.	A	B	C	D	**33.**	A	B	C	D
9.	A	B	C	D	**34.**	A	B	C	D
10.	A	B	C	D	**35.**	A	B	C	D
11.	A	B	C	D	**36.**	A	B	C	D
12.	A	B	C	D	**37.**	A	B	C	D
13.	A	B	C	D	**38.**	A	B	C	D
14.	A	B	C	D	**39.**	A	B	C	D
15.	A	B	C	D	**40.**	A	B	C	D
16.	A	B	C	D	**41.**	A	B	C	D
17.	A	B	C	D	**42.**	A	B	C	D
18.	A	B	C	D	**43.**	A	B	C	D
19.	A	B	C	D	**44.**	A	B	C	D
20.	A	B	C	D	**45.**	A	B	C	D
21.	A	B	C	D	**46.**	A	B	C	D
22.	A	B	C	D	**47.**	A	B	C	D
23.	A	B	C	D	**48.**	A	B	C	D
24.	A	B	C	D	**49.**	A	B	C	D
25.	A	B	C	D	**50.**	A	B	C	D

CHAPTER 15

SAMPLE OMR ANSWER SHEET

IMPORTANT: *PLEASE FILL IN NAME, SCHOOL CODE, CLASS, SECTION & ROLL NO. CORRECTLY*

PERSONAL DETAILS

1. STUDENT NAME (IN ENGLISH CAPITAL LETTERS ONLY)

2. SCHOOL CODE

A–Z	A–Z	0–9	0–9	0–9	0–9

3. CLASS

0–1	0–9

4. SECTION

A B C D E F G H I	J K L M N O P Q R	S T U V W X Y Z

5. ROLL NO.

0–9	0–9	0–9	0–9	0–9

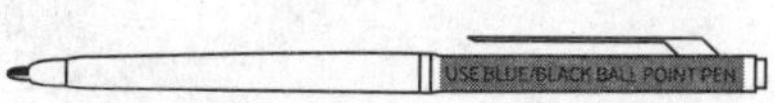

MARK YOUR ANSWERS

No.					No.				
1.	A	B	C	D	26.	A	B	C	D
2.	A	B	C	D	27.	A	B	C	D
3.	A	B	C	D	28.	A	B	C	D
4.	A	B	C	D	29.	A	B	C	D
5.	A	B	C	D	30.	A	B	C	D
6.	A	B	C	D	31.	A	B	C	D
7.	A	B	C	D	32.	A	B	C	D
8.	A	B	C	D	33.	A	B	C	D
9.	A	B	C	D	34.	A	B	C	D
10.	A	B	C	D	35.	A	B	C	D
11.	A	B	C	D	36.	A	B	C	D
12.	A	B	C	D	37.	A	B	C	D
13.	A	B	C	D	38.	A	B	C	D
14.	A	B	C	D	39.	A	B	C	D
15.	A	B	C	D	40.	A	B	C	D
16.	A	B	C	D	41.	A	B	C	D
17.	A	B	C	D	42.	A	B	C	D
18.	A	B	C	D	43.	A	B	C	D
19.	A	B	C	D	44.	A	B	C	D
20.	A	B	C	D	45.	A	B	C	D
21.	A	B	C	D	46.	A	B	C	D
22.	A	B	C	D	47.	A	B	C	D
23.	A	B	C	D	48.	A	B	C	D
24.	A	B	C	D	49.	A	B	C	D
25.	A	B	C	D	50.	A	B	C	D

Space for Rough Work

Space for Rough Work

Space for Rough Work

Space for Rough Work

Space for Rough Work

Space for Rough Work